12/6.

TEXTBOOK ON SOUND

TEXTBOOK ON SOUND

by

J. W. WINSTANLEY, M.Sc., A.Inst.P.

Formerly Physics Master, Manchester Grammar School

WITH DIAGRAMS
AND PHOTOGRAPHS

LONGMANS, GREEN AND CO
LONDON • NEW YORK • TORONTO

LONGMANS, GREEN AND CO LTD
6 & 7 CLIFFORD STREET LONDON W 1
BOSTON HOUSE STRAND STREET CAPE TOWN
531 LITTLE COLLINS STREET MELBOURNE

LONGMANS, GREEN AND CO INC
55 FIFTH AVENUE NEW YORK 3

LONGMANS, GREEN AND CO
20 CRANFIELD ROAD TORONTO 16

ORIENT LONGMANS PRIVATE LTD
CALCUTTA BOMBAY MADRAS
DELHI VIJAYAWADA DACCA

First published 1952
New impression 1957

PRINTED IN GREAT BRITAIN AT
THE UNIVERSITY PRESS
ABERDEEN

PREFACE

Sound, unfortunately, has always been a somewhat neglected branch of Science. In many cases the experiments and demonstrations require apparatus of considerable dimensions and, therefore, do not lend themselves so conveniently to laboratory work as light, for example. This neglect has been a pity, for many of the phenomena are of general interest and play an important part in everyday life.

In this volume I have not restricted the contents to the syllabuses laid down by examining bodies. I have added sections on phenomena of a general nature which, I believe, will interest most students. The book is intended primarily for the use of students in Grammar and Technical Schools who are preparing for the General Certificate of Education, at the Advanced or Scholarship level, or other examinations at a similar standard, and it will also cover most of the first year work at the University.

In many schools the pupil first comes into contact with sound as a scientific subject when he reaches the Sixth Form, and so the book has been written in the hope that the senior pupil, who is making his first acquaintance with this " Cinderella of the Sciences ", will find all he needs between its covers. Considerable care has been exercised in the selection of questions. In practically all cases these consist of a descriptive portion, together with a numerical exercise, the latter, in my opinion, being a first-rate test as to whether the student has really understood the principles expounded in the text.

In preparing the book I have had the help, advice, criticism and encouragement of many friends and colleagues. Dr. E. J. F. James, M.A., B.Sc., Mr. G. Darwin, B.Sc., Mr. S. Clynes, B.Sc., Mr. I. Tenen, M.A., of the staff of the Manchester Grammar School, have read the work in MS. and proof, and have made valuable suggestions. I am likewise greatly indebted to my old friend, Mr. J. A. Clayton, B.Sc., who has also provided his original contribution on the velocity of longitudinal waves in an elastic solid.

Acknowledgment with thanks is also made to the Examining Bodies of Oxford, Cambridge, London and the Northern Universities who, together with the Central Welsh Board, gave permission for questions set in Public Examinations to be reprinted in this book. Messrs. Griffin & Tatlock Ltd. provided ripple tank photorgaphs and Messrs. Mullard kindly provided the photograph showing various types of photo-electric cells.

Acknowledgments for permission to include copyright material are due to Messrs. Macmillan & Co. Ltd., for an extract from *A Textbook of Sound* by E. H. Barton, and the University Press Cambridge for a quotation from *The Physical Basis of Music* by Dr. A. Wood.

Finally, I should like to thank the publishers who have shown patience and understanding, and have co-operated fully with me in trying to make this volume complete and interesting.

J. W. W.

CONTENTS

PLATES

CHAPTER I

THE NATURE OF SOUND

1. Sound is always due to Vibrations

When a tuning fork is sounding, it can be seen that the prongs are moving, although the motion is too rapid to be followed completely by the naked eye. If the prongs are touched their vibration stops, and so does the sound. The action of bowing a violin is to set up, and maintain, a suitable motion of the string. The vibration of the string can be seen and felt; stopping the vibration again stops the sound. The vibration of the column of air in an organ pipe can be demonstrated by lowering a light tray carrying a suitable powder, such as lycopodium, into the pipe. The motion of the powder shows that at certain places in the pipe the air is stationary, but between these points it is in motion. The vibration of the air can actually be felt when an organ pipe sounds a loud note of low frequency. It must not be assumed that the air as a whole is in motion. An observer standing in front of a trombonist playing a fortissimo passage hears a loud sound, but does not feel a blast of air proceeding from the instrument. A similar experiment may be carried out using the human voice and singing a loud note whilst holding a lighted candle about a foot away from the mouth. A good singer disturbs the flame but little.

Smoke a piece of plane glass, using a camphor or turpentine flame, and place it on the bench. To the end of one prong of a tuning fork attach a small piece of thin wire by means of a suitable material such as sealing wax, Chatterton's compound, etc. Strike the fork on a piece of wood covered with felt and move the fork in a straight line above the glass so that the style touches the smoked surface. The style on the fork traces out a wavy line on the smoked glass. Each complete oscillation represents the same interval of time, even though the velocity with which the fork moved may have been non-uniform. A modification of this method (the falling plate) will be described later, showing how the frequency of the tuning fork may be calculated from the dimensions of the curve traced out on the smoked plate when the plate moves with uniform acceleration.

When a bell is sounding, the note emitted by it can be considerably reduced, and in some cases completely stopped, by touching the bell with the hand. The vibrations can actually be felt before the pressure of the hand stops them. A pith ball hanging from a piece of cotton thread is thrown violently to one side when the thread is held so that the pith ball touches the vibrating bell. Careful observation shows that the cone of the loudspeaker of a wireless set is moving when it is giving forth sound. The pressure of the hand will considerably reduce, and in some cases stop, the sound.

In a telephone mouthpiece (or microphone), and earpiece, the vibration of a disc of metal is responsible for the transmission of speech. In the microphone, vibration of a membrane causes variations in the electric current flowing through the instrument. These fluctuations are passed along a wire, with suitable precautions to prevent them from dying away, and when they pass through the earpiece at the other end of the wire, cause a similar membrane, or thin sheet of steel, to vibrate with practically the same motion as that given to the diaphragm

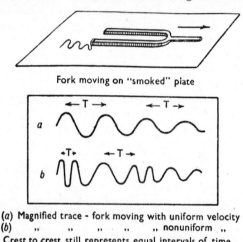

Fork moving on "smoked" plate

(a) Magnified trace - fork moving with uniform velocity
(b)   ,,   ,,   ,,   ,,   ,, nonuniform ,,
Crest to crest still represents equal intervals of time
Fig. i.

in the microphone. This motion is given to the air, which transmits it to the ear, and the listener is conscious of the sensation of sound.

The preceding examples all show that whenever sound is produced it is always the result of vibration.

2. The Frequency of the Vibrations

Although it is possible to make a body vibrate by means of a system of cogs and levers, sound almost always arises from vibrations which are due to the elasticity of the body. A body is said to be elastic if, on the removal of the force which has been causing a deformation, it resumes its original size and shape. In many cases, such as a spiral spring or lead wire, there are definite limits beyond which the deformation must not go, otherwise it becomes permanent. These limits are known as the elastic limits, and in the case of lead the amount of permissible distortion is very small. Within these small limits, however, lead is elastic since it will carry sound, and, as will be shown later, sound is passed through a body by virtue of the elasticity of the body.

Liquids and gases have no elastic limits in the ordinary sense of the term. They can be deformed in one way only, namely by change of volume or bulk. Hooke's law originally stated for solids only, that stress is proportional to strain, provided that the body has not passed its elastic limits. For a spiral spring this is often stated as load is proportional to extension. There seems to be no apparent reason why this law should not apply to the compression of liquids and gases, since in these cases also the change of pressure is proportional to the change in volume when these changes are small.

Hooke's law leads to the important result that the vibrations of a body due to its elasticity are *isochronous*, i.e. the time of a complete oscillation is constant and independent of the amplitude of vibration. For a simple pendulum making small oscillations the time of an oscillation is given by $T = 2\pi \sqrt{\dfrac{L}{g}}$, where L is the length of the pendulum, and is independent of the amplitude, except in so far as it must be small so as to make the oscillations Simple Harmonic. The balance wheel of a watch is kept oscillating, and its frequency determined, by the hair spring, the main spring supplying the necessary impulses to maintain the oscillations which would otherwise die away due to friction and air damping. The accuracy of the watch does not depend upon the degree to which the mainspring is wound, provided that there is sufficient tension in it to keep the watch going. If the balance wheel can oscillate sufficiently to allow correct movement of the escapement then the watch will keep correct time.

A simple harmonic vibration is the only one which gives rise to a pure tone of a definite pitch or frequency, i.e. a note without the admixture of notes of other pitches. The note given out by a tuning fork is pure. Notes from musical instruments, such as the violin, can be resolved into a whole series of notes of different pitch, all related to each other, and all of which can be produced by Simple Harmonic vibrations. If elastic vibrations were not isochronous, music would be rather strange, since if frequency varied with amplitude then a change in loudness would alter the pitch of the note.

The vibrator on Fletcher's Trolley, and the Ribbon Atwood, consists of a thin strip of steel. This is used for measuring intervals of time and is usually adjusted to vibrate 8 or 10 times a second. The strip can be seen vibrating, the brush it carries makes a trace on the paper, but no sound is heard. As the length of the vibrating strip is shortened, however, the vibrations become more rapid and a sound is heard which rises in pitch as the length of the vibrating strip is decreased. Most students will have performed the simple experiment of placing a ruler firmly on the desk, with a portion overhanging, and setting the projecting part into vibration, thus producing a note. The pitch of the note produced is raised by shortening the vibrating length of the ruler. If this is too long then an audible note is not produced. Similar variations in pitch can be produced by shortening the length of a piece of stretched elastic vibrating under tension. These simple experiments show that, for a sound to be heard, the frequency of vibrations must not be less than a definite number per second. Experiments with a Galton's whistle, which is used for the production of high-pitched notes, show that there is also an upper limit to the number of vibrations per second to which the ear will respond. Above this limit there is no sensation of sound. These limits vary considerably with different observers and, since the response of the ear falls

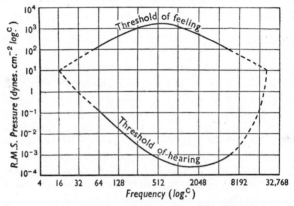

FIG. 2. Range of human ear (after Wegel).

off with frequency (see Fig. 2), it is essential that the intensity of the high-pitched notes should be sufficient to allow for this reduction in sensitiveness.

It is generally agreed that the lower limit of the number of vibrations which give the sensation of sound is about 20 vib./sec. Below this value the vibrations are sensed as separate impulses on the ear-drum and not as a note. Rayleigh [1] states that bird calls cannot be heard above 10,000 vib./sec., although a sensitive flame can be used to detect up to 50,000 vib./sec. There is little doubt that sounds up to 20,000 vib./sec., provided they are intense enough, can be heard by children. The sensitiveness of the human ear falls off with age, so that in adults the upper limit becomes 15,000 vib./sec. Thus the limits of audibility for the human ear are from 20 to 20,000 vib./sec. ; certain animals, such as bats, are sensitive to much more rapid vibrations.

[1] Rayleigh, *Sound*, **2**, p. 433.

The frequency range of the electrical system must be carefully considered when designing apparatus for the electrical reproduction of sound. The frequency range required for perfect reproduction varies with different sounds (see Fig. 4). For speech and music the ranges are 100 to 10,000 and 60 to 15,000 vib./sec.[1] respectively. In practice it is found that a frequency range of 80 to 8000 vib./sec. gives quite good reproduction except for a few sounds. Many inexpensive broadcast receivers only cover 100 to 5000 vib./sec., but give satisfaction to the owner who has not too critical an ear.

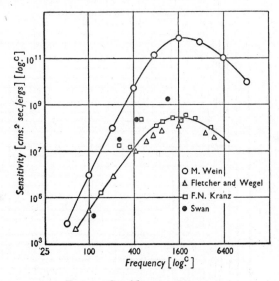

Fig. 3. Sensitiveness of the ear.

3. The Finite Time of Transmission of Sound

Many everyday happenings demonstrate the fact that sound has a finite time of transmission. When watching a cricket match from a considerable distance it may be observed that the batsman has completed his stroke, and the ball is speeding towards the boundary, before the noise of bat meeting ball reaches the ears. The distant observer of duck, pheasant, or grouse shooting sees the flash of the gun and the puff of smoke, the hit bird falling, and then the sound of the shot reaches his ears.

Probably the most familiar example of the finite time of transmission of sound is the interval of time between the lightning flash and the thunder clap. These are generated at the same instant but the interval of time between the arrival of the lightning flash, which travels at 186,000 miles/sec., and the thunder, which has a velocity of

[1] Terman, *Radio Engineering.*

about 1100 ft./sec., is often used to find the distance away of the storm ; a time interval of 5 sec. indicating that this is about 1 mile. During the war it was quite usual to see the flash of anti-aircraft guns, and the bursting of shells over a distant town, followed after some considerable time by the noise of firing.

In athletics the timekeeper often starts his stop watch when he sees the flash of the pistol. Because of the very large velocity of light, the only error in timing worthy of consideration is his own personal

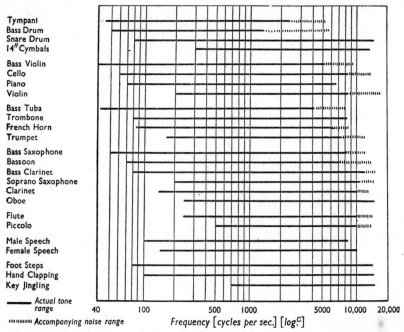

FIG. 4.   Frequency range of representative musical instruments as determined by listening tests (W. B. Snow).

error. If, however, he starts his stop-watch in a 100 yd. race when he hears the sound he then introduces an error of $\frac{300}{1100}$ or $\frac{3}{11}$ sec. irrespective of his personal error.

4. A Medium is required for Transmission

A tuning fork and a wooden bench are all the apparatus required to show that sound can pass through a solid and that air is not essential for its transmission. If the handle of the vibrating fork is placed in contact with the head or teeth the sound heard is much greater than that heard when the fork is held just not in contact with head or teeth. When the ears are plugged with cotton wool, and the head placed in contact with one end of a long wooden bench, the note given out by a vibrating fork with its handle in contact with the other end of the bench is quite audible. When not in contact with the bench the sound is inaudible even to unplugged ears.

When the ear is placed close to a telegraph pole the Aeolian tones or "singing" of the wires due to the air currents through them can clearly be heard, the sounds transmitted by the wood being little attenuated, whilst those passing through the air are soon absorbed. About 50 years ago, Professor Tyndall performed a simple but most instructive experiment at the Royal Institution. A musical box was placed in the basement and a rod in contact with it passed through two floors to the lecture room. When the musical box was playing it was inaudible in the lecture room unless the ear was placed close to the rod. By placing a suitable tray on the end of the rod a considerable

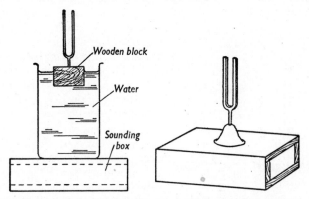

FIG. 5. Experiment to show that water transmits sound.

volume of air was set into vibration and the sounds were audible throughout the room. In schools and buildings equipped with central heating the kicking of the pipes in one room causes a sound of considerable intensity to be heard in many other rooms, the sound being transmitted through the pipes. Even small sounds given to the pipes carry well, thus showing that the sound loses little energy in its transmission in this medium.

The echo sounder, which will be dealt with in a later chapter, shows that sound is transmitted through water, but a simple laboratory experiment can be arranged to demonstrate this fact. When a vibrating tuning fork is placed with its stem on a hollow box a considerable increase in loudness is apparent. This is because a much increased quantity of air is set into vibration and so the fork loses its energy at a greater rate. When this sounding box is constructed for a fork of a particular frequency it is termed a resonance box, a point fully dealt with in the chapter on resonance. If the prong of the fork is fixed in a piece of wood which will float the fork on water, the sound is increased a little. When a large vessel containing water is placed on top of the resonance box, and the vibrating fork floated on the water, a considerable increase in the loudness of the note is apparent. The fork is floated clear of the sides thus showing that the vibrations are passed through the water to the resonator beneath the vessel (Fig. 5).

It is very obvious from everyday experience that sound is transmitted through air, and the preceding experiments have shown that sound is transmitted through media which have elastic properties. The final question is : can sound be transmitted without the aid of a medium ? i.e. can it pass through a vacuum, like light, heat, electromagnetic and gravitational effects ?

The Hon. Robert Boyle (1627-91) made the first recorded experiment to test this, although the experiment is often named after Hauksbee. He suspended a watch, by means of thread and wax,

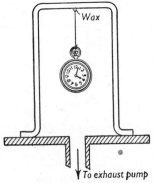

inside the receiver of an exhaust pump (Fig. 6). The sides of the vessel were sealed, but the ticking of the watch could be heard distinctly at the outset of the experiment. As the vessel was exhausted of air the ticking of the watch became fainter and fainter, until it could be heard no longer. The movement of the hands, however, showed that the watch had not stopped. As air was allowed into the vessel the ticking became more and more audible until it again reached its original intensity. This showed that sound cannot pass through a vacuum. Nowadays an electric bell with a battery strapped to

FIG. 6. Boyle's experiment to show that sound cannot pass through a vacuum.

it usually replaces the watch. The bell is suspended, in a vessel which can be exhausted of air, by means of thread and a split cork. If the bell touches the sides of the vessel then the vibrations are transmitted to the air outside even when the vessel is exhausted. As in Boyle's experiment the sound becomes fainter and fainter as the air is withdrawn from the vessel although the hammer can be seen striking the gong with undiminished violence. From these experiments it is to be expected that the intensity of sound will fall off with altitude, and Professor Tyndall stated that on Mt. Blanc the sound of a pistol shot resembled the noise made by opening a bottle of champagne.

When transmitting a sound the air does not move bodily but each particle moves about its own natural position. Lord Rayleigh has estimated that for sounds of normal loudness in air the movement of the particles is of the order of 10^{-3} in., and may be as small as 10^{-6} in.

Even very intense sounds carry little energy, average speech having a power of 10 micro-watts, a very small amount. Dr. Kaye has estimated that if the population of greater London shouted at the top of their voices, the total power generated would only be of the order of 1 h.p. As a further illustration of the small amount of sound energy coming from quite a considerable amount of physical energy it may be stated that, if all the inhabitants of the earth talked simultaneously, the average power produced would be less than that radiated from a large broadcasting station.

The preceding experiments, and everyday experiences, show that sound is a disturbance which requires a medium and a finite time for its transmission. The medium does not move bodily with the sound although the energy of the sound is moved in the direction of propagation.

5. Musical Notes and Noises

The character of the sensation produced determines whether a sound is musical or otherwise. Musical notes may be considered as those sounds which are smooth, regular, pleasant and of definite pitch. Noises are irregular, rough, unpleasant and of no definite pitch. What one person considers a noise may be considered a musical note by another, and it must be noted that all noises usually have associated musical notes, and almost all musical notes have associated noises. Dr. Alex Wood [1] dealing with noise states : " It has now been defined by international agreement as sound which is unpleasant to the recipient ", and goes on to say " a siren is not a noise if it is sounding the ' all clear ', whereas a Bach Fugue faultlessly performed is a noise if we are trying to settle ourselves to sleep ".

As well as having a predominant frequency a musical note must have intensity, otherwise it could not be heard, and quality or timbre which makes it possible to distinguish between notes of the same intensity and frequency played on different musical instruments, such as the violin and clarinet. Frequency, Quality and Intensity are termed the characteristics of a musical note. They will be considered separately, and more fully, later in the book but require some further explanation at this stage.

(a) *Frequency, Pitch.* These terms are distinct quantities, although it is possible to observe a relationship between them. The frequency of a vibration is the number of vibrations performed per second. Very few musical notes are made up of vibrations of one frequency, but these notes have, however, a predominant or fundamental note. Musical notes arrange themselves in a natural order according to pitch, and when stating the pitch of a note we refer to the frequency

[1] Alex Wood, *The Physics of Music*, p. 39.

of vibration of the fundamental or predominant note. All sound waves travel with the same velocity when in the same medium and under the same conditions of temperature, pressure and humidity, and since for a wave motion the velocity $v = n\lambda$, the lower frequency note must be of longer wavelength than the higher frequency note.

(b) *Intensity or Loudness.* It is important to realise that intensity and loudness, although related, are not the same. The loudness of a sound depends on the energy of the particles striking the ear-drums. If the amplitude of the vibration is large it will cause large changes in pressure on the ear-drum and a loud sound will be heard. The energy per unit volume of the medium is proportional to the square of the amplitude, and inversely proportional to the wavelength, of the sound wave. Thus the intensity of a sound is a measure of the energy carried, i.e. a definite physical quantity, whereas loudness involves the response of the ear to a sound of definite intensity. As the sensitiveness of the ear varies considerably with the frequency of the sound, sounds at the limits of audibility will appear very feeble although the energy carried is large.

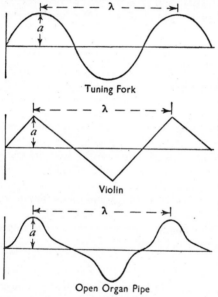

Tuning Fork

Violin

Open Organ Pipe

FIG. 7.   Notes of the same frequency and amplitude but of different quality.

(c) *Quality or Timbre.* Notes of the same pitch and loudness, but produced by different instruments, are distinguished by their quality or timbre. The note emitted by a tuning fork is a simple tone whilst the note of the same frequency sounded by a violin has a different quality. This is due to the fact that, when a string is made to vibrate, by bowing it fairly close to one end, as well as the fundamental or predominant frequency, of n vib./sec., notes of other frequencies are present. These have values $2n$, $3n$, $4n$, etc., and are termed harmonics or overtones. A harmonic is defined as a note having a frequency an integral number of times that of the fundamental, the integral number giving the value assigned to the harmonic. Thus the note of frequency $2n$ is the second harmonic or the first overtone, that of value $3n$ is the third harmonic or second overtone. As various quantities of pigment give rise to a definite colour on the artist's canvas, so mixtures of fundamental and overtones give rise to a definite quality or " colour " in music. The number of overtones present determine the quality, and, as will be shown later, an open and a closed organ pipe sounding the same fundamental note have different qualities, since all the harmonics present in the note from an open pipe are not present in that from a closed pipe. Helmholtz considers that the cutting characteristic of the note of the violin is due to the strength of the sixth and tenth harmonics as compared with the same note from other instruments.

In a displacement/time graph (see Chapter II) : (1) Frequency is characterised by wavelength. (2) Loudness is characterised by amplitude. (3) Quality is characterised by the shape of the curve (see Fig. 7) since with curves of the same amplitude and wavelength, it is possible to have an infinite variety of shapes and, as will be discussed later, a complicated curve can be constructed from a series of sine curves of frequency n, $2n$, $3n$, etc.

CHAPTER II

WAVE MOTION

6. In physics there are two distinct types of waves which are of considerable interest and importance. These are the pulse, which consists of a short burst of waves or even a single wave, and the regular wave train. Both of these types of waves can be produced by pushing up and down a board on the surface of water, or by making a strip of metal vibrate in air. The most important type of regular wave is the simple harmonic train which obeys the symmetrical sine or cosine law, since, as will be shown later, all waves can be split up into a series of waves which obey these laws. The diagram shows how the displacement from its position of rest of a particular particle in a simple harmonic wave train varies with time. The same shape of curve can also show how the displacement of the particles, from their

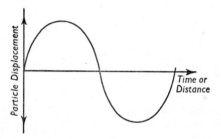

Fig. 8. Displacement graph of a S.H. wave representing the displacement of the particles transmitting the wave, from their undisturbed position, against time or distance in the direction of the wave motion.

undisturbed positions, varies with distance in the direction of propagation of the wave, thus giving an instantaneous picture of the wave train as a whole.

Transverse and Longitudinal Vibrations

7. Transverse

Consider a long string, india-rubber cord, or thick-walled tube with one end fixed to a wall and the other end attached to a rod or held *tightly* in the hand (see Fig. 9). As the rod is moved from *A* to *B* and thence to *C* the end of the string attached to the rod undergoes exactly the same displacement. The motion of the end of the cord is communicated to adjacent particles, and so the particles move up and down, but a disturbance moves along the cord (to the left in the diagram). Each particle undergoes the same motion as the end of the rod, but not necessarily at the same time. As the end of the string or cord, which is attached to the wall, cannot undergo a displacement, it means that when a single pulse in the form of a crest is sent down the cord it will be reflected at the wall and return along the cord as a trough. If the cord is held rigidly in the hand the same thing takes place at this end as well, and the pulse will run backwards and forwards until the imperfect elasticity of the cord causes it to die away. When the cord is lightly held in the hand then the trough moving along the cord is reflected as a trough.

If the rod or hand holding the cord vibrates harmonically then the same harmonic motion is passed on to each particle, the motion of the hand with time being represented by a sine wave. If the vibrations of the hand are not harmonic there will be a progressive wave but it will not obey the sine or cosine law. Similar waves are produced when a stone is thrown into water. A series of corks floating on the

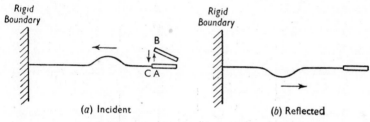

Rigid Boundary

Rigid Boundary

B

C A

(a) Incident

(b) Reflected

FIG. 9.   Reflection of a crest at a rigid boundary.

surface perform only an up and down movement about their position of rest, provided they are not so near the stone as to be disturbed by the splash.

Thus in a transverse wave the direction of motion of the particles of the medium propagating the wave is at right angles to the direction of propagation. It is important to realise that in this, as in all other waves, the vibrating particles do not travel with the wave. Every particle, of a medium which transmits waves, travels repeatedly over the same limited path, passing on the shape or arrangement of the particles and handing on the energy of the wave in the direction of propagation. .

8. Longitudinal Vibrations

When an engine is shunting waggons, the bump as the engine hits the buffers of the first waggon is passed down the line of waggons, each waggon moving backwards and forwards in the distance determined by its couplings. The energy supplied by the engine is thus handed on from waggon to waggon, although each waggon moves but little from its undisturbed position. When one end of a rod is stroked longitudinally certain layers are displaced from their normal position. When released they overshoot their equilibrium position and, in so doing, displace other layers, thus handing on energy in a manner very similar to that of the trucks and the engine.

Consider a body having a considerable surface area, such as a fan or piece of cardboard, moving from D to E and back again (Fig. 10). As the fan moves towards E the air in contact with it will be pushed away causing a local rise in pressure or a compression. As the fan moves back to D it will leave behind a degree of vacuum or a rarefaction. When the air is compressed it tends to relieve the strain on

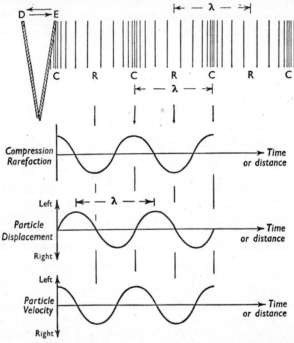

FIG. 10. Propagation of sound wave in a gas (longitudinal vibrations).

itself by moving away from the compression, thus compressing the layers of air to the right of it (see Fig. 10). These layers do likewise and so pass on the compression. When the fan moves to the left to D the air at E is rarefied and there is a local fall in pressure (at the same time a compression is sent out to the left of the figure). The air in a layer to the right of the rarefaction tends to move to make up the loss in pressure and so the rarefaction is also passed from layer to layer. If the motion of the fan is regular then there will be a regular interval of time between compressions and rarefactions, and this interval will be maintained as the wave moves along.

Thus in longitudinal vibrations the movement of the medium is in the direction of propagation of the wave, the individual particles performing only a small oscillation about their undisturbed position, but handing on the shape and energy of the wave. The importance of this type of wave lies in the fact that it is the only kind of wave which can be transmitted by a gas. A gas offers no permanent resistance to change of shape. The only change in a gas which gives rise to elastic forces is change in volume, and so changes in volume, or compressions and rarefactions, are the only vibrations which it can transmit. If the vibrations of the fan are simple harmonic then the oscillations of every particle which transmits the wave will be of the same kind, and when each particle has handed on its momentum it will also have rid itself of its compressions and rarefactions and will return to its original state of rest.

A suitable long horizontal spring can be used to demonstrate longitudinal vibrations.[1] " A helical coil should be wound in a lathe, the wire being of soft copper about $1 \cdot 5$ mm. in diameter, its turns being 10 cm. in diameter ; their pitch or distance apart longitudinally may be about 1 cm., the whole coil, being 2 m. long, thus containing about 200 turns. Each turn of the coil should be supported by a fine silk thread in the form of a ' V ', each limb of the V being about 1 m. long, its two upper ends being fixed $\frac{1}{2}$ m. apart to a wood framework. These dimensions are chosen to ensure a slow advance of the disturbance from one end to the other, and cannot without disadvantage be departed from at random." If one end of the coil is pushed in a little the turns are brought closer together, thus forming a compression which will travel slowly to the other end of the spring. On the other hand, when one end of the spring is pulled outward the end turns are more widely separated and a rarefaction travels along the spring. If the end of the spring is moved in and out, with simple harmonic motion, then compressions and rarefactions move down the coil at regular intervals.

The distance from crest to crest, trough to trough, or neighbouring points in the same phase is termed the wavelength of the disturbance. This is easy to visualise in a transverse vibration, such as a wave on water, but the wave through a gas, or any longitudinal vibration, does not show crests and troughs. In this case the wavelength is the distance between adjacent compressions or rarefactions (which are in the same phase) or the distance from crest to crest as measured on the particle displacement graph (Fig. 10). If n complete oscillations of wavelength λ are sent out each second then the wave front moves a distance $n\lambda$ in 1 sec. and therefore the velocity of the wave is given by

$$v = n\lambda.$$

[1] Barton, *Textbook of Sound*, p. 7.

The displacement of the vibrator from its mean position at a time t may be represented by

$$y = a \sin \omega t$$

or, since the period T of the vibrator is given by

$$T = \frac{2\pi}{\omega}, \quad y = a \sin \frac{2\pi t}{T}.$$

A particle of air at a distance x from this mean position will move in the same way, but at a time $\frac{x}{v}$ later, if v is the velocity of sound in air so that for it

$$y = a \sin \frac{2\pi}{T}\left(t - \frac{x}{v}\right),$$

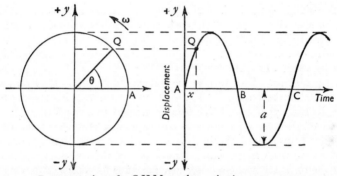

FIG. 11. Representation of a S.H.M. as the projection on to a diameter of a point on the circle moving with uniform angular velocity.

for if $t' = t + \frac{x}{v}$, the displacement of the particle at the time t' will be the same as that of the source at the time t, and will be

$$y = a \sin \frac{2\pi}{T} \cdot t = a \sin \frac{2\pi}{T}\left(t' - \frac{x}{v}\right).$$

The displacement of the air particle at any time t is thus

$$y = a \sin \frac{2\pi}{T}\left(t - \frac{x}{v}\right) = a \sin 2\pi\left(\frac{t}{T} - \frac{x}{vT}\right) = a \sin 2\pi\left(\frac{t}{T} - \frac{x}{\lambda}\right).$$

It is evident that when $t = 0$, the source has no displacement and when $t = \frac{x}{v}$, the air particle has none either. This equation embodies the two characteristics of wave motion : (i) when x is constant, y is a periodic function of the time, and (ii) when t is constant y is a periodic function of x.

The same periodic motion is handed on from particle to particle in the medium which is transmitting the train of waves.

9. Progressive and Stationary Waves

When a stone is thrown into a pond, the first waves sent out by the disturbance progress, or travel outwards, towards the edge of the pond. Each particle on the surface of the pond in turn goes

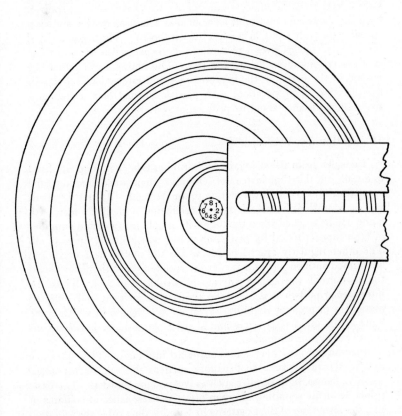

FIG. 12. Crova's Disc.

through a similar up and down motion about its position of rest while the energy of the wave is travelling outwards. This is a progressive wave, the shape and energy of which is continuously advancing. When the first wave is reflected at the edge of the pond the incident and reflected waves interfere and the waves now formed can no longer be termed progressive. The surface of the pond takes on a definite pattern, some points, termed nodes, being permanently at rest.

2

Crova's disc (Fig. 12) is a simple device for illustrating progressive waves. On a piece of fairly stout cardboard draw a circle about $\frac{3}{8}$ in. in diameter. Divide its circumference into a number of equal parts, say 8 or 12, and number them, 1, 2, 3, 4, etc., successively round the circle. With centre point 1 and radius $\frac{1}{2}$ in. draw a circle. Increase the radius by a suitable amount, say 0·2 in. and with centre point 2 draw a circle. Increase the radius by equal amounts each time and draw circles at 3, 4, etc., progressing round the numbered circle in the same direction until a sufficient number of circles have been constructed. Spin the disc about a suitable axle, such as a knitting needle, and view the disc through a slit in a piece of cardboard. The movement of the eccentric circles gives a picture of progressive waves, such as those in a gas or longitudinally stroked rod. This shows a concertina like motion of the particles, the compressions and rarefactions moving in the direction of propagation, each particle moving only a comparatively short distance about its position of rest.

10. Stationary Waves

Consider again the string, or india-rubber tube, with one end fixed to a wall, but this time instead of sending a single pulse along the tube apply a steady up and down motion to the free end. At first the result will be confusion, but, if the rate of oscillation is gradually increased, a rate will be reached when the tube will be split into a definite number of segments separated by nodes, or points which hardly move at all. The other regularly spaced points where the motion is a maximum are termed antinodes (Fig. 13). If the speed of oscillation is increased the motion of the string will again become confused. Thus the interference of two suitable wave trains (the incident and reflected motions) can produce standing waves, the wavelength of which is the same as the interfering waves and is twice the distance between consecutive nodes or antinodes.

Standing or stationary waves also exist in a fluid. Their presence can be shown by suitable detectors such as the ear, microphones, sensitive flames, light powder such as lycopodium powder. The basic principle of the sounding of organ pipes, the resonance of columns of gas, the formation of dust patterns in Kundt's dust tube, the vibration of strings on the sonometer or in Melde's experiment, is the formation of standing waves.

Consider a longitudinal wave, such as a sound wave in a gas, reflected normally from a rigid obstacle, such as a wall. Since the portion of the medium immediately in contact with the rigid wall must be at rest, the displacement of the particles produced by the incident and reflected waves at that point must be equal and opposite. When a compression reaches the wall the only way it can relieve its strained condition is by pushing back the neighbouring layers of gas, i.e. it is reflected as a compression, and similarly a rarefaction is reflected as a rarefaction. Since the gas in contact with a rigid wall is permanently at rest, the velocities of the particles in contact with the wall, due to the incident and reflected waves, must be equal and opposite, i.e. the particle velocity is reversed on reflection. It must be noted that when a wave train is reflected at a non-rigid barrier, such as the open end of a tube, the compression moves out of the tube and leaves behind a rarefaction, i.e. a compression is reflected as a rarefaction. This reflection is only partial as some of the energy is transmitted to the gas outside the tube.

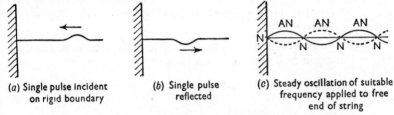

(a) Single pulse incident on rigid boundary   (b) Single pulse reflected   (c) Steady oscillation of suitable frequency applied to free end of string

FIG. 13.   Standing waves due to transverse vibrations of a string.

11. Longitudinal Standing Waves

In Fig. 14 the thin curve 1 represents the particle displacement/time graph for a sound wave in air falling on a rigid obstacle, such as a wall. Bearing in mind that at a rigid boundary, a compression is reflected as a compression and the particle velocity is reversed, the reflected wave can be constructed. This is often termed change of phase, but it must be realised that the change of phase applies to the velocity and that the reflected wave cannot be obtained by finding a point in anti-phase on the displacement/time sine curve and using that point as the start of the reflected wave. A few simple rules are sufficient to enable the student to construct easily the reflected wave for any position of the incident wave. These are:

1. Continue the incident wave beyond the boundary or y axis (curve 2).
2. Turn over this part of the wave about the x axis (curve 3, change of phase).
3. Now turn the wave over about the y axis (curve 4, reflection).

Curve 4 now represents the reflected wave which fulfils all the necessary conditions, and by compounding it with the incident wave the resultant disturbance is obtained (curve 5). Using the above method of construction, and starting from any arbitrary instant (calling it $t = 0$), and then representing the wave motions at intervals of $\frac{1}{8}$ of a period, the series of curves shown in Fig. 15 is obtained. With regard to these curves it should be noted :

1. There are a number of equally spaced points where the medium is undisturbed. These are termed nodes and denoted by the letter N.

2. Between the nodes the particles undergo different displacements. The places where this is a maximum are antinodes.

3. The amplitude of the resultant wave at any point varies with time. At the antinodes it varies from a maximum of twice the maximum amplitude of the incident wave to zero. It varies from a maximum positive amplitude, or displacement, to an equal maximum negative displacement and back again in a complete cycle.

4. The wavelength of the standing waves is the same as that of the incident (and reflected) wave train.

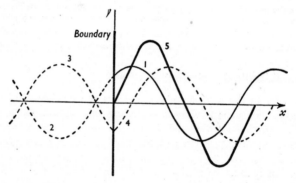

FIG. 14.   Construction of reflected and resultant wave.   1, Incident wave; 2, Continue on ; 3, Turn up ; 4, Fold back; 5, Resultant wave.

12. *Cheshire's disc* is a simple piece of apparatus for demonstrating compressive standing waves or standing waves in a gas. In construction it is very similar to Crova's disc, but there is one important difference which makes the waves appear stationary instead of progressive. In Crova's disc the progressive waves appear to move outwards from the centre of the disc, whereas in Cheshire's disc the particles move in concertina fashion about fixed points. The compressions and rarefactions are set up about fixed points which undergo no displacement and are, of course, nodes. At some instants, as shown in Fig. 15, there are no compressions and rarefactions present and the particles are all instantaneously undisturbed. To construct the disc draw a circle, about $\frac{3}{4}$ in. in diameter, on a piece of cardboard

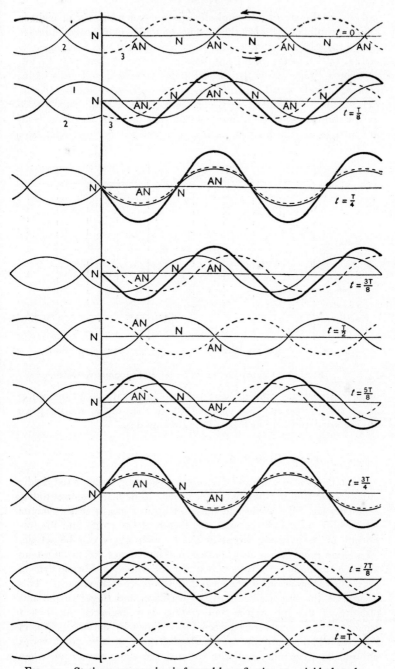

FIG. 15. Stationary waves in air formed by reflection at a rigid obstacle.

and divide the arc of one semi-circle into equal parts, six or eight is a suitable number. Project these points on to the diameter and number these projections 1, 2, 3, 4, etc., from left to right and back again as in Fig. 17. Starting with point number 1 as centre, and radius $\frac{1}{2}$ in., describe a circle. Now with centre point number 2 and radius $\frac{1}{2}$ in. plus a suitable small amount, say 0·2 in., describe another circle. Repeat this from points 3, 4, 5, etc., increasing the radii of the circles by the same amount each time, and moving the compass point from left to right and back again, until a sufficient number of circles have

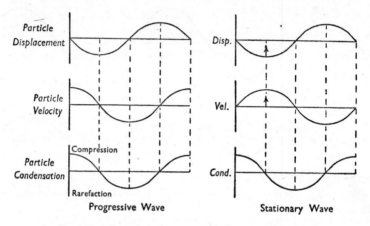

FIG. 16. Comparison of stationary and progressive waves.

been constructed. Spin the disc, on a suitable shaft, about the centre of the small circle *AB*, and view it through a slit cut in another piece of cardboard and held in front of the rotating disc.

13. Transverse Standing Waves

Standing waves can also be set up in a vibrating string, fixed rigidly at both ends, and in suitably clamped rods. The main point of difference between these waves and those set up in a gas, is that a definite relationship must exist between the length of the string and the frequency of the exciting vibration before such waves can be set up. This same relationship also holds if standing waves are to be set up in a gas contained in a tube closed at both ends. A vibrating string has a blurred appearance when standing waves are formed on it. This is because the displacements of the particles, and therefore the amplitudes of the sine waves representing their displacement, do not remain constant but vary between those shown by curves 1, 2, 3, in Fig. 18. The amplitude of the displacement at any point varies sinusoidally with time, and with the distance along the string, when

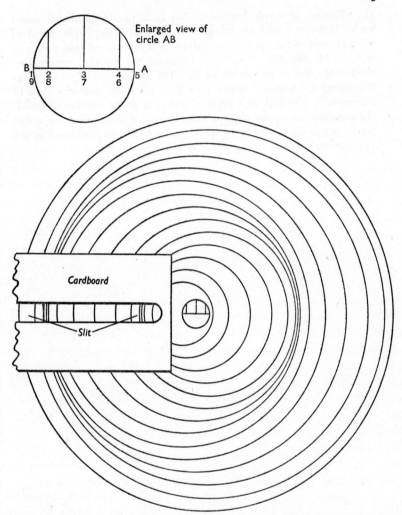

Enlarged view of
circle AB

Fig. 17. Cheshire's Disc.

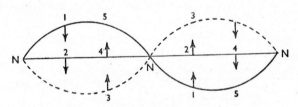

Fig. 18. Standing waves in a vibrating string.

the vibration is simple harmonic. At an antinode the displacement varies between o and 2*a*, where *a* is the maximum displacement of the particles of the applied oscillation, if it is assumed that energy is not lost by reflection, transmission through the medium surrounding the string, and in the string itself. The persistence of vision gives the string a " bowed " appearance as it takes on itself the form of curves 1, 2, 3 of Fig. 18 with the frequency of the applied vibration. As standing waves are really a special case of interference of sound waves, methods of detecting their presence will be discussed in the appropriate chapter.

CHAPTER III

THE VELOCITY OF SOUND

* 14. Equations of Motion of Simple Harmonic Waves

The simple harmonic wave is the most important type of sound wave, since, by Fourier's theorem, complex wave forms may be split up into simple harmonic components.

If a progressive S.H. wave is proceeding with velocity v in the positive direction along Ox, the displacement y of a particle of the medium, whose equilibrium position is specified by x is given by

$$y = a \sin \omega\left(t - \frac{x}{v}\right) \qquad . \qquad . \qquad . \qquad (\text{I})$$

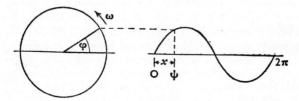

FIG. 19.

The velocity of this particle is $\dfrac{\partial y}{\partial t}$, the differentiation being partial, i.e. x is regarded as constant since we are considering a particular particle whose position is defined by x.

$$\frac{\partial y}{\partial t} = a\omega \cos \omega\left(t - \frac{x}{v}\right).$$

Its acceleration is similarly given by $\dfrac{\partial^2 y}{\partial t^2}$, and

$$\frac{\partial^2 y}{\partial t^2} = -a\omega^2 \sin \omega\left(t - \frac{x}{v}\right) = -\omega^2 y \qquad . \quad (2)$$

which merely confirms that the particle is executing a S.H.M. of the same frequency as the source. Also at a particular instant, i.e. when the time is regarded as constant

$$\frac{\partial y}{\partial x} = -\frac{a\omega}{v} \cdot \cos \omega\left(t - \frac{x}{v}\right)$$

so that

$$\frac{\partial y}{\partial t} = -v \cdot \frac{\partial y}{\partial x} \qquad . \qquad . \qquad . \qquad (3)$$

which connects the velocity of a particle in the medium with the slope of its displacement curve.

★ This section may be omitted at the first reading.

25

A second partial differentiation of $\dfrac{\partial y}{\partial x}$ with respect to x gives

$$\frac{\partial^2 y}{\partial t^2} = -\frac{a\omega^2}{v^2}\sin\omega\left(t - \frac{x}{v}\right) = -\frac{\omega^2}{v^2}\cdot y \qquad . \qquad . \quad (4)$$

whence $$\frac{\partial^2 y}{\partial t^2} = v^2\frac{\partial^2 y}{\partial x^2}, \text{ or } \frac{\partial^2 y}{\partial x^2} = \frac{1}{v^2}\frac{\partial^2 y}{\partial t^2} \qquad . \qquad . \qquad . \quad (5)$$

from equations (2) and (4).

Equations (2), (4), (5) and especially (5), are the differential equations of a wave motion. In equation (5), the coefficient of the derivative on the right-hand side represents the square of the velocity of the wave.

* 15. The Velocity of a Longitudinal Wave in an Elastic Solid

The wave in question consists of a succession of compressions and extensions which travel forward with the required velocity v. Consider a uniform rod of cross section A sq. cm. and density ρ gm./cc.

If a blow or impulse $F \cdot \delta t$ is given to one end of this, it will produce a compression δx cm. which will travel forwards a distance $v\delta t$ cm. in the interval δt sec. The momentum acquired by the length of rod $v\delta t$ cm. is thus $v\,\delta t \cdot A \cdot \rho \cdot \dfrac{\delta x}{\delta t} = A \cdot \rho v \cdot \delta x \cdot$ dyne sec.

It is only this length of rod which suffers a movement δx cm. in the time δt, the remainder of the rod is so far unchanged as the wave has not yet reached there.

The force F can be associated with the compression δx it produces in a length $v\delta t$ by considering the elastic properties of the rod. If Young's modulus for the material is E dynes/sq. cm., then

$$E = \frac{\text{stress}}{\text{strain}} = \frac{F}{A}\bigg/\frac{\delta x}{v \cdot \delta t} = \frac{Fv}{A}\frac{\delta t}{\delta x}\text{ dynes/sq. cm.}$$

or $$F = \frac{E \cdot A}{v}\frac{\delta x}{\delta t}\text{ dynes.}$$

The impulse is thus $F\delta t = \dfrac{EA}{v} \cdot \delta x.$

Equating the impulse to the change of momentum produced

$$\therefore \frac{EA}{v}\cdot\delta x = A\rho v\cdot\delta x$$

or $$v = \sqrt{\frac{E}{\rho}}\text{ cm./sec.} \qquad . \qquad . \qquad . \qquad . \quad (1)$$

* 16. Transverse Vibrations of a Stretched String

Suppose the string or wire to be stretched with a tension T and that its mass per unit length is m. The axis of x is taken along the equilibrium position and y denotes the transverse deflection at a distance x from one end O of the string, at the time t.   It is assumed that the gradient $\dfrac{\partial y}{\partial x}$ of the curve formed by the string at any instant is so small that the change of tension may be neglected.   Consider the equilibrium of an element δs of the string, of mass $m\delta s$.   The component of the tension T pulling downwards at the left end of the element is $T \sin \psi$, where ψ represents the inclination of the tangent to the x axis at this end of the element.   Since $\sin \psi = \dfrac{\partial y}{\partial s}$ this component is $T\dfrac{\partial y}{\partial s}$.   Hence the force acting upwards at the other end of the element is

$$T\frac{\partial y}{\partial s} + \frac{\partial}{\partial s}\left(T\frac{\partial y}{\partial s}\right)\delta s,$$

the second term representing the total change in $T\dfrac{\partial y}{\partial s}$ from the beginning to the end of the element, on the assumption that its rate of

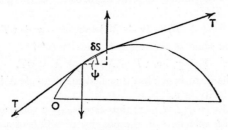

Fig. 20

change with respect to the arc s is sensibly constant over the small length δs.   The resultant force acting on the element in the direction to increase y is therefore

$$\frac{\partial}{\partial s}\left(T\frac{\partial y}{\partial s}\right)\delta s = T\frac{\partial^2 y}{\partial s^2} \cdot \delta s$$

since T is assumed to be constant.   As the acceleration of the element in this direction is $\dfrac{\partial^2 y}{\partial t^2}$ the force causing it is $m\delta s \cdot \dfrac{\partial^2 y}{\partial t^2}$ so that

$$T\frac{\partial^2 y}{\partial s^2}\delta s = m\delta s \frac{\partial^2 y}{\partial t^2}$$

or

$$\frac{\partial^2 y}{\partial s^2} = \frac{m}{T} \frac{\partial^2 y}{\partial t^2}.$$

By virtue of the assumption stated at the outset, $\sin \psi \eqsim \tan \psi$, so that $\dfrac{\partial y}{\partial s}$ may be replaced by $\dfrac{\partial y}{\partial x}$ and $\dfrac{\partial^2 y}{\partial s^2}$ by $\dfrac{\partial^2 y}{\partial x^2}$.

The equation of motion then becomes

$$\frac{\partial^2 y}{\partial t^2} = \frac{T}{m} \frac{\partial^2 y}{\partial x^2} \qquad . \quad . \quad . \quad . \quad (1)$$

and comparison with equation (5) of section 14, shows that this represents a wave motion of velocity $v = \sqrt{\dfrac{T}{m}}$.

Replacing $\dfrac{T}{m}$ by v^2 equation (1) may be re-written

$$\frac{\partial^2 y}{\partial x^2} = \frac{1}{v^2} \frac{\partial^2 y}{\partial t^2} \qquad . \quad . \quad . \quad . \quad (2)$$

Solutions to this equation are $y = f_1(vt - x)$ and $y = f_2(vt + x)$, as is verifiable by differentiation. Hence the general solution is

$$y = f_1(vt - x) + f_2(vt + x) \qquad . \quad . \quad . \quad (3)$$

where f_1 and f_2 are arbitrary functions.

Considering the first term alone which represents the disturbance at a point x at the time t, then the disturbance at the point $x + X$ at the time $t + T$ is

$$Y = f\{v(t + T) - (x + X)\} = f\{vt - x + vT - X\}$$

and this is the same as the original disturbance if

$$Y = y, \text{ i.e. } vT - X = 0 \text{ or } X = vT.$$

In this case the disturbance has travelled the distance X in the time T, so that its velocity is v.

The equation $y = f(vt - x)$ thus represents a wave-form travelling unchanged with velocity v in the positive direction of x and therefore $y = f(vt + x)$ will represent a similar disturbance travelling along the string with velocity $- v$, i.e. backwards. It thus appears that the most general free motion of the string may be regarded as made up of two such wave systems superimposed.

* 17. A relationship between frequency, length of vibrating string, tension and mass per unit length of the string may be obtained by dimensional analysis.

Assuming that frequency $n \propto l^a m^b \overline{T}^c$ where $\overline{T}$ is the tension and is so designated as not to be confused with T indicating time.

Then $[T]^{-1} = [L]^a \left[\dfrac{M}{L}\right]^b [MLT^{-2}]^c$. Equating indices of the units of mass length and time, it follows that

$$[L] \quad a - b + c = 0$$
$$[M] \qquad b + c = 0$$
$$[T] \qquad - 2c = - 1.$$

Hence

$$c = \tfrac{1}{2}, \; b = -\tfrac{1}{2}, \; a = -1.$$

$$\therefore \; n \; \propto l^{-1} m^{-\frac{1}{2}} \overline{\overline{T^{=\frac{1}{2}}}}.$$

$$\text{or} \; n \propto \frac{1}{l} \sqrt{\frac{\overline{\overline{T}}}{m}}.$$

18. Velocity of Sound in a Gas

Newton's formula showed that the velocity of sound as a medivm was given by $c = \sqrt{\dfrac{E}{\rho}}$, where E is the modulus of elasticity, ρ is the density of the medium, and c now replaces the symbol v used to denote the velocity of sound in the first investigation, so as to avoid confusion with the symbol used to represent volume.

In the case of a gas E must be the bulk modulus, the only modulus of elasticity it possesses.

$$E = \frac{\text{stress}}{\text{strain}} \backsimeq \frac{\delta p}{-\dfrac{\delta v}{v}} = -v \frac{\delta p}{\delta v}$$

where the symbols have their usual significance.

Assuming the changes are isothermal and so $pv = $ constant.   Then

$$p\delta v + v\delta p = 0. \quad \therefore \; \frac{-v\,\delta p}{\delta v} = p,$$

and hence the velocity of sound in a gas $c = \sqrt{\dfrac{p}{\rho}}.$

Assuming the gas to be air at S.T.P.   Then

$$p = 76 \times 13 \cdot 6 \times 981 \text{ dynes/sq. cm.}$$
$$\rho = 1 \cdot 29 \times 10^{-3} \text{ gm./cc.}$$

whence

$$c = \sqrt{\frac{76 \times 13 \cdot 6 \times 981}{1 \cdot 29 \times 10^{-3}}} \text{ cm./sec.}$$

$$\backsimeq 280 \text{ m./sec.}$$

or $\backsimeq 934$ ft./sec.

Working from his data Newton obtained a value of 916 ft./sec. By experiment, however, he found the velocity to be 1090 ft./sec., but he could not account for the difference between the calculated and observed values.   In 1816, about 100 years later, the problem was solved by Laplace.

Laplace's Correction.   Laplace decided that the compression and rarefactions took place so rapidly that the gas has not sufficient time to lose heat to or take heat from the surrounding air, i.e. the compressions and rarefactions take place adiabatically (at constant heat) and so the air in the path of a sound wave undergoes temperature fluctuations. Newton assumed that the compressions and rarefactions took place isothermally and so assumed Boyle's law to be true. For adiabatic compression and expansion the equation relating pressures and volumes is $pv^\gamma = $ a constant where γ is the ratio of the specific heats of the gas at constant pressure and constant volume. Hence

$$v^\gamma \delta p + \gamma v^{\gamma-1} . \delta v . p = 0$$
$$\therefore \ v \delta p + \gamma p \delta v = 0$$

and so
$$-\frac{v . \delta p}{\delta v} = \gamma . p.$$

Thus
$$c = \sqrt{\frac{\gamma p}{\rho}}.$$

For air $\gamma = 1\cdot40$ and assuming the value of p and ρ for S.T.P.

$$c = \sqrt{\frac{1\cdot4 \times 76 \times 13\cdot6 \times 981}{1\cdot29 \times 10^{-3}}} \text{ cm./sec.}$$

$$\backsimeq 331\cdot6 \text{ m./sec. at } 0^\circ \text{ C.}$$
$$\backsimeq 1100 \text{ ft./sec. at } 0^\circ \text{ C.}$$

For 1 gm. of gas $pv = rT$ or $\dfrac{p}{\rho} = rT.$

$$\therefore \ c = \sqrt{\gamma . rT} = k\sqrt{T},$$

where k is a constant and $c_0 = k\sqrt{T_0}.$

$$\therefore \frac{c}{c_0} = \sqrt{\frac{T}{T_0}} = \sqrt{\frac{273 + t}{273}} = \sqrt{1 + \frac{1}{273} . t} = \sqrt{1 + \alpha t},$$

where $\alpha = 0\cdot00367/^\circ$C. for air.

Hence
$$\frac{c}{c_0} = (1 + \alpha t)^{\frac{1}{2}} \backsimeq 1 + \tfrac{1}{2}\alpha t \backsimeq 1 + 0\cdot00184t.$$

$$\therefore \ c = c_0 + 0\cdot00184 \ c_0 t$$

since
$$c_0 \backsimeq 33{,}200 \text{ cm./sec.} \quad c \backsimeq 33{,}200 + 61t \text{ cm./sec.}$$

19. Factors Affecting the Velocity of Sound in a Gas

1. *Pressure.* For a given temperature, the velocity of sound in a gas is given by $v = \sqrt{\dfrac{\gamma p}{\rho}}$. In a gas, a change in pressure is accompanied by a change in density and vice versa, since if Boyle's law is assumed to be true $p . V = $ a constant or $\dfrac{p}{\rho} = $ a constant. Hence the velocity of sound is independent of change in pressure, or density, and experi-

ments carried out at high altitudes in the Tyrol have confirmed this result. It must be noted that at high pressures, when Boyle's law is not obeyed, this statement is no longer true.

2. *Temperature.* Consider a mass M of gas under constant pressure at $0°$ C. and then at $t°$ C. Then $M = V_0\rho_0 = V_t\rho_t$ where V_0, V_t, ρ_0, ρ_t, are the volumes and densities at $0°$ C. and $t°$ C. respectively. But $V_t = V_0(1 + \alpha t)$ where α is the coefficient of volume expansion of a gas at constant pressure. Hence $\rho_0 = \rho_t(1 + \alpha t)$ so that

$$\frac{v_t}{v_0} = \sqrt{\frac{\rho_0}{\rho_t}} = \sqrt{\frac{1 + \alpha t}{1}},$$

where v_t, v_0 are the velocities of sound at $0°$ C. and $t°$ C. Now as α is very nearly $\dfrac{1}{273}/°$C for all gases

$$\frac{v_t}{v_0} = \sqrt{\frac{273 + t}{273}} = \sqrt{\frac{T}{T_0}},$$

$$\text{or } v \propto \sqrt{T},$$

where T is the temperature on the absolute scale.

3. *Density.* The factor γ, in the equation relating the velocity of sound with the pressure and density of the gas, was necessary because the ratio $\dfrac{p}{\rho}$ is only constant if the temperature is constant. The compressions and rarefactions take place adiabatically, i.e. at constant heat instead of constant temperature, and so the temperature of the air in the path of the sound wave undergoes rapid fluctuations. Thus, other things being constant, the velocity of sound is proportional to the square root of the ratio of the specific heats of the gas. This ratio depends upon the number of degrees of freedom of the molecules, and it can be shown that $\gamma = 1 + \dfrac{2}{r}$ where r is the number of degrees of freedom. As is shown in text books on heat,[1] the molecules of a monatomic gas have three degrees of freedom (since three co-ordinates are required to fix it in space), those of a diatomic gas have five degrees, and those of a triatomic gas have six degrees of freedom. It follows that :

Helium and other monatomic gases . .	$r = 3$	$\gamma = 1·66$
Air, oxygen, hydrogen, and other diatomic gases	$r = 5$	$\gamma = 1·40$
Carbon dioxide and other triatomic gases .	$r = 6$	$\gamma = 1·33$

[1] Preston, *Heat*, p. 289.

Comparing gases having the same atomicity, e.g. oxygen and hydrogen, then, for the same temperature and pressure, the velocity of sound is inversely proportional to the density, and therefore

$$\frac{v_0}{v_H} = \sqrt{\frac{\rho_H}{\rho_0}} = \sqrt{\frac{1}{16}} = \frac{1}{4},$$

where v_0, v_H are the velocities in oxygen and hydrogen.

This fact can be demonstrated convincingly by means of a police type whistle and a long piece of Bunsen tubing. Since the physical dimensions of the whistle determine the wavelengths of the sound emitted, and $v = n\lambda$, any variation in the velocity will cause a corresponding variation in the frequency of the note emitted. One end of the tube is attached to the whistle and the other end to the gas supply. When the gas is turned on the whistle is first blown by the air in the tubing, and when this is all expelled it is blown by coal gas. The note emitted rises very obviously when the coal gas begins to pass through the whistle, the frequency being quadrupled and so the rise in pitch is two octaves. The gas supply is now turned off and the end of the tubing fastened to the gas tap is detached. Using the lungs, the coal gas is driven through the whistle and the whistle once more blown by air. This time the note falls in pitch as the coal gas is replaced by air.

It was pointed out by Blaikley,[1] that if the earth's atmosphere were hydrogen, instead of oxygen, a piccolo would have to be a yard long, and a contra-bass saxhorn as long as a cricket pitch, to give notes of the same range of pitch as those produced under present conditions.

4. *Humidity.* The velocity of sound in air is only altered slightly by the presence of water vapour. The effect of the vapour is to produce a slight lowering of the mean density of the air. The effect on γ, the ratio of the specific heats, is negligible at ordinary temperatures, even when the air is saturated. This lowering of the mean density means that the velocity of sound is increased when water vapour is present. At $10°$ C. the velocity in saturated air is greater than that in dry air by about 3 ft./sec. In dealing with problems on this point the method of solution consists of finding the mean density of the saturated air from the data provided, using, of course, Dalton's Law of Partial Pressures.

EXAMPLE. If the velocity of sound in dry air at $0°$ C., and under a pressure of 76 cm. of mercury, is 332 m./sec., find :

1. The velocity in dry air at $20°$ C. and a pressure of 76 cm. of mercury.

2. The velocity in air, saturated with water vapour, at $20°$ C. and 76 cm. of mercury. It may be assumed that the saturation

---

[1] Blaikley, *Cantor Lecture,* 1904.

vapour pressure of water at 20° C. is 1·74 cm. of mercury, and that the ratio of the densities of aqueous vapour and dry air is 1 : 1·6.

1. Since the pressure is constant $v \propto \sqrt{T}$ and hence

$$\frac{\text{velocity at 20}^\circ \text{ C.}}{\text{velocity at 0}^\circ \text{ C.}} = \sqrt{\frac{293}{273}}, \quad \text{velocity at 20}^\circ \text{ C.} = 332\cdot0 \times \sqrt{\frac{293}{273}}$$

$$= 344\cdot0 \text{ m./sec.}$$

2. Let ρ' and ρ be the densities of the mixture and dry air respectively then $\dfrac{\rho}{1\cdot6}$ is the density of water vapour.

Consider unit volume of the mixture and let x be the fractional

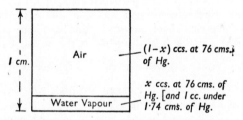

FIG. 21. Diagram showing the volume occupied if the water vapour and air are separated and both put under a pressure of 76 cm. of mercury.

volume occupied by the water vapour. By Dalton's Law of Partial Pressures

pressure of mixture = pressure of air + pressure of water vapour,
∴ 76 cm. = pressure of air + 1·74 cm.,
pressure of air = 74·26 cm. of mercury.

Equating masses of air + water vapour in 1 cc. of the mixture,

$$1 . \rho' = (1 - x)\rho + x . \frac{\rho}{1\cdot6}$$

$$= \rho(1 - 0\cdot375 . x)$$

$$= \rho\left(1 - \frac{0\cdot375 \times 1\cdot74}{76\cdot00}\right)$$

$$= \rho(1 - 0\cdot00858)$$

$$\therefore \rho' = 0\cdot9914 . \rho$$

(since $1\cdot74 \times 1 = 76\cdot00 \times x$ by Boyle's Law).

3

Since the pressure is constant,

$$\frac{\text{velocity in dry air}}{\text{velocity in moist air}} = \sqrt{\frac{\text{density of moist air}}{\text{density of dry air}}}$$

$$\text{velocity in moist air} = 344 \cdot 0 \sqrt{\frac{\rho}{\rho'}}$$

$$= 344 \cdot 0 \times \sqrt{\frac{1}{0 \cdot 9914}}$$

$$= 345 \cdot 3 \text{ m./sec.}$$

i.e. the velocity is increased by 1·3 m./sec.

5. *Frequency.* Everyday experience shows that the order of the notes in a piece of music is unchanged when the music is heard at different distances from the source. This shows that the velocity of sound in air is constant for the particular range of frequencies which affect the ear. Rayleigh,[1] using a stationary wave method, carried out a series of experiments on sounds beyond the limits of audibility. Since a sensitive flame is least disturbed at the nodes, and the nodal separation is $\dfrac{\lambda}{2}$, then the velocity can be calculated from $v = n\lambda$, provided that the frequency is known. Galton's whistle, later modified by Edelmann, is a simple form of adjustable organ pipe. The column of air is set into vibration by a jet of air which impinges on the round lower edge of the tube which contains it. Using the modified form of Galton's whistle two screw adjustments are made simultaneously. These are (1) move the nozzle or jet nearer the pipe, (2) alter the length of the pipe by means of the piston. The note produced then rises through the musical scale and finally becomes inaudible. Some idea of the size of the instrument can be gained if it is realised that a stopped organ pipe $4\frac{1}{4}$ mm. long will give a note of 20,000 vib./sec. Sounds which are propagated in the same way as audible sounds, but whose vibrations are so rapid that the human ear cannot respond to them, are termed *ultrasonics*. Professor J. Hartmann developed a ultrasonic source based on Galton's whistle but using a jet of much greater velocity.

The introduction of the wireless, or thermionic, valve made possible more elegant and precise methods of producing and maintaining supersonic vibrations, and hence finding their velocity from a measurement of frequency and wavelength. In 1880 Jean and Pierre Curie discovered the piezo-electric effect which led to the piezo-electric oscillator as constructed by Langevin during the 1914-18 war. His researches, however, were not published until some time later. G. W. Pierce,[2] an American physicist, carried out important experiments on

[1] *Sound*, **2**, p. 403.   [2] *Proc. Amer. Acad.*, **60**, p. 271, 1925.

the velocity of high frequency sounds using a crystal controlled valve oscillator producing ultrasonic vibrations. He found that, with free air, the velocity behaved in a very peculiar manner, e.g. at 0° C.

Frequency	Velocity
1000 vibs./sec.	331·94 metres/sec.
50,000 ,, ,,	332·47 ,, ,, (maximum value)
1,500,000 ,, ,,	331·64 ,, ,,

More important still was the behaviour of the waves in carbon dioxide. At 10^5 cycles/sec. the velocity was found to exceed that at sonic frequencies and the radiations were strongly absorbed. His results are shown graphically. Since then similar experiments have been carried out on nitrous oxide and sulphur dioxide and a similar effect has been found.[1] Up to the present limit of high frequency sounds (2×10^6 cycles/ sec.), similar effects have not been found using oxygen, nitrogen and the rare gases. The presence of a little water vapour with oxygen and nitrogen, however, does cause them to show a change in velocity and absorption with change of frequency. It may be that these gases will behave like CO_2, SO_2, N_2O if the frequency of vibration is

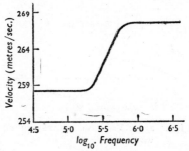

FIG. 22.   Variation of velocity of sound with frequency.

sufficiently high. What is important, however, is that at frequencies to which the human ear responds the velocity of sound is independent of frequency. Beyond the limits of audibility the velocity of sound in some gases does vary with frequency.

Amplitude. For sound waves of small amplitude, such as are normally met in everyday life, the equation $v = \sqrt{\dfrac{E}{\rho}}$ is sufficiently accurate to give the velocity. These waves travel through the medium without change of type. In the case of sounds of large amplitude, such as from explosions, the velocity of sound is considerably altered from that given by the formula above.

Poisson, Stokes, Earnshaw, Riemann, Rankine, Rayleigh,[2] and others have shown that a progressive wave of large amplitude changes

[1] *Discovery*, vol. iv, 1943, p. 245.
[2] Rayleigh, *Sound*, 2, p. 32 ; Lamb, *Sound*, p. 174 ; *Hydrostatics*, p. 470.

in type and velocity as it is propagated through a medium. The velocity increases with increase in density or condensation, i.e. the velocity in the more highly compressed part is greater than in the less compressed parts of the wave and so the shape of the wave alters. This effect is shown in an advancing sea wave. The velocity of the wave decreases as the depth of the water decreases, i.e. the velocity at the crest is greater than that nearer the sea bed. The crest gains on the trough, altering the shape of the wave, until the wave finally curls over and breaks. Regnault found, in experiments on the velocity of sound in pipes, that the velocity of sound increased with the amount of explosive charge used, and the velocity decreased as the distance of the observer from the source increased. Angerer and Ladenburg found that in the vicinity of a loud explosion the velocity of sound was 1150 m./sec., but at a distance of about 10 km. it had fallen to

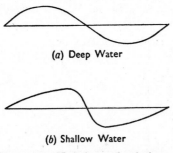

(a) Deep Water

(b) Shallow Water

FIG. 23. Variation of velocity of wave with depth of water.

its normal value. A bullet or shell travelling at a velocity less than that of sound gives out a spherical sound wave moving with normal velocity. If the velocity of the bullet is greater than that of sound then the condensation at the nose can be transmitted laterally but not forwards. Here, due to the large condensation, the velocity is greater than normal, and the nearer the tip of the bullet the greater will be this effect, i.e. the angle of the cone will increase towards the tip of the bullet so that the actual wave-front will resemble a blunted cone. As the speed of the bullet decreases the velocity of the wave will approach its normal value and the angle of the cone will increase. A sharp crack, sounding like an explosion, is heard when a body travelling with a velocity greater than that of sound passes an observer. This is known as the *onde de choc*, or *onde balistique*. Behind this is the *onde de bouche* or gun wave, of very low pitch, often inaudible, and is the sound used in sound ranging since its velocity is normal. The frequency of these sounds may be as low as 1 vib./sec. and they are described by Esclangon [1] as *Infra Sounds*. As they are usually accompanied by audible sounds the apparatus for sound ranging is made so as not to respond to the latter.

In conclusion it may be stated that sounds of small amplitude have a velocity which is constant and independent of the amplitude. Sounds of large amplitude travel with a velocity which depends upon, and increases with, amplitude and which gradually falls away to the normal value.

[1] E. Esclangon, *L'acoustique des projectiles et des canons.*

20. Methods of Finding the Velocity of Sound

These may be divided roughly into four main groups :—
1. Direct measurements in free air.
2. Direct measurements using air or gas in tubes and making a correction for the physical dimensions of the tube.
3. Indirect methods. These include methods using stationary waves and methods in which the frequency and wavelength are found and the velocity calculated instead of finding the velocity from the distance travelled by the sound in an observed time. Under this section are therefore included Hebb's and Pierce's (supersonic) methods, and other indirect methods such as vibrating strings, resonant columns of gas, Kundt's dust tube, etc. Of the methods mentioned in this section only those due to Hebb and Pierce will be treated at this stage, the others being dealt with under more appropriate sections of the book.
4. Direct methods using hydrophones for liquids in bulk.

21. Velocity of Sound in a Gas

Unlike light, with its very large velocity, the velocity of sound may be determined easily by direct measurement of the time required for the sound to travel a measured distance. Using free air and a large distance, so as to minimize the effect of timing errors, it is very likely that other errors are introduced due to the effect of wind, changes in temperature and humidity along the path of the sound.

The method of reciprocal observation appears to have been the first recorded careful observation on the velocity of sound in free air. It was made by the French Academy in 1738 and the effect of wind was eliminated by making almost simultaneous observations of the velocity along the same course in opposite directions. Cannon were fired at half-hourly intervals at distances of 18 miles apart, and observers at each end of the measured distance observed the interval of time between the flash of the powder and the noise of the explosion. The time of approximately one ten-thousandth of a second for the light to leave the cannon's mouth and reach the observer was negligible compared with the ordinary timing errors. When the temperature of the air was allowed for, the value of the velocity of sound obtained by this method was 332 m./sec. in dry air at 0° C.

In 1822 a similar method was tried by the Bureau des Longitudes. In this series of experiments the reciprocal firing took place at intervals of 5 minutes and the pendulum clocks of the first series of experiments were replaced by more accurate chronometers. The corrected value of the velocity of sound was 331 m./sec. at 0° C.

It must be noted that the value obtained is also an average value over a considerable distance, a distance which is so great that the conditions may vary considerably along it. As the velocity was required for the locating of guns, however, this average value was just as useful for this purpose as a value found in the laboratory to a higher degree of accuracy. The chief inaccuracy of these experiments lies in the personal equation of the observer. This is due to the time lag in response between seeing the flash, hearing the sound, and the muscular effort to operate the stop watch. Modern methods using microphones and electrical recordings reduce this error to a small constant value.

22. Regnault carried out an experiment to find the velocity of sound in free air using electrical recording and so removed the personal equation of the observer. The receiver itself had a "personal" equation which depended on the intensity of the sound wave. Regnault applied a correction for this. The method is shown diagrammatically in Fig. 24. The firing of the gun breaks the circuit

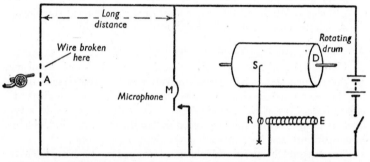

FIG. 24. Regnault's method for finding the velocity of sound in air.

of the electromagnet thus allowing the spring R to move to the left, and style S making a mark on the drum D which is rotating at a constant speed. When the sound wave reaches the microphone it closes the circuit containing electromagnet and battery thus drawing the spring R towards the electromagnet. This time the style S makes a mark to the right on the revolving drum. From the speed of rotation of the drum, the time interval represented by the distance between the appropriate marks made on the drum by the style can be calculated, and hence the average value of the velocity of sound over the distance AM.

Regnault obtained the following mean values of the velocity of sound at 0° C. :—

Distance AM	Velocity
0–1280 m.	331·37 m./sec.
0–2445 ,,	330·71 ,,
1280–2445 ,,	329·9 ,,

This showed that the velocity of sound was dependent on the intensity of the sound.

23. Echo Method (method of coincidences)

Kahl simplified methods used by Bosscha and König using an electromagnetic tapper and the echo from a wall. The observer moved away from the wall and noted points at which echo and direct sound coincided. If these are denoted by A, B, C, then the time required to go a distance $2d$ is the interval of time between the taps. If N is the number of taps made per sec. then $v = \dfrac{2d}{\dfrac{1}{N}} = 2Nd$.

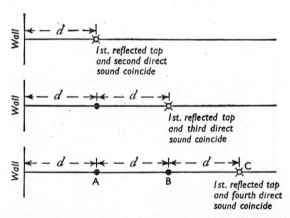

FIG. 25. Kahl's echo method of determining the velocity of sound in free air.

An alternative method is to alter the rate of tapping until taps and echo are heard simultaneously. Szathnari (1877) estimated that the accuracy of timing using this method of coincidences is $\dfrac{1}{400}$ sec.[1]

24. Esclangon [2] during 1917-18 made what are probably the most accurate observations of the velocity of sound in the open air. His method was essentially a modification of that of Regnault. His sources of sound were provided by a variety of guns. As detectors of sound he used tuned hot-wire microphones at distances of 1400 and 14,000 m. along the same line. The Tucker or tuned hot-wire microphone was designed during the first world war for the detection of enemy guns. It consists of an electrically heated platinum wire mounted in the neck of a Helmholtz resonator (see Chap. VII). This consists of a large vessel about 16 litres capacity which will respond only to the low

[1] Wood, *Textbook of Sound*, p. 236.
[2] *Comptes Rendus*, **168**, p. 165, Jan. 1919.

frequency sound of the gun wave or *onde de bouche*. The grid is
heated to just below red heat by a small steady electric current. When
the appropriate sound reaches the resonator the air in the neck is
set into vibration and the grid is cooled. This change in temperature
causes a change in resistance of the wire, and as the microphone is
placed in one arm of a previously balanced Wheatstone bridge circuit,
the bridge is no longer balanced, and the galvanometer registers a
deflection. The galvanometer must have a rapid response and so the
Einthoven string galvanometer is used. This consists of a fine wire
suspended in a strong magnetic field, the movement of the string being
viewed through one of the pole pieces of the magnet. (Fleming's
left-hand rule gives the direction of motion.)

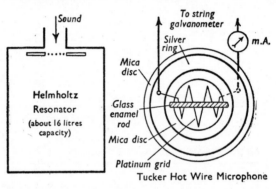

FIG. 26

Esclangon considered that the time difference between the instants
of arrival and the recording of the sound wave were accurate to within
$\pm$ 0·002 sec. and the final result of the velocity of sound in dry air
was 339·8 m./sec. at 15° C., as compared with that of 339·7 m./sec.
obtained by Regnault in 1864.

In 1921 Angerer and Ladenburg performed a series of experiments
using a charge of powder which broke a wire in a recording circuit.
An Einthoven string galvanometer was used to record the instant of
arrival of the sound. In the immediate vicinity of a loud explosion
the velocity was found to reach 1150 m./sec., the value falling to a
more normal value at distances away of about 10 km. At this distance the mean velocity was found to be 330·8 $\pm$ 0·1 m./sec. for dry
air at 0° C.

25. Hebb's Method

Finding the velocity of sound by measuring the time taken for the
sound wave to travel a large distance means that intense sounds have
to be used. As mentioned in the previous paragraph, Angerer and

Ladenburg showed that the velocity of sound in the vicinity of a large explosion was three times the velocity some distance away. Hebb pointed out that the uncertainties of the preceding methods were :

1. Temperature, wind and humidity variations at different points along the base line.

2. Very intense sounds have to be used. This means that the velocity of sound varies with distance.

These two uncertainties, together with various personal equation errors, he considered sufficient to account for the different values obtained by different observers. At the suggestion of Michelson, he devised and carried out an experiment which removed these uncertainties. The fundamental difference between his experiment and those of Regnault, Esclangon and others, lies in the fact that the velocity is not determined from the time required for the sound wave to traverse a known distance. He used a source of sound whose frequency was known accurately, measured accurately the wavelength of this sound wave and calculated the velocity from the equation $v = n\lambda$. The experiment was carried out in a hall 120 ft. $\times$ 10 ft. $\times$ 14 ft. This meant that there was no wind, the humidity was constant and could be found, and the temperature was determined from the readings of thermometers arranged along the walls. Fig. 27 shows the schematic arrangement of his experiment.

Two parabolic reflectors M_1, M_2, made of plaster of Paris, 5 ft. in diameter and 15 in. focal length, were arranged co-axially with about 100 ft. between the foci. The wavelength of the sound was approximately 6 in. and so the mirrors had to be large compared with this length. At the foci F_1, F_2 of the reflectors were placed carbon granule microphones or transmitters T_1, T_2, each being connected, together with a suitable battery, to a primary winding of a telephone transformer. The transformer had two primary windings and one secondary winding to which was connected a telephone earpiece. A high-pitched whistle S of frequency 2376 vib./sec. was placed at the focus F_2 of the mirror M_2. This source of sound consisted of a tube 0·75 in. in diameter and closed at one end. The sound was produced by blowing a stream of air across the open end. The pitch was compared with that of an accurately calibrated tuning fork and was kept constant to 1 part in 5000. (The frequency was determined by standard methods.)

Sound from S fell directly upon T_2, and upon T_1 after reflection at M_2 and M_1. These two sounds set up alternating currents in their respective primary windings. The change in magnetic flux through these windings induced a voltage across the secondary windings, which caused an alternating current in the secondary, which gave rise

to a note in the phones.   The sound heard was the resultant effect of
two alternating currents flowing in the secondary circuit.   When the
path $F_2M_2M_1F_1$ was an even number of half wavelengths then the
sounds falling on T_1 and T_2 were in phase or in step.   Thus the alternating currents in the secondary windings were in phase, and so rein-
forced each other, and this was shown by the presence of a loud sound
in the earphones.   When $F_2M_2M_1F_1$ was an odd number of half-
wavelengths, then the sounds, and hence the currents in the secondary,
were in antiphase, i.e. they tended to neutralise each other since they

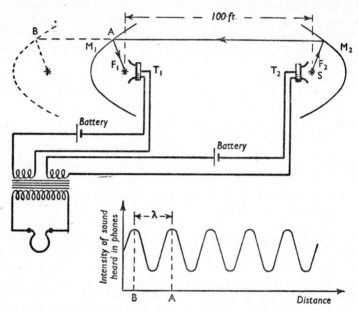

FIG. 27.   Hebb's telephone method for measuring the velocity of sound in
free air.

were in opposition, and the sound heard was a minimum.   In short,
the vector sum of the two effects determined what was heard by the
operator.   Thus keeping M_2 fixed and moving M_1 either towards or
away from M_2, the sound heard in the earphones passed through various
maxima and minima, the distance between each corresponding to
half a wavelength of the sound.   Hebb moved the mirror M_1 through
a distance corresponding to 100 wavelengths.   By determining the
position of the maxima and minima to one-tenth of a wavelength, and
using 100 wavelengths, this would give an error of the order of $\frac{1}{10}$ in
100, or 1 in 1000.

Hebb gave as his result $331 \cdot 29 \pm 0 \cdot 04$ m./sec. at $0°$ C.   It is
interesting to note that using the value $1 \cdot 405$ for the ratio of the specific

heats of air, as determined by Röntgen, the calculated value of the velocity of sound at 0° C. is 331·80 m./sec.

26. Pierce's Method for Sounds of High Frequency

The ear does not respond to all sounds and so it cannot be used as a detector of high frequency sounds. For sounds beyond the limits of audibility, the velocity is most conveniently measured by a method based on an experiment of Rayleigh in which he found the wavelength

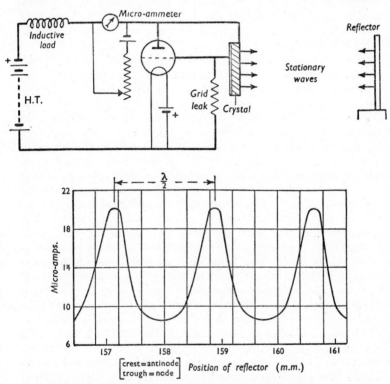

FIG. 28.   Pierce's method for sounds of high frequency.

of the sound by means of stationary waves. In his original experiment Rayleigh [1] used a bird-call as his source of sound. This consisted of a thin metal plate through a hole in which was blown a stream of air. This stream then fell on a similar hole fixed in a telescopic tube. By varying the distance apart of the holes, or the strength of the air stream, the frequency of the note was altered, the upper limit being inaudible. This source of sound was placed about 2 m. away from a plane reflector, such as a sheet of metal or glass. When the sound waves were reflected at the rigid boundary, stationary waves were set up, and

[1] *Sound*, **2**, p. 403.

the positions of the nodes and antinodes were located by means of a sensitive flame. The positions of the nodes were well defined, the flame being least disturbed at these places. The nodal (and antinodal) separation is $\frac{\lambda}{2}$, and hence, if the frequency were known, the velocity of sound could be found. For a bird-call the frequency is not known, but recent developments, using piezo-electric crystals and magneto-strictive rods (nickel) as the source of sound, have made it possible to determine the velocity of sound, using stationary wave methods, to a high order of accuracy, since the frequency of vibration can be accurately found.

Pierce for gases, and Boyle, Wood, Loomis and Hubbard for liquids have done noteworthy work in this connection.

Pierce [1] used a crystal of quartz, electrically maintained at its own natural frequency, as a source of high frequency sound. The compressions and rarefactions were given to the air by the vibration of the faces of the crystal. The frequency of the vibrations was determined by accurate wave-meter methods, as in standard radio-frequency measurement,[2] the ultimate standard of time being a master clock. The vibrating crystal was placed in front of a plane reflecting surface, the position of which could be accurately adjusted by means of a fine lead screw. The wave trains coming from the face of the crystal and reflected at the plane surface set up a system of standing waves. The measurement of the nodal separation (and hence the wavelength) of these waves was carried out by noting the effect of the sound waves on the oscillating crystal. Thus, when the sound waves falling on to the crystal tend to help its vibration, the oscillation of the crystal will be more violent (the two frequencies being the same) and vice versa. These effects are shown by the readings of the micro-ammeter in the anode circuit which fluctuate visibly with the phase of the oscillations which fall on the face of the crystal. As the reflector is moved, the current through the valve will fluctuate, the distance moved by the reflector to give two consecutive maxima or minima being half a wavelength. For precision measurements, the micro-ammeter was shunted, using a potentiometer arrangement. This neutralised the direct current through the valve so that the instrument only registered the fluctuations in current.

Pierce found that the position of the maxima could be located to 0·05 mm., and a hundred or so successive half-wavelengths could be counted giving an accuracy of the order 1 in 3000. He also showed that the loading of the crystal, due to the reflected wave, had a negligible effect upon its frequency of vibration.

---

[1] *Proc. Amer. Acad.*, **60**, p. 271, 1925.
[2] *Dictionary of Applied Physics*, **2**, p. 627 : Radio Freq. Measurement.

Pierce gave the following conclusions :

1. For free air.

(a) Between 40,000 and 1,500,000 vib./sec. the velocity varied with frequency in a peculiar manner, e.g. at 0° C.

Frequency	1,000	50,000	$1 \cdot 5 \times 10^6$
Vel. m./sec.	331·94	332·47 (max.)	331·64

(b) The effect of humidity is negligible. For 80 per cent. humidity the velocity differed by less than 0·02 per cent. from the velocity in dry air.

2. For CO_2.

(a) At 0° C.

Frequency	42,000	200,000 vibs./sec.
Vel. m./sec.	258·52	260·15

(b) At higher frequencies, CO_2 was found to become opaque to sound waves.

Two theories have been put forward to explain this behaviour. The Relaxation Theory supposes that a molecule has a sort of stiffness and so takes a definite time in responding to a vibration. Each molecule takes the impulse and, as it relaxes, hands it on to the next. Thus the speed of handing on the impulses will be undisturbed if the time between them is greater than the relaxation time. When the next impulse reaches the molecule before it has time to relax, then the molecules behave like a system of rigidly connected bodies, and the vibration is now transmitted at a higher speed. The Dispersion Theory lays emphasis on the scattering effect of radiation. The gases and vapours which scatter ultrasonics most are also noted scatterers of light. These substances tend to form aggregates, so that they are no longer truly isotropic. These media show changes of velocity with frequency, due to interference.[1]

Experimental data collected to date are insufficient to give a really satisfactory theory, although at the moment the relaxation theory has most supporters.

E. Griffiths [2] has used Pierce's method of finding the velocity of sound as a means of determining the percentage of CO_2, or other gases, mixed with air. If the gases do not react chemically, the nodal separation is an indication of the composition of the gaseous mixture.

27. R. W. Wood, A. L. Loomis, and J. C. Hubbard [3] made measurements of the wavelength of high frequency sounds in various liquids by a method analogous to that of Pierce. A quartz oscillator, 10 cm. in diameter, vibrating at 200,000 to 400,000 vib./sec., produced practically plane waves in a small dish of liquid placed upon it. The

---

[1] *Discovery*, Aug. 1943, p. 249.   [2] *Proc. Phil Soc.*, **39**, p. 300, Aug. 1927.
[3] *Phil. Mag.*, **4**, p. 417, 1927, and *Nature*, Aug. 6, 1927.

waves were reflected from a suitable surface placed in the liquid, the position of which could be accurately adjusted. The method of measuring the nodal separation was quite ingenious. A neon lamp was loosely coupled to the oscillating crystal thus receiving some energy from this circuit. The coupling was such that, as the reflector passed through each nodal point of the stationary waves, the neon was extinguished due to the reaction of the stationary waves on the crystal reducing the amplitude of oscillation, and so the amount of energy fed to the neon. The neon would glow more brightly when the reflector was at the antinodal points, but the maximum brightness would not be so obvious as the minimum.

No variation of velocity with frequency was detected, although it was found that small quantities of dissolved air materially affected the velocity. Typical results of the experiment are as follows :—

VELOCITY OF SOUND IN M./SEC.

Liquid	Temp. °C.			
	5	15	25	35
Distilled water	1439	1477	1509	1534
1 per cent. NaCl . . .	—	1487	1520	1542
Mercury	—	—	1469	1468
Carbon disulphide . . .	1215	1184		
Chloroform	1066	1027		

28. Velocity of Sound in Water

Water, either fresh or salt, is the only liquid which permits the direct measurement of the velocity over a considerable distance.

In 1826 Colladon and Sturm carried out on Lake Geneva the first recorded experiment to find the velocity of sound in water in bulk. A submerged bell, suspended from a boat, was struck by a hammer which simultaneously ignited a quantity of gunpowder. An observer in another boat about 9 miles away started a " quarter-second " stop watch when he saw the flash from the powder. To make this more obvious the experiment was carried out at night. A large ear trumpet, closed by a membrane and immersed in water, was used to detect the arrival of the sound through the water. Although water is denser than air it has a much greater elasticity, and so the velocity of sound in water is approximately four times that in air. Thus the sound through the water arrived after about 9 sec. and the direct sound after about half a minute.

Considering the primitive form of apparatus, and the conditions of the experiment, the results obtained were extremely good, giving a value of 1435 m./sec. at 8·1° C. against a calculated value of 1436·4 m./sec.

The great strides in submarine signalling have resulted in many elaborate and accurate experiments on the velocity of sound in the sea. In 1919 M. Marti[1] carried out experiments, in the Cherbourg roadstead at a depth of 13 m., using hydrophones to detect the sound produced by the explosion of a charge of gun-cotton. His results were rather high, probably due to the quantity of explosive used, although A. B. Wood found, in the experiments next described, that increasing the explosive charge from 2¼ to 300 lb. produced no change in the velocity when the nearest microphone was 12 miles away from the explosion. Marti, however, used smaller distances than this and the estimated velocity in the neighbourhood of a source increases with the quantity of explosive.

Between 1920-22 an extensive series of experiments was made in the sea off St. Margarets, Dover, by A. B. Wood, H. E. Browne, and C. Cochrane.[2] Four microphone receivers (hydrophones) were laid at intervals of about 4 miles on a N.S. line east of the Goodwin Sands. The position of these microphones was known to one part in 10,000. A six-stringed Einthoven galvanometer was used to record photographically the time intervals of the passage of the explosion wave. Four strings were connected to the microphones, the fifth string to a microphone receiving the ticks of an accurate chronometer, and the sixth string recorded the wireless signal from a destroyer each time a charge was fired. The time intervals were estimated to be correct to ± 0·001 sec. while the sound took about 14 sec. to traverse the measured distance. Continuous observations, of the salinity and temperature of the sea, were made throughout the experiment at various points along the base line. It was possible to calculate the velocity of sound in two ways :—

1. By measuring the interval between the arrival of the wireless signal from the destroyer exploding the charge and the arrival of the sound at any one of the four microphones.
2. By measuring the interval between the arrival of the sound at any of the four microphones.

Since there was some doubt about the exact position of the explosion the latter method was adopted.

Further experiments were made, at different times of the year and in different places (Gareloch and Dover), in order to study the effect of temperature and salinity. The results of the complete investigation showed that

$$v = 4266 + 13\cdot8t - 0\cdot12t^2 + 3\cdot73S \text{ ft./sec.}$$
or $$v = 1410 + 4\cdot21t - 0\cdot037t^2 + 1\cdot14S \text{ m./sec.}$$

where t is the temperature in °C. and S the salinity in parts per 1000.

[1] *Comptes Rendus*, **169**, 281, 1919. [2] Wood, A. B., *Textbook of Sound*, p. 246.

Methods of finding the velocity by echo depth sounding are not as reliable as might appear at first sight. The elasticity and density of water increase with pressure, the elasticity increasing the more rapidly. It has been calculated, for example, that at 30,000 ft. (5000 fathoms) the pressure is about 1000 atmospheres (67 tons/sq. in.) and the velocity is about 160 m./sec. greater than the surface value. Several other difficulties present themselves, since a considerable depth of water is desirable to ensure a high degree of accuracy in timing.

(a) The reflected sound may not come from directly under the ship, since the sea bed may be sloping.

(b) At great depths the echoes are weak.

(c) Wire depth soundings are doubtful at great depths due to the drift of the ship.

These factors do not detract from the use of echoes in the location of submarines, sunken wrecks or finding the undulations of the sea bed, since an accurate value of the velocity of sound in water is not required.

PRACTICAL APPLICATION OF THE VELOCITY OF SOUND

29. Multiple Point Sound Ranging

If the velocity of sound under the existing atmospheric conditions is known, then the position of a source of sound, such as a gun or mine, can be located by means of the sound wave only. To carry out this project three or more sound receivers are mounted at known positions on a surveyed base line. Suppose S is the source of sound and the spherical wave front WW, which originated at S, passes over the receivers 1, 2, 3, 4, at intervals of time 0, t_1, t_2, t_3. Denoting the velocity of sound by v, construct circles with centres 1, 2, 3, 4, having radii 0, vt_1, vt_2, vt_3 respectively. The origin of the sound wave must be the centre of the circle of which the circumference touches the smaller circles. Considering the distances, $S1$, $S2$, the difference between them is t_1v and so S lies on a hyperbola of which the points 1, 2, are the foci. Similarly S lies on a hyperbola having stations 1 and 3 as its foci, and so on for the other stations. Therefore the exact position of S is the point of intersection of a family of hyperbolae. The approximate position of S is given by the intersection of the asymptotes. When an accurate position is required an asymptote correction is applied.[1]

30. Army Sound Ranging

The above mentioned principles were extensively applied during the static warfare of 1914-18 for the location of heavy guns. Six

[1] *Aspects of Science*, by H. S. Toy, pp. 123 *et seq.* *The World of Sound*, Sir W. Bragg, pp. 181 *et seq.*

receivers were spaced along a 900 yd. base line, three additional receivers being deployed in case of failures and as a means of providing

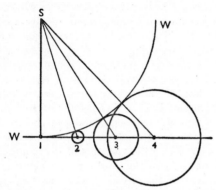

(a) Four microphones equally spaced on a base line

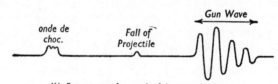

(b) Response of vessel of large volume to
firing of a gun (Esclangon)

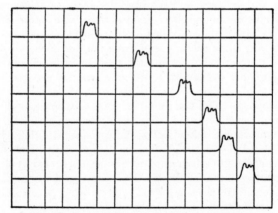

(c) Typical sound ranging record using six microphones
and showing response to the Onde de Bouche

FIG. 29.   Multiple point sound ranging.

check locations. The receivers were Helmholtz resonators, about
16 litres capacity, in the mouth of which was placed a Tucker Hot

4

Wire microphone (see Fig. 26). The large capacity ensured that the receiver resonated, or responded, only to the low frequency gun wave (*onde de bouche* or *infra son*). A six-stringed Einthoven galvanometer, fitted with a timing device, automatic photographing, and placed about a mile behind the resonators, was used for the recording of the gun wave. A lamp illuminated the strings of the galvanometer and produced a shadow of the strings on a photographic film. Between the lamp and the film was a toothed wheel, the revolutions of which were controlled by a tuning fork of known frequency. As the wheel revolved it cut off the light and so gave a series of timing lines across the moving film. The film was exposed, developed and fixed automatically so that the results were available a few minutes after the recording had been made. From the vibration of the strings and the timing lines as shown on the film the observer calculated the values of t_1, t_2, t_3, etc., as mentioned in the preceding section. The apparatus was switched on by an " observer " or " sentry microphone " as soon as the report of the gun was heard. In all cases a correction had to be applied for wind and temperature, and, under certain conditions of wind gradient, sound ranging was not possible. Under normal conditions the position of guns 3 to 10 miles from the microphones could be located to within 100 yd.

31. Navy Sound Ranging

The same principles were applied to locate the explosions of mines, depth charges and torpedoes. Hydrophones (steel diaphragms covering carbon granule microphones) were used instead of the ordinary type of microphone. Four of these were spread over a base line of 12 miles, the recording station was about 20 miles away. An Einthoven string galvanometer similar to that described previously was used to record and measure the time intervals. The position of the hydrophones was known to within a few feet and, using this arrangement, the position of an explosion 100 miles away could be located very accurately. The sea transmits sound extremely well, the absorption of water for sound being about 2000 times less than that of air. As an example of how well sound is transmitted through water it may be stated that a charge of 9 oz. of gun-cotton exploded under water is sufficient to send recordable sounds over a radius of 40 miles. Sound ranging in the sea also has the advantages that the sea is homogeneous and there is no need for a meteorological correction. The temperature fluctuations are also small and slow being from 6° C. to 17° C. in the North Sea between England and Holland.

32. The Binaural Effect

One of the most important functions of the ear can only be carried out when they are used as a pair, namely, the sense of direction. This instinctive sense is a problem which has been solved only partially so far. In many cases the senses of sight and touch assist the sense of hearing, but without these aids an average person can usually locate the direction of a sound to within a few degrees. The directional accuracy is good if the sound proceeds from left or right, but there may be an error of 180° if the sound is in front or behind. Two explanations have been given of this sense :

(a) There is a difference of intensity of the sounds received at the two ears. The sound is judged to be on the side of that ear which receives the greater intensity.

(b) There is a difference of phase in the sounds at the two ears. The sound is judged to be on the side where the phase leads.

In practice there is both phase and intensity difference at the ears except when the sound is directly in front or behind. Stewart [1] carried out extensive work on this subject. He found that :

1. The upper limit of the phase difference effect lies between 1000 to 1500 vib./sec. and hence this is the most important effect in locating a pure tone of 100 to 1200 vib./sec.

2. Above 1200 vib./sec. the intensity plays a very important part.

3. There are more factors to be considered than the simple theory suggests, e.g. reflection and changes in quality may have an important effect.

Detection of Aircraft by Sound Waves

Among the sounds produced by an aircraft are those due to the exhaust and the lateral vibration of the air-screw blades. Beats may occur if two engines are used, and Aeolian tones from the struts are present, but the latter are not audible over a considerable distance. The prominent sounds were found to range between 100 and 400 vib./sec. In order to locate the direction of an aircraft four collecting trumpets were used either in the form of a " + " or a " T ". The trumpets were used in pairs, one pair being used to give the bearing and the other pair the elevation. The four cones were fixed to a frame which could be rotated about a horizontal and a vertical axis by the operators. Accurately matched microphones, specially designed for use on sounds of 100 to 400 vib./sec. were placed at the narrow ends of the cones. The cones were then rotated about their respective axes until the sounds heard in ears of the observer were equally loud. The direction of the cones then gave the bearing and elevation of the plane. At the beginning of the 1939-45 war, the microphones were connected to selective amplifiers, the output of which was applied to a cathode ray tube and the apparatus was then known as Visual Indicating Equipment. When a related pair of

[1] *Phys. Rev.*, **15**, pp. 254 and 432, 1920.

microphones was directed towards the target, or plane, this was indicated by a vertical line on the cathode ray tube. When the microphones were receiving sounds which were not in phase the line on the tube was inclined to the left, or the right, thus indicating to the operator the direction in which to rotate the apparatus. The theory, design, and construction of this equipment were excellent, but the results obtained, although useful, were not up to the same standard. Considerable trouble was met due to the effect of moisture on cables, which gave untrue readings. The range of the instrument was not

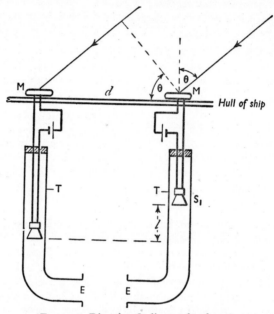

FIG. 30. Direction finding under the sea.

very great and the angle between the direction of the sound and the true direction of a plane travelling at 250 m.p.h. was considerable. Accurate and steady following of the target was difficult and so when radar was introduced, giving long range, pick-up, identification, practically instantaneous positions, and continuous following of the target, which could be fed directly to the predictor, the days of the sound locator were numbered.

33. Direction Finding under the Sea

Due to the excellent transmission of sound by water the binaural effect was used with great success to locate a source of sound which was moving, such as a ship or submarine. It was also used to take bearings on a fixed point, such as a lightship or buoy, sending out submarine signals. When the sounds received in hydrophones on opposite sides of the ship were of equal intensity then the ship was pointing in the direction of the source of sound. When the sounds were not equally loud, then it was desirable to know the bearing of the source. Instead of turning the ship until the sounds received in the two microphones were equally loud, simple methods were devised of calculating the bearing. Fig. 30 shows the principle of a method used by the Germans. The two microphones M, at a known distance apart in the water, fed loudspeaker telephones in tubes T which were applied to the ears of the operator at E. When the loudspeaker S_1 was moved it meant that the path difference of the sound in air in tube 1 was not equal to that in tube 2. S_1 was therefore adjusted until the sounds heard at E were in phase and this meant that the extra path difference in air in one tube was compensating for the extra path difference in water to the other tube. Suppose S_1 moved a distance l. Then for binaural balance $d \cdot \sin \theta = 4 \cdot 3 \times l$, where $4 \cdot 3$ is the ratio of the velocity of sound in water to that in air, i.e. $\sin \theta \alpha l$. Hence from the reading of l the bearing θ was found. The Americans used a system similar in principle, the adjustment being carried out by rotating a dial (a Binaural Compensator). The reading on the dial when the sounds at E were equally loud indicated the bearing in degrees.

34. Echo Depth Sounding

In the Behm-Echolot system a small charge is exploded in the water near one side of the ship. The initial and reflected pulses are received by microphones on the other side of the ship and recorded stylographically. On the same graph and side by side with the microphone traces is a sine wave due to a tuning fork of frequency 1440 vib./sec. The velocity of sound in sea water is approximately 1440 m./sec. so that the number of waves between the kicks of the microphones represents the depth of the sea (or the distance from the surface to the nearest large solid mass) in half metres, since the sound traverses the distance twice. In a modified form (the dial recorder) a disc is set in motion by the firing of the charge and stopped by the arrival of the echo. The angle of rotation of the disc is proportional to the depth, and so the periphery of the disc is calibrated in metres.

35. The British Admiralty uses a sonic, or audio frequency, source of sound in order to find the depth of the sea (Fig. 31). The sound source is a steel diaphragm, about 5 in. in diameter, which emits three times a second a short train of waves of frequency about 2000 vib./sec. An electromagnetically operated hammer excites the vibrations by a sudden blow when the current through the electromagnet, which holds off the spring-loaded hammer, is cut off.   The echo, and a small amount of the direct sound, are received by a hydrophone receiver mounted on the side of the ship opposite from the transmitter. Two commutators are driven, through suitable gearing, by a constant speed motor.   Each commutator has an insulating segment.   When the brushes on one disc come in contact with this segment the current through the electromagnet holding off the hammer is broken, the diaphragm is struck and a sound is emitted.   The second commutator short circuits the headphones, except when the brushes come in contact

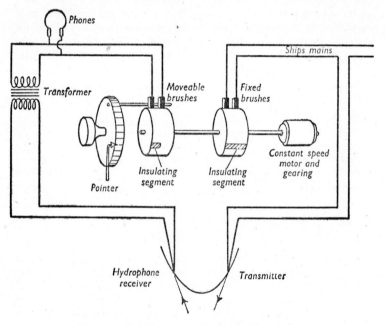

FIG. 31.   British system of echo depth sounding.

with the insulating segment (for about $\frac{1}{300}$ sec.).   Then the phones are live and it is possible to listen to the reflected sound if it happens to reach the headphones at this instant.   The position of the brushes on the commutator in the telephone circuit can be altered by rotating the disc which carries them.   The angular distance between the brushes in the two circuits is proportional to the interval of time between the sending out of the sound and when the phones can receive the re-flected sound.   The brushes are therefore rotated until the operator receives an echo.   Suppose the transmitter gives 3 impulses/sec. Then $360° \equiv \frac{1}{3}$ sec.   Assuming the velocity of sound to be 4920 ft./sec. in sea water, then a relative displacement of 90° of the brushes indicates an interval of time of $\frac{90}{360} \times \frac{1}{3}$ sec. $= \frac{1}{12}$ sec. Hence the depth of the sea $= \frac{1}{2} \times \frac{1}{12} \times 4920 = 205$ ft.

In practice, the calculations are unnecessary, the depths being indicated on the dial carrying the telephone brushes. This form of apparatus is used to measure depths up to about 200 fathoms (1200 ft.).

Ultrasonic Methods of Depth Finding

There are three principal ways of producing ultrasonic sounds of considerable energy.

1. Using the Hartmann oscillator. This is based on Galton's whistle and differs mainly in the velocity of the jet which provides the energy.

2. Piezo-electric effect. In 1880 the brothers Jean and Pierre Curie discovered that when certain crystals were compressed along their axes they developed charges, which was apparent as a potential difference, on two opposite faces. Conversely, if a potential difference was applied to the unstressed crystal, strains were set up in the form of a compression or extension.

If alternating current of the same frequency as the natural frequency of the crystal is applied then resonance takes place and much increases the mechanical vibrations. Commonly used substances are quartz, Rochelle salt and tourmaline. During the 1914-18 war Langevin realised the piezo-electric resonator, details of which were kept secret for some considerable time.

3. Magneto-strictive effect. This is similar in many respects to the piezo-electric effect. The potential difference is replaced by a magnetic field and the crystal by a rod of magnetic material, usually an alloy of nickel. A valve oscillator provides an alternating magnetic field at the natural frequency of the rod and when the rod is laid in a coil, it alternates in length, sending out longitudinal waves from its ends.

The Langevin system is based on a suggestion made by L. F. Richardson at the time of the *Titanic* disaster (April 1912). He proposed the use of a beam of ultrasonic waves as a means of detecting submerged objects, such as icebergs or wrecks, by echo. In order to radiate a considerable amount of energy the source must have a considerable area (cf. the vibrating area of a loudspeaker with that of a headphone). To give this necessary area Langevin built up a sandwich, made up of a large number of little crystals side by side, all having their axes of vibration parallel, and enclosed between two metal plates to act as electrodes. The vibrations of the slab of quartz move the lower plate relative to the upper in concertina fashion. A spark energised high frequency circuit is tuned to the natural frequency of the steel-quartz sandwich which then gives out a signal of short duration. Some of the waves reflected from the submerged object fall on the crystal oscillator which in the meantime has been connected automatically to the receiver. An important feature of the quartz oscillator is that it is " dead beat ". This means that as soon as the energising spark is cut off, the crystal stops oscillating. If this were not so the crystal might still be oscillating when the reflected wave returned. Various methods have been devised of observing or recording the interval of time between the initial and reflected pulse. In one method of visual recording, a spot of light is set moving at a constant speed. The return of the wave is shown by a kink in the path of the spot of light. For greater accuracy the constant speed of the beam of light is controlled by a phonic wheel controlled by a tuning fork. As a modification of this idea, the action of

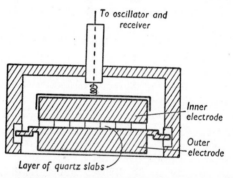

FIG. 32.   Piezo electric echo depth sounder.   Crystal sandwich tuned to a known frequency by thick metal electrodes.

sending out the ultrasonic pulse (about $\frac{1}{10}$ sec.) starts a pointer moving at constant speed over a dial graduated in fathoms or metres. The arrival of the first wave of the reflected pulse stops the pointer.

Distance is not the only information given by the echo sounder. The nature of the echo tells quite a lot about the sea bed. With a sharp and distinct echo a hard bed is indicated. If the echo is fuzzy (cf. light reflected from a mirror which is losing its silvering) then the sea bed is oozy or soft. The position of wrecks may also be determined, as shown by an abrupt change in the depth of the sea over an area corresponding to the size of a ship.

36. Practical Applications of Ultrasonics

When radiation passing through a metal arrives at a boundary within the metal, such as a crack, most of the radiation is reflected. The presence of cracks and internal flaws is determined by means of an oscillator and a receiver. If these are fixed on opposite sides of the metal a discontinuity will be shown by a drop in the energy received by the ultrasonic receiver. If the transmitter and detector are placed side by side a discontinuity causes an increase in the energy received at the detector. By placing an ultrasonic oscillator in a liquid the occluded air can be driven out. Metallurgists have been experimenting with this idea in order to remove traces of gas which sometimes occur when metals are melted down to form alloys. When the alloy is cold the gas bubble leaves a cavity inside which weakens the structure. Because of the temperature of the melt, the crystal or magnetostrictive oscillator cannot be placed inside, but it exerts its influence through a thin metal diaphragm. Two liquids of different density, such as aniline on water, can be emulsified by ultrasonics. When the oscillator is placed below the surface the liquid is forced up in the form of a continuous fountain, the aniline being emulsified as a cloud of small drops into the water. Ultrasonic radiation has also a disruptive effect on the cellular structure of plants and animals. As the specimen is usually placed in a liquid bath this may be due to the formation of cavities, or vacua, in the liquid due to the ultrasonic wave. Experiments showing the lethal effect of these waves have been carried out on small plant forms such as algae and bacteria in liquid suspension. Langevin's first experiments were carried out in a sea water tank and were found to be lethal to the small fish therein. In the dissipation of ultrasonic energy a considerable amount of heat is evolved, and account must be taken of this when judging the results of an experiment using these waves. When an ultrasonic oscillator is used in a liquid, a glass rod held with one end touching the surface of the liquid rapidly becomes unbearably hot, even when the rod is well away from the ultrasonic source.

37. Direction Finding on Land, Oil and Salt Prospecting

The Geophone [1] was invented by French engineers during the 1914-18 war and was used to find the direction of enemy tunnellers or sappers. It is used nowadays for rescue work in mines, tunnel construction, and in studying the depth of various strata in the earth. It consists of a hollow cylindrical wooden box, about 3 in. in diameter and 2 in. deep, containing a large mass of mercury enclosed between two mica discs. Between these discs and the ends of the box are two air cavities which are connected to the ears by stethoscope tubes. Due to its large inertia, the mercury remains still when pulses coming through the ground shake the box. The air spaces, however, are alternately compressed and expanded and sounds are heard by the observer. The device is very sensitive to thudding sounds. When used binaurally two geophones are used but one cavity in each is closed

[1] Bragg, *World of Sound*, p. 178.

by means of a plug. In order to find the direction of sound the observer moves one geophone until the sounds are heard simultaneously in both ears. The instrument is used in geophysical prospecting, i.e. locating deposits of ores, salt, oil, etc., to detect the arrival of artificial seismic waves. An artificial miniature earthquake is set up by means of dynamite in a region where it is suspected there is a salt dome, which is usually associated with oil deposits. The arrival of the waves, which have travelled through the earth, is recorded at points such as *A, B, C, D*, etc. From the distances *SA, SB*, etc., and the

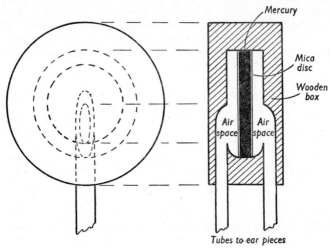

FIG. 33.   The geophone.

times to travel these distances, the velocity of sound can be calculated. If all the waves travel through the same medium then their velocities will be the same, but if one wave travels through a medium of different density this will be indicated by an anomalous velocity. By repeating the experiment several times the intersection of the directions giving anomalous velocities locates the salt dome with considerable precision.

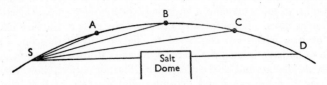

FIG. 34.   Oil prospecting.

QUESTIONS

1. Obtain expressions for the isothermal and adiabatic expansions of a gas. Explain the necessity for Laplace's correction in the expression for the velocity of sound in a gas in terms of pressure and density.

   Find the velocity of sound in air given that: Atmospheric pressure = 76 cm. of mercury, density of air = 1·293 gm./litre, γ = 1·40, g = 981 cm./sec./sec., density of mercury = 13·6 gm./cc.

2. How does the velocity of sound in a gas depend upon pressure, temperature, density of the gas, and the frequency and amplitude of the sound?

   If the velocity of air at 0° C. and 76 cm. of mercury is 330 m./sec., calculate the velocity at 27° C. and a pressure of 74 cm. of mercury.

3. Explain fully the difficulties inherent in the measurement of the velocity of sound in free air, and describe in detail one method of finding it.

   A short sound is made in front of an extensive wall and the echo is heard after 1·6 sec. After walking towards the wall for a distance of 33 m. the observer repeats the experiment and the time is 1·4 sec. How far is the observer from the wall and what is the velocity of sound?

4. A ship sounds its siren when approaching a cliff and the echo is heard after an interval of 8 sec. After moving steadily towards the cliff for another 5 min. the siren is again sounded and the interval between sound and echo is 3 sec. Find the distance of the ship from the cliff at this instant and calculate the velocity of the ship in a direction perpendicular to the face of the cliff (velocity of sound = 1120 ft./sec.).

5. Give an account of the experiments which have been made to determine the velocity of sound in water.

   Given that the bulk modulus of water at 15° C. is 2·23 × 10^{10} dynes/sq. cm. find the velocity of sound in water at that temperature.

6. Describe how the velocity of sound in either (1) air, or (2) water, may be determined by the use of echoes.

   An observer A fires a pistol in the angle between two high walls at right angles to each other, and the sounds produced are heard by an observer B. A is 110 yd. from one wall and 220 yd. from the other; B is 440 yd. from each wall. Draw a diagram to scale (110 yd. = 1 in.) showing the path of " rays " of sound from A to B, and calculate the time intervals between the sounds heard by B.

   (Velocity of sound in air = 1100 ft. per sec.)

   (N.U.J.M.B.)

7. Describe an experiment to find the velocity of sound in air at room temperature. A ship at sea sends out simultaneously a wireless signal above the water and a sound signal through the water, the temperature of the water being 4° C. These signals are received by two stations, A and B, 25 miles apart, the intervals between the

arrivals of the two signals being $16\frac{1}{2}$ sec. at A and 22 sec. at B. Find the bearing from A of the ship relative to AB. The velocity of sound in water at $t°$ C. $= 4756 + 11\,t$ ft./sec. (N.U.J.M.B.)

8. If the velocity of sound in air at S.T.P. $= 330$ m./sec., the ratio of the specific heats of air $= 1\cdot4$, the density of mercury $= 13\cdot6$ gm./cc., and $g = 981$ cm./sec./sec., prove that the height of the homogeneous atmosphere is nearly 5 miles. (1 ft. $= 30\cdot45$ cm.)

9. Find the velocity of sound in hydrogen given that the velocity of sound in air is 332 m./sec., and that under the same pressure the volumes of 1 gm. of hydrogen and air are $11\cdot161$ and $0\cdot774$ litres respectively.

10. Given that the velocity of sound in air at 0° C. and 760 mm. of mercury pressure is 332 m./sec. and the density of air at S.T.P. is $1\cdot293$ gm./litre find the adiabatic coefficient of elasticity for air.

11. Calculate the velocity of sound in air, at 15° C. and 745 mm. of mercury pressure, given the following data : density of air at S.T.P. $= 1\cdot293$ gm./litre, ratio of the specific heats of air $= 1\cdot407$, density of mercury at 0° C. $= 13\cdot596$ gm./cc., $g = 981$ cm./sec./sec., coefficient of expansion of air $= 0\cdot003665$ per deg. C.

12. How would you find by experiment the velocity of sound in air ? Calculate the velocity of sound in air in cm./sec. at 100° C. if the density of air at S.T.P. is $0\cdot001293$ g./cc., the density of mercury at 0° C. $13\cdot60$ gm./cc., the specific heat of air at constant pressure $0\cdot2417$, and the specific heat of air at constant volume $0\cdot1715$.

(Lond. H.S.C.)

13. Give an account of any important and characteristic wave phenomena which occur in sound. Why are sound waves in air regarded as longitudinal and not transverse ?

An observer looking due north sees the flash of a gun 4 sec. before he records the arrival of the sound. If the temperature is 20° C. and the wind is blowing from east to west with a velocity of 30 m.p.h., calculate the distance between the observer and the gun. The velocity of sound in air at 0° C. is 1100 ft./sec. Why does the velocity of sound in air depend upon the temperature but not upon the pressure ? (N.U.J.M.B. Schol.)

14. A ship travelling due north at 1 m./sec. in a thick fog fires a detonator in the sea alongside and receives an echo from a buoy on the port side $1\cdot2$ sec. later. Fifteen minutes later a repetition of the experiment yields the same result. What is the bearing and distance of the buoy ? Describe the type of apparatus you would use to make these measurements. (Velocity of sound in sea water $= 1500$ m./sec.)

(O.S.)

15. An observer standing close beside an anti-aircraft gun notices that the shell explodes 5 sec. after it has been fired. The sound of the explosion reaches him 9 sec. later. If the angle of elevation of the gun is 45°, calculate to within the nearest hundred feet the height

at which the shell explodes. (Velocity of sound in air = 1110 ft./sec. ; $g = 32$ ft./sec./sec.) (C.S.)

16. Find the specific heat of air at constant volume given that the velocity of sound in air at 20° C. and 760 mm. of mercury is 344 m./sec., the density of air at the same pressure and temperature is 1·240 gm./litre, the density of mercury is 13·6 gm./cc. and the mechanical equivalent of heat is 4·2 joules per calorie.

17. State briefly how you would show by experiment that the characteristics of the transmission of sound are such that (a) a finite time is necessary for transmission, (b) a material medium is necessary for propagation, (c) the disturbance may be reflected and refracted. The wavelength of the note emitted by a tuning fork, frequency 512 vib./sec., in air at 17° C. is 66·5 cm. If the density of air at S.T.P. is 1·293 gm./litre, calculate the ratio of the two principal specific heats of air. Assume that the density of mercury is 13·6 gm./cc. (N.U.J.M.B.)

18. On what does the velocity of sound in a gas depend ? Explain fully why an organ pipe blown in hydrogen might be expected to have a frequency two octaves higher than when blown in oxygen.

Calculate the velocity of sound in air which is saturated with water vapour at 18° C. and at a pressure of 76 cm. of mercury. Saturation pressure of water vapour at 18° C. : 15·5 mm. of mercury. Velocity of sound in dry air at 0° C. : 332 m./sec. The relative densities of hydrogen, water vapour, air, and oxygen under the same pressure and temperature conditions are 1 : 9 : 14·4 : 16. The ratio of the two specific heats of air may be taken as unaffected by the moisture content. (N.U.J.M.B. Schol.)

CHAPTER IV

REFLECTION, REFRACTION, INTERFERENCE AND DIFFRACTION OF SOUND

38. Reflection of Sound

When a sound wave meets a boundary between two media it is partially reflected, the reflected wave moving in the negative direction with the same velocity. In many cases the length of the sound wave is comparable with the linear dimensions of the " reflecting " object and diffraction takes place. In order to demonstrate the laws of reflection of sound it is essential therefore to use a sound of high frequency, i.e. short wavelength or very large reflecting surfaces. When these conditions are fulfilled then it can be shown that sound waves obey the ordinary laws of geometrical optics.

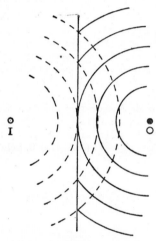

FIG. 35. Production of sound image.

Huyghens' construction of secondary wavelets can also be applied to sound waves in order to study the formation of sound images as shown in Fig. 35.

To demonstrate the laws of reflection of sound a suitable sound source is a ticking watch. Two metal tubes A and B about 3 in. in diameter and a yard in length are placed on a well padded table (Fig. 36). C is a suitable board, such as a drawing board, placed vertically, and another similar board or damp cloth D is desirable so as to cut off the direct sound from the watch W. One tube, say B, is fixed and the other tube adjusted until the observer, with his ear placed to the end of the tube D, hears most clearly the ticks of the watch. Under these conditions it is found that $\hat{r} = \hat{i}$, and also the incident ray, reflected ray and the normal at the point of incidence all lie in one plane.

As a further demonstration an experiment similar to that often used to show that radiant heat obeys the simple laws of reflection may be used. The watch W is hung at the principal focus of a large concave mirror A. A similar mirror, B, is placed about 6 ft. away so that the principal axes are collinear. An ear trumpet, such as a glass funnel connected to the ear by Bunsen tubing is then moved about in front of the mirror B until a position is found where the ticks of the watch are loud. This point is the principal focus of the reflector B. Moving the funnel away from F_2 causes the ticks to become inaudible. For a more elaborate experiment the funnel can be conveniently replaced by a microphone connected to an amplifier and loudspeaker.

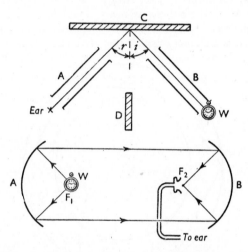

FIG. 36. To demonstrate the laws of reflection of sound.

39. Examples of the Reflection of Sound

1. In a narrow passage or corridor the sound of footsteps is louder due to reflections from walls and ceilings. Cf. also the noise of tube trains with similar trains in the open air.

2. In megaphones and horns of loudspeakers the sounds are reflected from the sides and the energy is concentrated in a cone of definite angle instead of being spread over a sphere.

3. The opposite is true of ear trumpets. The sound is collected by a large area, reflected down the tube and concentrated at the ear.

4. In deep wells (such as in Carisbrooke Castle, Isle of Wight, which is 200 ft. deep and 12 ft. wide) the noise made by a tiny stone striking the surface of the water is clearly heard at the top.

5. Whispering galleries such as in St. Paul's Cathedral. A person whispering at A can be heard quite clearly at B on the other side of the gallery and about 100 ft. away. Because of the dimensions of the gallery many of the waves keep close to the wall and by reflection are passed round the gallery.

6. Echoes are due to the reflection of sound. The reflector is large compared with the wavelength of the sound since it is usually a wall, block of buildings, hillside, etc. As mentioned in the preceding chapter an echo can be used to calculate the velocity of sound and for depth sounding. For a clear echo the distance must be such that the sound can go and return in the time taken to utter the syllables. The first syllable of the echo should not be heard before the speaker has finished. Multiple echoes, such as those set up by sounding a horn in the Alps, where there are many mountains to provide suitable reflecting surfaces, are caused by the repeated reflection of sound. If the reflectors are close together this gives rise to the echelon effect

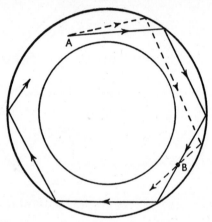

Fig. 37. Reflection of sound in the whispering gallery.

(see Chap. VIII). The rolling of thunder may be due partly to the reflections from clouds.

7. Reverberation or the prolonged reflection of sound in a building.

8. Stationary waves in rods, strings and gases (see Chaps. VI and VII) are produced by the interference of wave trains which are reflected at normal incidence.

40. Refraction of Sound

When sound from one medium enters another medium it suffers a change in velocity (cf. light) and so Huyghens' idea of secondary waves is a useful method of demonstrating the change in direction of the sound wave. If WW' is the incident plane wavefront, then a secondary wave starts from W with a velocity v' in the second medium. If the time t is required for W' to reach R then $W'R = vt$ where v is the velocity in the first medium and $WR' = v't$. Thus a semicircle drawn with centre W and radius $v't$ gives a section of the wavelet sent out from W. Each point of WW' will similarly have reached a corresponding point of RR'. From the diagram

$$\frac{\sin i}{\sin r} = \frac{\dfrac{W'R}{WR}}{\dfrac{WR'}{WR}} = \frac{W'R}{WR'} = \frac{vt}{v't} = \frac{v}{v'}$$

which is the law of sines as used in light. Thus the normal to the wavefront is deviated towards or away from the normal to the surface according as the velocity in the first medium is greater or less than that in the second. If v' is greater than v then when r is $90°$ the value of $\hat{i}$ is the critical angle, then $\sin i = \dfrac{v}{v'}$ and so total reflection may occur

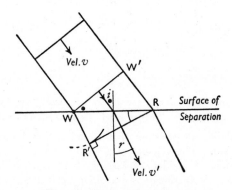

Fig. 38.   Refraction of sound.

when a wave tries to go from a medium of low to one of high wave velocity. The velocities of sound in air and sea-water at $15°$ C. are $0·331 \times 10^5$ and $1·501 \times 10^5$ cm./sec. respectively and so

$$\sin i_c = \frac{0·331 \times 10^5}{1·501 \times 10^5} \fallingdotseq 0·221$$

which gives $\hat{i}_c \fallingdotseq 12° \; 43'$.

In 1852 Sondhaus demonstrated the refraction of sound through a gas filled prism and determined a refractive index $\mu \left(= \dfrac{v}{v'} = \dfrac{\sin i}{\sin r} \right)$. Using a Sondhaus lens consisting of a thin envelope of collodion filled with carbon dioxide he demonstrated the focusing effect of such a lens. Nowadays the experiment is usually demonstrated by means of a lens formed by thin rubber membranes and filled with CO_2. A high frequency source (i.e. the wavelength is small compared with the

linear dimensions of the lens) such as a Galton's whistle is placed at
A (Fig. 39). A sensitive flame placed on the side of the lens remote
from A is moved about until it reaches a point of maximum disturbance at B—which may be called the sound image of A. The point B
is nothing like so definite as the location of the image in light. If
the lens is filled with hydrogen (i.e. velocity of sound in it is greater
than in air), it acts like a concave lens. To demonstrate this the flame
at B is adjusted to flare before the lens is interposed. When the lens
is placed between whistle and B the flames ceases to flare.

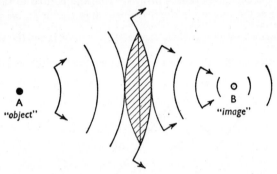

FIG. 39.   Refraction of sound through a CO_2 " gas " lens.

41. Refraction due to Wind and Temperature Gradients

It is a familiar observation that sound travels better with than
against the wind. The velocity of a wind increases from the earth's
surface upwards. Consider a plane wave front travelling over the
earth's surface. If the wave is travelling against the wind then its
upper portion will be retarded more than the lower. This process
is continuous and the direction of propagation of the wave front is
gradually changed until the wave is going upwards and may easily
pass over the head of an observer. The opposite is true when the
sound travels with the wind. In this case the upper portion moves
with a greater velocity than the lower by virtue of the assistance of a
greater wind velocity. The direction of motion of the wave front is
gradually brought down towards the ground and the observer may
experience a concentration of sound.

Since the velocity of sound is proportional to the square root of
the absolute temperature ($v \propto \sqrt{T}$), the direction of a sound wave will
change when it enters a region at a different temperature. On entering colder air the wave is retarded and so acts in a manner similar to
a ray of light entering a more dense medium, i.e. it bends towards the
normal at the surface of separation. On entering a region of warm
air the opposite is true. Temperature and wind refraction are analogous to mirages in light. On a summer's day the air in contact with

the ground is hot and that above it is cool.   Sound from S is therefore refracted as shown and appears to come from S'.   Owing to the refraction of sound audibility at ground level is low on a hot day, but in the evening, when the earth has cooled more rapidly than the air, audibility at ground level is high.

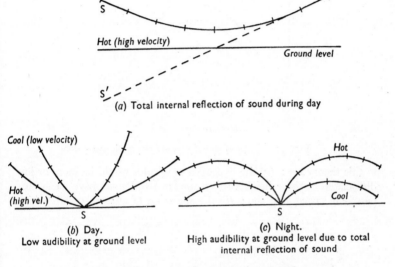

(a) Total internal reflection of sound during day

(b) Day.
Low audibility at ground level

(c) Night.
High audibility at ground level due to total internal reflection of sound

FIG. 40.   Refraction of sound in the atmosphere.

42. Zones of Silence

These are associated with large explosions such as the blowing up of an ammunition dump, munitions factory, etc.   When such large explosions take place four zones are usually found.

1. Near the explosion where the velocity of sound is abnormally great and there is considerable movement of the air.
2. A second zone where the velocity of sound is normal.
3. A zone of silence.
4. A zone where the sound reappears with unusual intensity after an exceptionally long time.

Two rival theories have been put forward to explain this zone of silence.   They agree that in zones 1 and 2 the sound reaches the observer directly, and that in zone 4 the sound reaches its objective after travelling in the higher part of the earth's atmosphere and being gradually bent down again, thus accounting for the abnormal interval of time between explosion and sound.   They disagree as to why the sound was bent down.   The older theory was put forward by von den Born.

He described the upper region as consisting mainly of helium and hydrogen which occasions the low density there.

This low density together with the value of γ for a mixture of hydrogen and helium causes an increase in the velocity of sound in the outer atmosphere and so brings the waves down to earth again. Objections

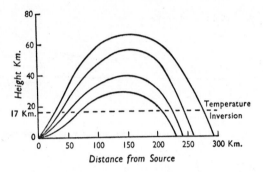

FIG. 41. Paths of sound waves from explosive source.

to this theory are : (a) the hydrogen molecules would be more or less dissociated at these heights (up to 60 km.) and must have been dispersed in space long ago ; (b) the spectrum of aurora borealis which

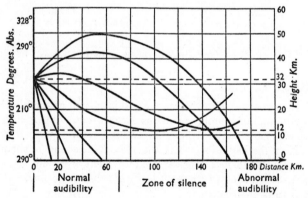

FIG. 42. Hypothetical track of sound rays from the explosion of a meteor.
(From Whipple's paper.)

has its origin at great heights in the atmosphere fails to show any spectral lines due to helium or hydrogen.

In view of these objections the second or temperature theory has been adopted although it leads to a result which is in direct contradiction to the older ideas on the atmosphere, namely, that there is a temperature inversion at about 17 km. above the earth's surface after which the temperature rises with height, reaches the surface temperature at 35 km. and at 60 km. is greater than 70° C.[1] Assuming this reversal of temperature gradient then the path of the sound wave is as shown in Fig. 41.

In January 1917, a munitions factory blew up at Silvertown, London. The sound of the explosion was heard in the Home Counties, Lincs. and Norfolk, but no sound in the intermediate region of Cambridge, Huntingdon, parts of Suffolk and Essex. In January 1923, a large ammunition dump at Oldebroek, Holland, blew up and sounds of the explosion were heard up to distances of 500 miles, but were not detected between 60 and 100 miles of the source. Similar observations were made of the Oppau and La Courtine explosions in 1924.

F. J. W. Whipple [2] described the zones of silence associated with a detonating meteor in September 1926. From numerous observations it was deduced that this meteor exploded at a height of 30 to 40 km. A heavy thunder-like explosion was heard at distances up to 60 or 70 km. This was followed by a zone of silence from approximately 70 to 150 km. after which was a second audible zone.

43. Interference

Huyghens in his *Principle of Superposition* first drew attention to the important fact that when one beam of light passes through an aperture it is not affected by the passage of another beam of light through the same aperture, i.e. the light waves cross at the aperture

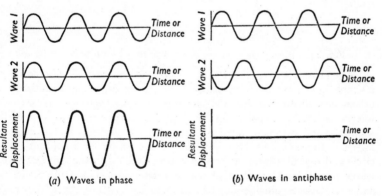

(a) Waves in phase   (b) Waves in antiphase

FIG. 43.   Combination of simple harmonic waves.

without interfering with each other's course. The same is true of sound waves. On this principle the resultant displacement of a particle of the medium through which two or more waves are travelling is obtained by the vector addition of the separate displacements due to each wave independently. If the waves are in the same phase the

[1] E. G. Richardson, *Sound*, p. 23.
[2] *Monthly Notices R.A.S.*, p. 89, Oct. 1928.

amplitude of vibration in enhanced, if in opposite phase the amplitude will be diminished.

If two simple harmonic waves of the same frequency are travelling in the same straight line, then, as shown earlier in the book, the resultant is obtained by adding the two displacements at any instant. As shown in Fig. 43 (*a*) and (*b*), the resultant displacement is a maximum if the wave trains are in phase, if the waves are of equal amplitude then, when the waves are in antiphase, the resultant displacement is zero. These effects are simple examples of interference.

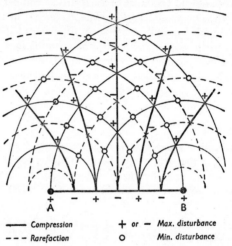

——— Compression   + or — Max. disturbance
– – – Rarefaction   o   Min. disturbance

FIG. 44.   Interference pattern due to two sound sources A and B.

When two stones are thrown into a pond the surface does not present a simple appearance. Some parts of the surface are much disturbed, others little disturbed, but the two sets of wave trains can be seen intermingling. Suppose *A* and *B* (Fig. 44) represent two sources of sound. Each complete wave consists of a compression and a rarefaction. Representing the middle of a compression by a continuous circle and that of a rarefaction by a dotted circle, then the two sets of waves pass through each other and interfere. When a compression and a rarefaction coincide they tend to annul each other's effect (shown by o). When two compressions or two rarefactions coincide (shown by a + or a —) the resulting amplitude is the sum of the separate amplitudes and the sound is correspondingly loud. As is shown in the diagram there are interference bands or alternate bands of loudness and comparative silence. These bands may be located experimentally by means of a sensitive flame (a jet of gas of suitable pressure passing through a fine nozzle made of drawn out glass tube).

The phenomenon of interference can be demonstrated also by

means of a single tuning fork. Each prong as it vibrates sends out
two waves in opposite directions which are in opposite phase. As
one prong of a tuning fork moves so that a compression is produced
on one side of the prong, a rarefaction is set up on the other side. These

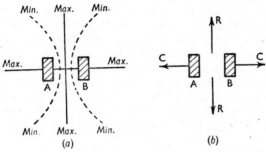

Fig. 45. (AB represents section of vibrating fork.) Interference due to a
vibrating tuning fork.

two simultaneous pulses in opposite phase will neutralise in certain
directions. A similar effect is produced by the other prong. The
result is that in the region of disturbance around the fork there are
regions of relative silence. As a vibrating fork is rotated in a vertical

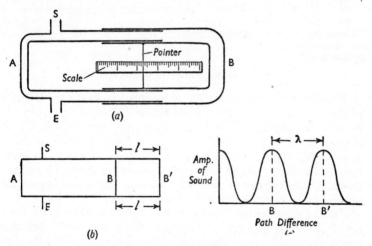

Fig. 46. Quincke's Tube.

position the amplitude of sound rises and falls four times in a revolution
(see Fig. 45).

Quincke's tube may be used to illustrate the phenomenon of
interference and to find the wavelength of a sound. The apparatus
consists of tubes as shown in Fig. 46, the right-hand tube being made

to slide in a manner similar to that of a trombone. As the sound
going from S to E has to travel farther by the right-hand than the
left-hand path it is usual to make the right-hand tube of material of
slightly greater diameter than the left so that the amplitudes of the
sound at E are equal (the narrower the tube the greater the dissipation
of energy). The source S should preferably be a pure note and of
fairly high frequency. If S is a tuning fork of frequency 1000 vib./sec.
or more, or an electric buzzer, then the ear is connected to E by means
of stethoscope tubes. When a high frequency source such as Galton's
whistle is used, a sensitive flame is placed at E. The sounds from S
going by each path start off in phase. If the path difference between
SAE and SBE is a whole number of wavelengths, they will arrive in
phase at E. If SBE is greater than SAE by half a wavelength, then
the waves arriving at E will be in antiphase and the resultant amplitude

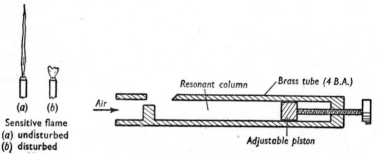

FIG. 47.   Simple model of Galton's whistle.

at E will be zero. Thus as SBE is increased in length the intensity
of the sound arriving at E rises and falls. The extra path difference
between two successive maxima or minima is one wavelength. If
SBE represents the adjustment of the tube B for maximum sound at
E, and $SB'E$ the next position of the tube B for maximum loudness,
then the length " l " is half a wavelength because of the double journey.
Hence, if the velocity of sound is assumed, the frequency of the
source can be calculated from $v = n\lambda$.

Using a sensitive flame instead of the ear the variations in the flame
are as shown in Fig. 47. A Galton's whistle is a small adjustable
closed pipe about 1 in. in diameter. The resonant length of the pipe
is altered by means of a piston controlled by a screw. As the piston
is moved outwards, so increasing the length of the pipe, the pitch of
the note rises until it becomes a sibilant hiss and then inaudible. A
whistle is easily made from 4 B.A. tube and 2 B.A. threaded brass rod.
In commercial instruments the screw piston has a graduated scale
indicating the frequency of the sound wave. In experimental work

the whistle is often blown by means of air from a cylinder, football
bladder or motor car inner tube.

As mentioned in the chapter dealing with wave motion, stationary
waves, the formation of nodes and loops in vibrating strings, rods and
air columns are due to the interference of wave trains moving in opposite
directions due to reflection.

Suppose S_1 and S_2 are two sound sources of the same wavelength
and in phase, then from the similar triangles S_1PS_2 and OCE (Fig. 48),

$$\frac{x}{D} = \frac{S_2P}{S_1P} \backsimeq \frac{S_2P}{S_1S_2} = \frac{S_2P}{a}.$$

If S_2P (i.e. path difference)$= n\lambda$, then the sound waves will reinforce.

Hence for maximum sound $x = \dfrac{Dn \cdot \lambda}{a}$,

for minimum sound $x = \dfrac{D}{a}(n + \tfrac{1}{2})\lambda$.

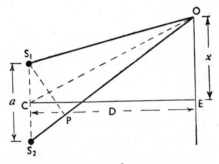

FIG. 48.   Interference of two sources, $s_1 \cdot s_2$.

As in light, there are alternate fringes of maximum and minimum
intensity with a fringe width of $\dfrac{D\lambda}{a}$.   In Lloyd's single mirror, fringes
are produced by interference between the waves from a source of
light and its image in a mirror.   An analogous experiment in sound
uses a single source of sound and a plane reflector such as a wall.
Sound fringes can also be produced using two related sources provided
either by double slits or inclined reflectors (cf. Young's slits and
Fresnel's inclined mirrors).   Tyndall noted the apparent variation in
strength of the signals from a fog siren at South Foreland.   The
sound periodically decreased and increased as the ship receded from
the shore.   This was clearly a case of interference between the sound
source and its image.

S. R. Humby,[1] using a high frequency sound source in air, has
demonstrated the existence of Lloyd's interference fringes in front of

[1] *Proc. Phys. Soc.*, **39**, p. 435, 1927.

a plane reflector. The observed hyperboloid fringes agreed exactly with the theoretical calculations.

Experiments by F. B. Young and A. B. Wood [1] have demonstrated the existence of interference of sound under water. The resulting fringes due to the interference between the source and its negative image formed in the surface were made more complicated by multiple reflections from the bottom and surface.

44. Beats

A special case arises when two sound sources of not quite the same frequency interfere with each other. Consider two tuning forks of frequency 500 and 501 vib./sec. Suppose the forks are sounding and are in phase. If not in phase to start with they will soon come into phase since the frequencies are unequal. As the higher frequency fork makes one more vibration per sec. than the lower frequency fork the sounds will again be in phase after 1 sec. has elapsed. Half a second after the sounds are in phase they must obviously be in antiphase

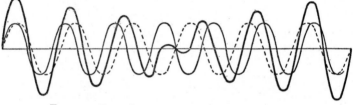

FIG. 49.   Beats due to two waves of 6 and 7 vibs./sec.

since one has gained half a complete vibration on the other and if the amplitudes of the vibrations are equal, then the resulting sound is zero. If the amplitudes are not equal the sound heard is a minimum. Thus once a second the sound heard by an observer rises and falls in intensity producing what is termed a " Beat ". In the general case where the difference in frequency is " n " vib./sec. the intensity of the sound rises and falls " n " times per sec., giving " n " beats.

The production of beats can be demonstrated by means of two tuning forks of the same frequency by loading the prong of one fork with a small piece of soft wax. The larger the piece of wax the greater the lowering of the frequency of the fork and the greater the number of beats set up. The number of beats per second is the difference in frequency of the two forks. If two forks when sounding together give beats it is possible to determine which fork has the lower frequency. One fork is loaded, if the number of beats per second is increased then it is very likely that the loaded fork had the lower frequency originally and the load has served to increase the difference in frequency between them. As it is possible that the higher frequency fork was the one

[1] *Proc. Phys. Soc.*, **100**, p. 261, 1921.

chosen to be loaded and has been overloaded, the experiment must be repeated with the other fork loaded, when the number of beats should be reduced.   The presence of beats is used in the laboratory as an indication that the sonometer or monochord is almost in tune with a vibrating fork.   In everyday life beats are used in the tuning of musical instruments and for testing a unison.[1]   The piano tuner sets out the octave from middle C by ear.   He then works up and down the piano by octaves.   If the piano is slightly out of tune, beats are heard between the first overtone of the lower note and the octave. When the notes are in tune beats are no longer heard.   Thus the presence of beats between octaves on a piano show that the instrument is in need of tuning.

45. Discords are due to beats.   When less frequent than 10 per sec. they can be heard separately.   When more frequent than this they produce an unpleasant sensation which reaches a maximum effect at about 25 beats/sec.   The sensation disappears when the rate is about 60 beats/sec. for a note in the neighbourhood of middle C (256 vib./sec.).

Consider two exactly similar organ pipes one of which is blown by pure air and the other by impure air.   Because of the difference in density of the gases the notes emitted will be different and if the difference in density is small the difference in frequency will be small and so beats will be heard.   This method has been used to detect the presence of fire-damp in coal mines.   One pipe is blown by pure air from a cylinder, the other by impure air in the mine.   Tables enable the operator to estimate the percentage of fire-damp from the number of beats heard per second.

46. Consider two simple harmonic motions of nearly the same frequency, and let them be represented by $y = a \sin (m + n)t$ and $y = b \sin (m - n)t$, where n is small compared with m.

The resultant displacement is given by

$$y = a \sin (m + n)t + b \sin (m - n)t \quad . \qquad . \qquad . \quad (1)$$

Assume
$$y = f \sin (mt + \theta) \qquad . \qquad . \qquad . \qquad . \qquad . \quad (2)$$

Expanding the right-hand sides of (1) and (2), it follows that

$$y = a \sin mt \cos nt + a \cos mt \sin nt + b \sin mt \cos nt - b \cos mt \sin nt$$

and
$$y = f \sin mt \cos \theta + f \cos mt \sin \theta.$$

Comparing these expressions gives

$$f \cos \theta = a \cos nt + b \cos nt = (a + b) \cos nt$$
$$f \sin \theta = a \sin nt - b \sin nt = (a - b) \sin nt$$

whence
$$f^2 = (a + b)^2 \cos^2 nt + (a - b)^2 \sin^2 nt$$

so that
$$f^2 = a^2 + b^2 + 2ab \cos 2nt$$

and
$$\tan \theta = \frac{a - b}{a + b} \cdot \tan nt.$$

_____

[1] Rayleigh, *Nature*, **19**, p. 275, 1879.

Thus f varies between $(a + b)$ and $(a - b)$ with a frequency of $\dfrac{2n}{2\pi}$, which equals the difference in frequency of the components $\dfrac{m + n}{2\pi}$ and $\dfrac{m - n}{2\pi}$, and the apparent frequency of the resultant is $\dfrac{m}{2\pi}$ which is equal to $\dfrac{1}{2}\left(\dfrac{m + n}{2\pi} + \dfrac{m - n}{2\pi}\right)$, i.e. the arithmetic mean of the components.

When two musical sounds of nearly the same frequency are heard simultaneously, the waxing and waning of loudness, which is readily discerned by the ear, is termed *beats*.

47. Diffraction of Sound

The elementary phenomena of light and sound are most easily explained on the assumption that light and sound travel in straight lines. Everyday experience shows that sound waves bend round corners whilst the propagation of light is sensibly linear. A carefully planned experiment is needed to show that light can also " bend round corners ". The apparent anomaly rises from the difference in ratio of the wavelength to the dimensions of the obstacle in the two cases. The wavelength of sound is of the order of a million times that of light and the extent of the encroachment inside the geometrical shadow increases with increase of wavelength. In order to obtain sharp shadows with sounds of long wavelength, large obstacles are needed. Even with sounds of short wavelength moderately large obstacles are required. In sound, as distinct from light, diffraction effects predominate, so that in experiments on the directional transmission, reception, reflection and refraction of sound it is important to know the relationship between the wavelength of the sound and the size of the obstacles which it encounters.

Using the principle of Huyghens, later added to by Fresnel and Kirchhoff, the diffraction patterns, familiar to the student of optics, can be derived. For a cylindrical wave diffracted at a straight edge, the distance PN to successive zones from the edge of the geometrical shadow is given by $PN = \sqrt{nr\lambda}$, where n has the values 1, 2, 3, etc., and r is the distance from the straight edge to the screen. Assuming the velocity of sound in air to be 1100 ft./sec. and a source of frequency 5500 vib./sec., then the wavelength is 0·2 ft. Assuming the distance r between edge and screen to be 20 ft., then the width of successive zones will be $\sqrt{1 \times 0·2 \times 20}$, $\sqrt{2 \times 0·2 \times 20}$, $\sqrt{3 \times 0·2 \times 20}$, etc., which gives 2, 2·82, 3·46, etc. ft. The diagram so familiar in light for a parallel slit is obtained by a mathematical treatment which does not differentiate between sound and light. The essential point of difference between the results obtained lies in the size of the aperture and the position of the fluctuations inside the geometrical shadow. " The amount of spreading of waves passing through an opening depends entirely on the relation between the wavelength and the width of the opening. This explains the apparent discrepancy between sound and light which delayed so long the general adoption of the wave theory of light." [1]

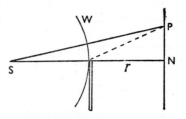

In light a good diffraction grating has about 14,000 lines to the inch. In sound a row of regularly spaced palings or a corrugated surface provides quite a suitable piece of apparatus. The usual grating law, $d \sin \theta = n\lambda$, applies for normal incidence of a plane wave, where d is the width of space + strip, n is the order of the spectrum and θ is the direction of a maximum. In sound, as in light, focusing devices are needed to set up parallel beams and to converge the transmitted beam on to a suitable detector.

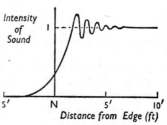

Diffraction at a Straight Edge

When Arago demonstrated that the optical shadow of a suitably illuminated disc had a bright spot at its centre, this was regarded as the final proof of the validity of the wave theory of light. Using a " birdcall " giving sounds about 1 cm. wave-length in air and a sensitive flame as a detector, Rayleigh [2] demonstrated the corresponding experiment in sound as well as the more obvious effects of diffraction.

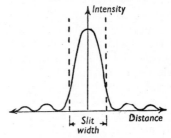

Diffraction at a Slit

Fig. 50. Diffraction patterns.

S. R. Humby [3] demonstrated qualitatively the various interference and diffraction effects of sound waves using a telephone excited by the high frequency current from a valve oscillator. This source had the advantages of steadiness and accurately known frequency. Both the ear and sensitive flames were used as detectors. Diffraction effects were detected at the straight edge of a large wooden screen, the effect on a sensitive flame as it moved from outside to inside the

[1] A. B. Wood, *Sound*, p. 307. [2] *Sound*, pp. 142 and 143.
[3] *Proc. Phys. Soc.*, **39**, p. 435, 1927.

geometrical shadow being very obvious.   Using a rectangular aperture 20 cm. wide and 43 cm. high and a sound source of wavelength 4·4 cm. placed 40 cm. from the aperture, a central maximum and several secondary maxima were located 40 cm. beyond the aperture.

48. Apart from laboratory demonstration, diffraction plays an important part in directional transmission and reception.   The mouth of a horn or reflector behaves like an aperture through which plane waves are diffracted.   This increases the directional efficiency of horns and reflectors as the wavelength decreases.   The energy reflected when a sound pulse of fairly long wavelength falls on a surface, such as a ship, will be small unless the source is very powerful since the sound is spread over a large area.   If very short waves are emitted through an aperture (supersonic waves for example), the waves diffracted out of the direct path are destroyed by interference and so a beam of sound waves is produced in a manner similar to that in which the very short light waves are concentrated into a beam on passing through an orifice.

49. Stroboscopic Observation

If a stone is thrown into a pond the appearance of the surface is constantly changing.   As described previously in this chapter two stones produce a more complicated changing picture.   Suppose that it is dark when the stone is thrown into the pond and the surface is viewed with the aid of short regular flashes from an electric torch. The appearance of the surface depends upon the interval between the flashes.   If one wave has been replaced exactly by another wave in the time between two illuminations then the surface will appear unchanged and the waves will appear quite fixed in their positions.   To produce this effect it is essential that the time of illumination is sufficiently short.   Instead of using a flashing light, short glimpses of the pond (or any vibrating body) can be made through a slit in a rotating disc.   For convenience the disc usually has a considerable number of slits equally spaced, and can be rotated at a constant controlled speed. If one wave succeeds the next in the time taken for one slit to replace another, then the surface of the pond will appear to be a series of stationary crests and troughs.

There are four possible ways of producing the interruptions necessary for stroboscopic observation.   These are interruption

1. Of light between object and eye.
2. Between the light and the object.
3. Light at the object.
4. The source of light itself.

Methods 1 and 3 require the use of some form of mechanical shutter, e.g. a disc with slits.   The first practical instrument of this kind is ascribed to Plateau (1801-83) and was first used to determine the speed of revolution of wheels and shafts. Other examples of method 1 are rotating and vibrating mirrors (König and Wheatstone for viewing a vibrating flame). The introduction of the neon lamp in 1911 provided a convenient method of interrupting the light at the source. This lamp which flashes 100 times a sec. on 50 cycle A.C. mains can be used to give flashes up to 10,000 per sec. If a rotating wheel, having a series of white dots painted at equal intervals round its circumference, is viewed by means of a neon lamp connected to 50 cycle mains, then if one dot replaces another in $\frac{1}{100}$ sec. the dots will appear stationary.

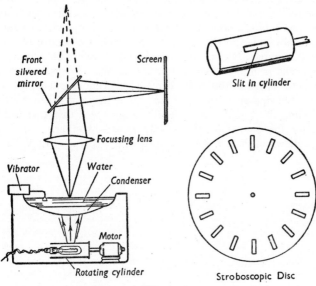

FIG. 51. The ripple tank.

This method can be used to check the speed of gramophone turntables and in the laboratory is used to check the frequency of vibration of a strip of metal as used in Fletcher's trolley, etc. In fluorescent lighting the light is given out in pulses at intervals of time equal to those of a neon. If a pencil, for example, is moved up and down at a suitable speed in such lighting, then a series of images of the pencil can be seen. These positions correspond to the position of the pencil when the light pulse was emitted. All these methods of observation depend for their success on the "persistence of vision". If the frequency falls below 25 per sec. the image on the retina is not continuous and a flicker is observed. Details of the methods of measuring frequency using this effect will be found under the appropriate section.

50. The Ripple Tank

In a ripple tank the ratio between the wavelength of the ripples and the dimensions of the obstacles used is approximately the same as that required to show interference and diffraction phenomena in light and sound. The principle of the apparatus is quite simple. A vibrator dipping into a shallow pool of water sets up ripples. A magnified picture of the ripples is projected on to a screen by means of a lens and mirror. The bottom of the tank containing the water is a condenser lens in conjunction with which a source of light illuminates the ripples. Unless a stroboscopic method of viewing is adopted the image on the screen consists of rapidly moving ripples. In the " microid " ripple tank, as supplied by Messrs Griffin and Tatlock, method 2 of interrupting the light is used. A cylinder having two diametrically opposite slits is made to rotate at a controllable speed round the source of light. The ripples are therefore only illuminated when a slit is immediately below the condenser lens. A rheostat controls the speed of the motor driving the cylinder and so, as well as showing the ripples as still, they can also be shown in " slow motion " by running the cylinder at a slightly slower speed than that which is necessary for one ripple to exactly replace another. The screen images shown in Plate 1 were obtained with this type of ripple tank.

PLATE 1

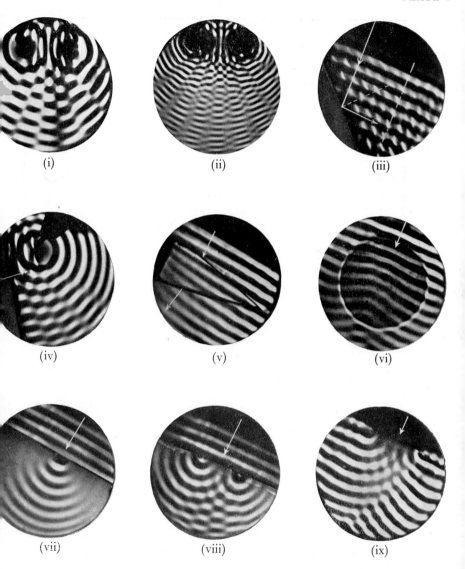

(i)   (ii)   (iii)

(iv)   (v)   (vi)

(vii)   (viii)   (ix)

SCREEN IMAGES OBTAINED BY USING A RIPPLE TANK

and (ii)   Interference between waves from two point sources.

i)   Reflection of plane waves at a plane boundary.

v)   Circular waves reflected at a plane boundary. (Lloyds' fringes).

) and (vi)   Refraction through a prism and a lens.

ii)   Diffraction through a slit.

iii)   Diffraction through two slits and consequent interference of two circular waves.

x)   Diffraction round an obstacle.

PLATE 2

(A)

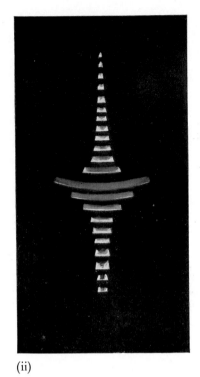

(i)   (ii)

BARTON'S PENDULUMS

Photographs, taken from the side of the paths of pendulum bobs which are executing forced vibrations, when the vibrations are (i) heavily damped, (ii) lightly damped.

(B)

INDUSTRIAL PHOTO CELLS

CV. Indicates caesium cathode, vacuum. High sensitivity to infra-red and white light.

AV. Caesium-antimony cells. High sensitivity to daylight and blue light.

PLATE 3

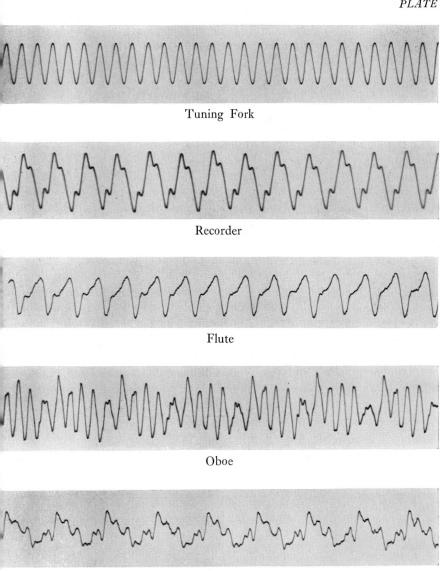

Tuning Fork

Recorder

Flute

Oboe

Clarinet

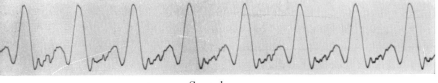

Saxophone

OSCILLOGRAMS

PLATE 4

(A) Early Gramophone
(Berliner)

(B) Edison's original phonograph

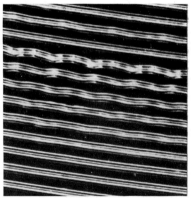

(C) Magnified grooves in a gramophone record (magnified about 12 times)

(i)

(ii)

(D) Portions of film (as recorded) showing (i) variable area and (ii) variable density sound recording

CHAPTER V

MEASUREMENT OF FREQUENCY

MEASUREMENT of frequency can be broadly divided into two classes.

(a) Absolute methods, in which the number of vibrations is determined by reference to a standard clock. This includes methods such as recording on film or paper calibrated by standard time marks, siren, toothed wheel, phonic motor, stroboscopic methods, standardised or electrically driven forks, multivibrators controlled by a standard fork (as is used to determine the frequency of a piezo-electric crystal).

(b) Comparative methods, in which the pure tone is compared with a source standardised by a direct method, such as sonometer, Lissajous' figures, resonant columns of gas, and Kundt's dust tube when the velocity of sound is assumed.

51. Savart's Toothed Wheel

When a piece of cardboard or thin wood is lightly pressed against a toothed wheel which is revolving (usually driven by an electric motor), a series of vibrations is set up. If the vibrations are sufficiently rapid they are not heard separately but as a musical note (cf. circular saw). The faster the speed of rotation the higher the note. If the wheel has N teeth and revolves at n rev./sec. then the frequency of the note is Nn vib./sec.

52. The Siren

This was first introduced by Seebeck and modified later by Cagniard de la Tour. It consists of a wind chest in the top surface of which is drilled a ring of evenly spaced holes. On top of this disc is placed a similar one, having the holes in corresponding positions, and arranged so that it can be rotated. The holes in the discs are drilled obliquely so that the pressure of the air causes the upper disc to rotate. When the holes in wind chest and disc coincide a puff of air passes through to the outside, i.e. a compression, and if the number of puffs per sec. is sufficiently rapid a note is heard. Thus if each disc has N holes and the upper disc revolves at n rev./sec., the frequency of the note is Nn vib./sec. It can be appreciated that to drive the upper disc at a slow speed a low air pressure is essential which means that the air movement is small and therefore the note is of small intensity. As the pressure of air, and therefore the speed of rotation, increases, the frequency and the intensity of the note increases. In its more modern form the disc is electrically driven, having speed control and indicator. This means that the air pressure controls the intensity of sound only. The note emitted by the simple form of the instrument contains a number of harmonics. Milne and Fowler [1] have devised a form of Seebeck siren which emits a pure note. The jet is rectangular in section and the holes are shaped so that the area of jet exposed varies sinusoidally. In adjusting the siren to find the frequency of a note the speed is increased until beats are heard between the two notes. The speed of rotation of the disc is then carefully altered until the beats become very slow and finally disappear.

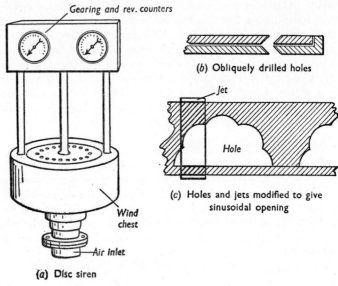

Gearing and rev. counters

(b) Obliquely drilled holes

Jet

Hole

(c) Holes and jets modified to give sinusoidal opening

Wind chest

Air inlet

(a) Disc siren

FIG. 52. The disc siren.

53. Falling Plate Method

In this experiment the value of the acceleration due to gravity is assumed. Using a fork of known frequency the same apparatus may be used to find " g ". A light style is fixed to a clamped fork which is adjusted so as to bring the style lightly into contact with the lower part of a suspended glass plate, which has been smoked by means of a camphor or turpentine flame. The plate is suspended by means of sealing wax and cotton, an electromagnet attracting a piece of ferro-magnetic material attached to the glass, or any other method which provides a suitable means of releasing the plate. The fork is then lightly bowed and the plate released by burning the cotton or breaking the circuit. As the plate falls the style traces a wavy line on the smoked surface. A rubber or felt pad placed on the base of the apparatus prevents the glass from breaking on impact, and wooden guides prevent it from falling on its side on hitting the pad. It is essential that

[1] *Proc. Roy. Soc.*, **98**, p. 414, 1921.

these guides do not interfere with its free motion under gravity since the value of " g " is to be used in the calculation. A point P is chosen clear of the indistinct portion of the curve made when the velocity of the plate was small. From P a whole number of waves " m " is counted to a point Q, from Q the same number of waves is counted to a point R. Let the distances PQ and QR be s_1 and s_2.

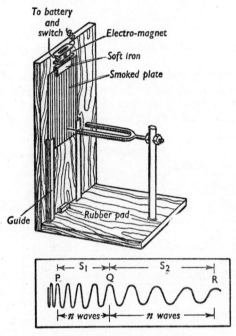

FIG. 53. Falling-plate experiment.

For the distance PQ

Let the initial velocity $= u$.
Acceleration due to gravity $= g$.
Time $= T$.
Distance $= s_1$.

Then since the acceleration is uniform,

$$\therefore \ s_1 = uT + \tfrac{1}{2}gT^2 \qquad . \qquad . \qquad . \qquad . \ (1)$$

For the distance PR the time taken is twice that to go PQ since each oscillation of the fork indicates the same interval of time.

It follows that

$$s_1 + s_2 = u \, . \, 2T + \tfrac{1}{2}g(2T)^2 \qquad . \qquad . \qquad . \ (2)$$

Multiplying equation (1) by 2 :

$$2s_1 = 2uT + gT^2 \qquad . \qquad . \qquad . \qquad . \ (3)$$

Subtracting (3) from (2) to eliminate " u " from the equation gives

$$s_2 - s_1 = gT^2$$

$$\therefore T = \sqrt{\frac{s_2 - s_1}{g}}.$$

But T is the time of " m " oscillations and so the time of 1 oscillation
$$= \frac{T}{m}$$

$$\therefore \text{ Frequency of fork} = \frac{m}{T} = m\sqrt{\frac{g}{s_2 - s_1}} \text{ vib./sec.}$$

The distances s_1 and s_2 are measured by means of a travelling microscope and the value of the frequency obtained is that for the fork vibrating with a load. The effect of the style can be accounted for by taking a fork of slightly higher frequency and loading it until no

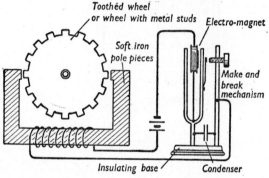

FIG. 54. Tuning fork driving a phonic wheel.

beats are heard when both sound together (the first fork is unloaded). Now place the style on the first fork, arrange it to come in contact with the smoked plate and sound both forks together. The number of beats now heard per sec. gives the number of periods lost due to the loading of the fork. For fairly obvious reasons the experiment is much more easily carried out using an electrically maintained fork.

54. Phonic Wheel

This instrument, which was the forerunner of the electric clock, was invented independently by Rayleigh [1] and La Cour (Fig. 54). It offers a very convenient and accurate way of finding the frequency of an electrically maintained fork. It consists of a toothed iron wheel, or a wooden wheel with iron studs with a small electromagnet embracing a whole number of teeth of the wheel. The vibrations of

[1] Rayleigh, *Nature*, **18**, p. 111, 1878 ; also *Sound*, 1.

the fork are turned into electrical impulses, by the make and break mechanism, which in turn are changed into magnetic impulses. The wheel is set into motion by hand or air thrust, and when the frequency with which the teeth pass the poles of the electromagnet and the frequency of the applied impulses are equal, then the revolutions are maintained indefinitely. If the wheel has N teeth and makes n rev./sec. then the frequency of the impulses, and therefore of the fork, must be Nn pulses or vib./sec. An important feature of the instrument is the high degree of accuracy attainable, which depends ultimately on the accuracy of the standard clock. When fitted with revolution counters the instrument can be left running for very long periods, the frequency so found being the average over this period. An accuracy of 1 in 10,000 is easily attainable and so the instrument is very useful for finding small changes in frequency such as the variation in the frequency of a tuning fork due to a small change in temperature.

In 1919 J. M. Ford and A. B. Wood [1] devised an improved form of phonic motor which gave a considerable driving torque and was capable of driving an electrically-operated chronometer or a moving-tape pen recorder.

55. Stroboscopic Methods

As stated in the chapter dealing with reflection, etc., of sound, if a vibrating body is viewed through a disc which has equally spaced radial slits round its periphery, then, if in the time that one slit replaces another the body makes 1 vibration, or returns to its original position, it does not appear to be vibrating. The method usually adopted to find the frequency of an electrically maintained fork is to use a black disc with white spots at equal distances apart along the periphery (or vice versa) instead of a disc with slits. To the ends of the prongs of the forks are attached light metal plates with a small hole through each through which the stroboscopic wheel is viewed. If the holes in the plates are coincident when the fork is at rest then it is possible to see through them twice in one complete oscillation. If the holes are coincident when the prongs are at their maximum displacement from the undisturbed position, then it is possible to see the disc once only in a complete oscillation. Assuming the first (and more usual) state of affairs the disc is set rotating and its speed increased until the dots appear stationary. Suppose there are N dots and the disc makes n rev./sec. Then in $\frac{1}{n}$ sec. N dots move past the holes in disc, i.e. each dot takes the place just previously occupied by its predecessor in $\frac{1}{Nn}$ sec. But this is the time of half a complete oscillation

[1] A. B. Wood and J. M. Ford, *Journ. Sci. Instrs.*, **1**, pp. 160-73, 1924.

of the fork. Therefore frequency of the fork $= \dfrac{Nn}{2}$ vib./sec. As the speed of the disc increases the dots appear stationary when its speed is 2, 3, 4, etc., times too fast (cf. Fizeau's method for velocity of light). If the wheel is going too slowly the spots do not quite replace each other in the interval between successive viewings and the disc appears to be going slowly backwards. If it is going a little too fast the dots seem to be going slowly forwards (cf. effect as seen on the films of motor wheels, etc.). The spots also appear stationary when the disc is going at $\frac{1}{2}$ or $1\frac{1}{2}$ times the correct speed, but in this case the distance between the spots appears to be half that when the disc is stationary. Stationary patterns are also obtained when the disc rotates at $\frac{1}{3}$, $\frac{1}{4}$, $\frac{5}{4}$, etc., times the correct speed. Without the aid of the persistence of vision this experiment would not be possible.

EXAMPLE

A stroboscopic disc has 20 equally spaced dots round its edge and they appear stationary when viewed through the holes in plates carried by the prongs of a tuning fork (as described above) when the disc makes 1800 r.p.m. What is the frequency of the fork?

1 rev. takes $\frac{1}{1800}$ min. $= \frac{1}{30}$ sec.

Angle between the spots $= \frac{1}{20}$ of a revolution.

Time to sweep out $\frac{1}{20}$ rev. $= \frac{1}{20} \times \frac{1}{30} = \frac{1}{600}$ sec.

Time of 1 vib. of fork $= 2 \times \frac{1}{600} = \frac{1}{300}$ sec.

Frequency of fork $=$ 300 vib./sec.

56. Graphic Method

A is a cylindrical metal drum covered with a smoked paper on which the style of a tuning fork B lightly presses (Fig. 55). The drum is rotated either electrically or by clockwork and is mounted on an axis with a screw thread. Thus as the drum rotates it also moves either up or down depending on the direction of rotation. This prevents the overlapping of the traces made on the smoked paper by the style of the tuning fork. S is the secondary winding of a transformer or induction coil, the ends being connected to the fork and drum respectively. The primary is connected to batteries and a standard seconds pendulum P (made of metal), on the end of which is a short piece of platinum wire arranged so that it makes contact with a mercury cup C once per sec. This passes a momentary current through the primary which gives rise to a large voltage in the secondary. This voltage is sufficient to cause a spark to pass from the style of the fork through the paper to the metal drum, so making a spot on the trace made by the fork. As the drum rotates, the wavy curve made by the fork is marked at intervals by spots due to the electric discharge, the distance between any two consecutive spots representing a time of 1 sec. The frequency is determined by counting the number of waves in any interval of time, measured by the dots on the paper, and dividing the number of complete oscillations by the time in seconds. The result is independent of the rate of revolution of the drum or on its regularity, but depends solely on the accuracy of the pendulum. A slight error is introduced, however, due to the addition of the style as well as the friction between style and paper.

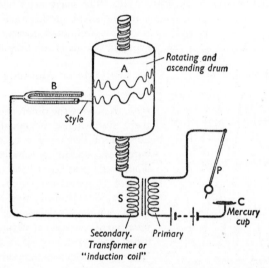

FIG. 55.   Graphic method of finding frequency of a fork.

57. Cathode Ray Oscilloscope Methods

One of the most accurate ways of determining the frequency of sound waves is to turn them into electrical waves of the same frequency by means of a microphone and determine the frequency of these waves by means of a cathode ray oscilloscope. As described in Chapter XI, the combination of two S.H.M.s at right angles gives rise to Lissajous' figures, and, when the figures are continuous, half the total number of peaks gives the relative frequency. For multiples up to 10 : 1 the Lissajous' figures are reasonably clear, above this value they become complex, and frequency comparison becomes difficult.[1]

For the comparison of frequencies when the multiple is large, a time base method is most suitable and this is most easily done with a double beam tube.[2]   In this instrument the electron beam is split by

[1] Parr, *The Cathode Ray Tube*, p. 53.
[2] Reyner, *Cathode Ray Oscillographs*, p. 145.

means of a wedge so that two time bases appear on the screen. The standard trace of known frequency is applied to one time base and synchronises both time bases, i.e. sets them going at a definite time. On the other time base is applied the unknown frequency. The frequency is found by finding how many waves of the unknown frequency corresponds to 1 wave of the standard frequency. In the figure (a) represents the standard frequency, (b) the unknown frequency which has a frequency of four times that of the standard. The standard wave can be of any known frequency, e.g. 50 cycle mains, 1000 cycle fork, valve oscillator or 100 kc. crystal, etc. The wave need not be pure since the shape of the wave does not affect the frequency measurement or synchronisation of the time-base.

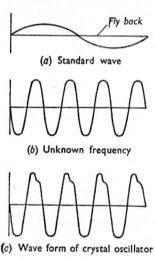

(a) Standard wave

(b) Unknown frequency

(c) Wave form of crystal oscillator

FIG. 56. Comparison of frequency using C.R.O.

58. Tonometer Methods

When two notes have nearly the same frequency the difference between their frequencies is equal to the number of beats per sec. when the notes are sounding simultaneously. This is the principle of the tonometer devised by Scheibler (1777-1837) for the rapid determination of frequencies within a definite range. The instrument consisted of 56 tuning forks tuned from a (220 vib./sec.) to a' (440 vib./sec.), the interval between any two consecutive forks of the series being such that they gave 4 beats/sec. Thus any note within this range may be made to beat with a number of forks. If a fork gave two beats with two consecutive forks, then its frequency was midway between them, and so by counting the number of beats made with several of the forks the frequency could be found accurately and quickly. An instrument of this kind requires accurate adjustment and takes a long time to construct. When completed, however, it is permanent, provides an answer quickly, and is little affected by moderate temperature changes. It is worth noting that as a result of his experiments Schiebler recommended in 1834 that 440 cycles/sec. should be adopted as standard pitch for a' in the musical scale. In 1899 piano manufacturers adopted 439 vib./sec. and in 1927 the Army Council adopted the same value as a' or the frequency of A in the treble clef.[1]

[1] Alexander Ellis, *History of Musical Pitch.*

König (1832-1901) made a more elaborate and accurate tonometer, which is preserved in the Conservatoire des Arts et Métiers in Paris, consisting of 150 forks covering the frequency range 16 to 21,845·3 vib./sec. The tuning and workmanship is first class, the largest fork weighing about 200 lb., having blades 5 ft. long and has a resonator about 8 ft. long.

59. The Sonometer or Monochord

As is shown in the chapter dealing with the vibration of strings the sonometer can be used for the comparison of the frequencies and, under certain conditions, to find the absolute frequency of a tuning fork. The instrument can also be modified to find the frequency of an alternating current of fairly low value such as from A.C. mains.

Resonant Columns of Gas. This method is also dealt with under its appropriate heading. Normally the apparatus is used with a fork of known frequency to find the velocity of sound from a measurement of the wavelength. It may be used to compare the frequency of two notes.

Helmholtz' Resonators. These instruments are also dealt with later in the work. The instruments were devised for sound analysis, i.e. to find the harmonics present in a note.

Kundt's Dust Tube. This is normally used to compare the velocities of sound in a solid and a gas and to find the ratio of the specific heats of a gas, but, as will be discussed later, it can be used to find the frequency of the note emitted by a loudspeaker, for example, if the velocity of sound in the gas is assumed.

60. Musical Scales

If four wheels having a number of teeth in the ratio 4, 5, 6, 8, are fixed on the same shaft and are made to rotate, then the notes emitted when a piece of cardboard is brought lightly into contact with the teeth are what are termed doh, me, soh, doh[1] on the musical scale. As the speed of rotation of the shaft increases the frequency of all four notes rises but they still have the same pitch relation, doh, me, soh, doh[1]. If the frequency of a given note c is twice that of another note C, the former is said to be an octave above the latter. The ordinary piano keyboard comprises 7 octaves and if it were tuned to scientific pitch, i.e. middle C 256 vib./sec., the frequencies of the other Cs would be 32, 64, 128, 256, 512, 1024, 2048 vib./sec. The bottom two of these differ by 32 vib./sec. whilst the top two differ by 1024 vib./sec., but the interval is so similar to the ear that each is termed an octave.

In the diatonic scale six notes are introduced between the fundamental C and its octave C' such that the frequency ratios to the fundamental or keynote are

	C	D	E	F	G	A	B	C'
Ratio of frequency .	I	$\frac{9}{8}$	$\frac{5}{4}$	$\frac{4}{3}$	$\frac{3}{2}$	$\frac{5}{3}$	$\frac{15}{8}$	2
Interval .		$\frac{9}{8}$ major tone	$\frac{10}{9}$ minor tone	$\frac{16}{15}$ semi tone	$\frac{9}{8}$ major tone	$\frac{10}{9}$ minor tone	$\frac{9}{8}$ major tone	$\frac{16}{15}$ semi tone

These notes with their peculiar ratios and intervals were chosen by ear, long before their frequencies were investigated scientifically, as giving the maximum amount of concord, i.e. they blended better than any others. They are a series of notes which are pleasing to European ears, and can be traced with fair certainty to the music of the Greeks,[1] but there are many other scales which are not pleasing to European ears.

When the beats between two notes are less than 10 per sec. they can be distinguished separately. Above this number the effect is a discord. As the number of beats increases the beats are perceived as a roughness and, according to the theory of Helmholtz, the dissonance between *pure* tones is due to beats between the tones, the degree of dissonance depending on the beat frequency and the interval between the tones. According to Stumpf,[2] for a tone of 256 vib./sec., the maximum dissonance occurs and dissonance disappears when the beat frequencies are 23 and 58 vib./sec. respectively. In the case of musical instruments which are designed so that the notes emitted are not pure tones but contain the harmonics responsible for their peculiar quality, the problem is very complicated and well beyond the scope of this book.

Reference to the table above shows that the intervals in the diatonic scale are $\frac{9}{8}$, $\frac{10}{9}$ or $\frac{16}{15}$. The first two intervals, although not quite equal, are termed tones (not to be confused with a pure note), and the last a semitone. If all music were played in the same key then it would give a sense of monotony. This is avoided by modulation or change of key. Starting with the keynote as C the intervals which follow are tone, tone, semi-tone, tone, tone, tone, semi-tone. If, however, the keynote is taken as E the intervals are semi-tone, tone, tone, tone, etc., i.e. the intervals do not follow in the right order and so, with this simple arrangement, a tune would be very much changed by playing it in a different key. To make all scales in different keys correct, a

[1] Alex Wood, *The Physics of Music*, p. 173.
[2] Sir James Jeans, *Science and Music*, p. 50, 1937.

large number of intermediate or black notes would be required. This would ensure that all the intervals would be correct in order and size but would make the instrument cumbersome and difficult to play. To avoid this a compromise, known as temperament, is made. Five black notes are introduced into each octave (as many as sixteen have been used) which simplifies the playing of the instrument, but the intervals are not quite correct. Only very sensitive ears, however, can discern the change in a tune when modulated or played in a different key. On the scale of equal temperament the octave interval of $2:1$ is divided into twelve equal intervals, i.e. each of $\sqrt[12]{2}:1$. The following table shows how well these intervals agree with the true diatonic scale.

	C	C$\sharp$	D	D$\sharp$	E	F	F$\sharp$	G	G$\sharp$	A	A$\sharp$	B	C'
Ratio of frequency Equal	1	$2^{\frac{1}{12}}$	$2^{\frac{2}{12}}$	$2^{\frac{3}{12}}$	$2^{\frac{4}{12}}$	$2^{\frac{5}{12}}$	$2^{\frac{6}{12}}$	$2^{\frac{7}{12}}$	$2^{\frac{8}{12}}$	$2^{\frac{9}{12}}$	$2^{\frac{10}{12}}$	$2^{\frac{11}{12}}$	2
temperament	1	1·059	1·122	1·189	1·260	1·335	1·414	1·489	1·587	1·682	1·782	1·888	2
Diatonic	1	—	$\frac{9}{8}$	—	$\frac{5}{4}$	$\frac{4}{3}$	—	$\frac{3}{2}$	—	$\frac{5}{3}$	—	$\frac{15}{8}$	2
scale	1	—	1·125	—	1·250	1·333	—	1·500	—	1·667	—	1·875	2

Temperament is only necessary in those instruments which give out notes of a predetermined and fixed frequency, and is therefore unnecessary for instruments such as the human voice, violin, etc., which can be controlled to produce any desired note or interval within the compass of the instrument.

61. Variation of Frequency with Motion. Doppler Effect

All students will be familiar with the change in pitch of the whistle of an express train as it rushes through a station or the horn of a swiftly moving car as it approaches and then recedes. To an observer in the train or automobile the pitch of the note is unaltered no matter with what speed the vehicle is moving. When a goods train passes slowly through a station, or a slow-moving car sounding its horn passes on the road, the change in the note of whistle or horn is very small, thus indicating that the change in frequency of a note is dependent on the relative speed of observer and source. The principle of the variation of frequency with motion is known as the Doppler or Doppler-Fizeau principle. It was first applied to the changing colour of certain stars as they approached or receded along the line of sight.

The earliest recorded experiments demonstrating the Doppler effect were carried out by Buijs Ballot and Scott Russell using musical instruments carried on locomotives. Some time later Mach devised a laboratory method using a whirling tube with a whistle at one end, the supply of air being sent along the tube while the whistle and tube were rotating. A simple but effective form of this apparatus consists of a police-type whistle fitted to the end of a piece of Bunsen tubing and blown by coal gas from the laboratory gas supply. If the operator makes the whistle describe a circle of constant radius with uniform speed, with his head at the centre of the circle, then he does not hear any change in pitch, but an observer in the plane of rotation of the whistle hears a rise and fall in the note emitted as it approaches and recedes.

König used two tuning forks, which gave a few beats per sec. when stationary, to demonstrate the Doppler effect. When one fork was made to approach or recede from the ear whilst the other remained at rest, then the number of beats per sec. was altered according to Doppler's principle, the increase or decrease in the number of beats depending on which fork had the higher frequency and in which direction it was moving.

As will be shown mathematically, the change in frequency does not depend simply on the relative velocity of source and observer. The effect is different according as to whether the source is moving relative to the observer or the observer relative to the source.

Thus, if an observer moves with a velocity of u ft./sec. relative to the source, the change in frequency is not the same as if the source moved with a velocity of u ft./sec. relative to the observer. Another point which causes some difficulty, unless thoroughly grasped, is that when a sound has left a source, its velocity through the medium is independent of the velocity of the source but depends solely on the physical properties of the medium. Thus, if a source moving at u ft./sec. sends out waves in air, the velocity of the waves relative to the air is v ft./sec., where v is the velocity of sound in air under the existing atmospheric conditions. When the medium is also in motion then it is convenient to express the frequency of the sound in terms of velocities relative to some fixed body, viz. the earth. The velocity of sound relative to the medium is its normal value v and if the velocity of the wind is w ft./sec. the velocity of the sound relative to the earth is $v \pm w$ ft./sec. depending upon whether the wind is blowing in the same or opposite direction to the direction of propagation of the sound. Consider the simplest case first.

62. Observer Moving, Source and Medium at Rest

Let S represent a stationary source of frequency n vib./sec. and O an observer moving with uniform velocity u towards the source (Fig. 57). The sound waves are sent out at regular intervals, the spacing being governed by the equation $\lambda = \dfrac{v}{n}$. If the observer were stationary at O, he would receive in 1 sec. the waves in a distance v, viz. n waves. But during each second he moves a distance u towards the source and so he receives the waves which occupy a distance $v + u$. But n waves occupy a distance v and each is of length λ,

$$\therefore \quad \text{number of waves in a distance } v + u = \frac{v + u}{\lambda} = \frac{v + u}{\dfrac{v}{n}}.$$

But these are received in 1 sec.

$$\therefore \quad \text{apparent frequency} = \frac{v + u}{v} \cdot n \text{ vib./sec.}$$

If the observer moves away from the source then he receives the waves

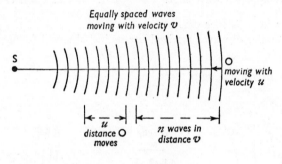

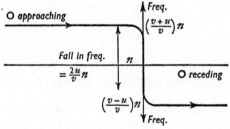

FIG. 57.

only in a distance $(v - u)$ ft. in 1 sec., therefore the apparent frequency of the source in this case

$$= \left(\frac{v - u}{v}\right) \cdot n \text{ vib./sec.}$$

Thus the fall in frequency as the observer passes the source is

$$\left(\frac{v + u}{v}\right)n - \left(\frac{v - u}{v}\right) \cdot n = \frac{2u}{v} \cdot n \text{ vib./sec.}$$

63. Source Moving, Observer and Medium Stationary

Suppose A is the first wave sent out by a source S of frequency n vib./sec. as it moves with a velocity u ft./sec. towards an observer O

(Fig. 58). Then the second wave B is nearer to A than if S were stationary by the distance S has moved in the time between the sending out of B. Similarly, C, D, etc., are all closer together than if S were stationary, since the velocity of the wave when it is in the medium is independent of the velocity of the source. By the same reasoning, waves A', B', C', etc., are all farther apart than if the source were stationary.

S sends out n waves in 1 sec. and since in each second S moves a distance u towards O, these n waves occupy a distance $v - u$ ft.

Therefore apparent wavelength $= \dfrac{v - u}{n}$ ft. But in 1 sec. O receives the waves in a distance v ft.

∴ Number of waves received per sec. or observed frequency

$$= \frac{v}{\text{new wavelength}} = \frac{v}{\left(\dfrac{v - u}{n}\right)} = \left(\frac{v}{v - u}\right) . n \text{ vib./sec.}$$

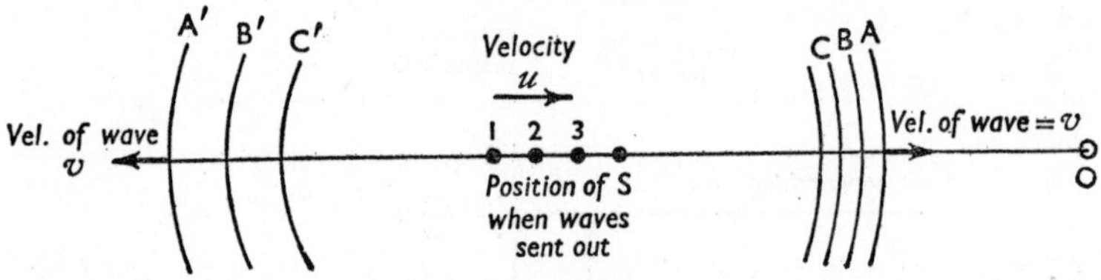

FIG. 58.

If the source moves with velocity u ft./sec. away from the observer, then n waves occupy a distance $v + u$ ft., new wavelength $= \dfrac{v + u}{n}$ ft. The observer receives the waves in a distance v,

$$∴ \text{ observed frequency} = \frac{v}{\dfrac{v + u}{n}} = \left(\frac{v}{v + u}\right) . n \text{ vib./sec.}$$

As the source passes the observer the drop in frequency will be

$$\left(\frac{v}{v - u}\right)n - \left(\frac{v}{v + u}\right)n = \frac{v^2 + uv - v^2 + uv}{v^2 - u^2} . n = \frac{2uv}{v^2 - u^2} . n \text{ vib./sec.}$$

64. Observer and Source Moving, Medium Stationary

Suppose the observer is moving with a velocity u ft./sec. away from the source and the source S of frequency n vib./sec. is moving with a velocity u' ft./sec. toward the observer. Whenever the source is moving it is useful to deal first with the change in wavelength due to the motion of S. It follows that :

$$n \text{ waves occupy a distance } v - u',$$

$$\therefore \text{ new wavelength} = \frac{v - u'}{n} \text{ ft.}$$

These travel with a velocity v and due to his motion the observer receives in 1 sec. the waves in a distance $v - u$ ft.

$\therefore$ Number of waves received per sec. or frequency

$$= \frac{v - u}{\dfrac{v - u'}{n}} = \left(\frac{v - u}{v - u'}\right) . n \text{ vib./sec.}$$

By similar reasoning, if O moves towards S with a velocity u then, etc., apparent frequency of S

$$= \left(\frac{v + u}{v - u'}\right) n.$$

If a wind is blowing, then the velocity of sound relative to the earth must be suitably altered so that if the wind is blowing at w ft./sec. in the same direction as that in which O and S are moving, the velocity of the waves relative to the ground becomes $v + w$ ft./sec. and hence for the previous set of conditions the observed frequency n' is given by

$$n' = \left(\frac{v + w - u}{v + w - u'}\right) n \text{ vib./sec.}$$

The student is advised to learn the principles involved in the preceding work and not to memorise a number of formulae.

EXAMPLE

Two cars are approaching each other at 30 and 60 m.p.h. along a straight road. Each car has a horn which when sounded emits a note of frequency 200 vib./sec. What would be the apparent frequency of the horn.

(a) to the driver of the second car if the driver of the first sounded his horn

(b) to the driver of the first car if the driver of the second sounded his horn ? Assume velocity of sound in air to be 1100 ft./sec.

(a) As both source and observer are moving, consider first the effect of the motion of the source.

For the sound going towards the observer

$$200 \text{ waves occupy a distance of } 1100 - \frac{30}{60} \times 88 = 1056 \text{ ft.}$$

$$\therefore \text{ apparent wavelength} = \frac{1056}{200} = \frac{132}{25} \text{ ft.}$$

In 1 sec. the observer receives the waves in 1100 + 88 ft.

∴ number of waves received or apparent frequency $= \dfrac{\dfrac{1188}{132}}{25}$

$$\begin{bmatrix} 3\cdot0749 \\ 1\cdot3979 \\ 4\cdot4728 \\ 2\cdot1206 \\ \overline{2\cdot3522} \end{bmatrix}$$

$$= \frac{1188 \times 25}{132}$$

$$= 225 \text{ vib./sec.}$$

(b) In this case the source moves at 88 ft./sec.

∴ for the sound going towards the observer

200 waves occupy a distance 1100 − 88 = 1012 ft.

∴ apparent wavelength $= \dfrac{1012}{200} = \dfrac{253}{50}$ ft.

In 1 sec. the observer receives the waves in

$$\begin{bmatrix} 3\cdot0584 \\ 1\cdot6990 \\ 4\cdot7574 \\ 2\cdot4031 \\ \overline{2\cdot3543} \end{bmatrix}$$

$$1100 + \frac{30}{60} \times 88 = 1144 \text{ ft.}$$

$$\therefore \text{ apparent frequency} = \frac{1144}{\dfrac{253}{50}} = \frac{1144 \times 50}{253}$$

$$= 226\cdot(1) \text{ vib./sec.}$$

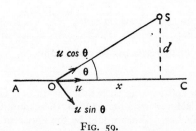

Fig. 59.

* **65.** When the observer is moving with a velocity which is not directed towards the source and vice versa, the results are a little more complicated, owing to the presence of trigonometrical functions. The principles involved, however, are the same as before, the difference being due to the fact that the component of the velocity of source or observer along the line joining them is not constant.

(a) *Source Stationary, Observer Moving.* Consider an observer O moving with velocity u ft./sec. along a line AOC (Fig. 59). Let the frequency of the source S at a distance d from AOC be n vibs./sec. The velocity of O towards S is $u \cos \theta$.

∴ In 1 sec. O receives the waves in a distance $v + u \cos \theta$ where v is the velocity of sound in the medium.

But n waves occupy a distance v

$$\therefore \text{ in I sec. } O \text{ receives } \frac{v + u \cos \theta}{\dfrac{v}{n}} \text{ waves,}$$

$$\therefore \text{ apparent frequency } = \left(\frac{v + u \cos \theta}{v}\right) n \text{ vibs./sec.}$$

Substituting $\dfrac{x}{\sqrt{x^2 + d^2}}$ for $\cos \theta$, $\quad n' = n\left(1 + \dfrac{u}{v} \cdot \dfrac{x}{\sqrt{x^2 + d^2}}\right).$

Considering u, v and n as constant and plotting apparent frequency n' against x for fixed values of d, curves are obtained as shown above. In each case when $x = 0$, the velocity u changes sign and so the general solution is $n' = \left(\dfrac{v \pm u \cos \theta}{v}\right) n$, which reduces to the value of n' obtained in the preceding section when $d = 0$.

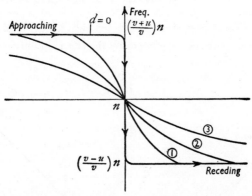

Fig. 60. Graph showing the variation in frequency as the observer passes a stationary source when the observer is not moving directly towards the source.

(b) *Observer Stationary. Source Moving.* Due to the velocity of the source the distance between the waves is altered. In I sec. S moves a distance $u \cos \theta$ in the direction SO (Fig. 61).

$$\therefore n \text{ waves occupy a distance } v - u \cos \theta.$$

The velocity of sound in the medium v is independent of the velocity of the source, and so O receives in I sec. the waves in a distance v,

$$\therefore \text{ In I sec. } O \text{ receives } \frac{v}{\dfrac{v - u \cos \theta}{n}} \text{ waves,}$$

$$\therefore \text{ apparent frequency } = \frac{v}{v - u \cos \theta} \cdot n \text{ vibs./sec.}$$

When S passes through P the sign of u changes and so the general solution is

$$n' = \frac{v}{v \pm u \cos \theta} \cdot n \text{ vibs./sec.}$$

7

Substituting for $\cos\theta$ in terms of x and d and differentiating, an expression is obtained for $\dfrac{dn'}{dx}$. This expression shows that when

$$x = 0 \qquad \frac{dn'}{dx} = \frac{n \cdot u}{v \cdot d}.$$

When x is large compared with d, then $\dfrac{dn'}{dx} = 0$ and n' has the value

$$\frac{v}{v \pm u} \cdot n.$$

(a) For small values of d, the source passing close to the observer the frequency remains at an approximately constant high value and suddenly changes to a low value; cf. express train rushing through a station.

(b) When d is large the change in frequency is more gradual and is not so easily noticed unless u is large; cf. high speed aeroplane passing overhead.

(c) If u is large and d is small, for example a low flying high speed aeroplane, $\dfrac{dn'}{dx}$ is also very large and the effect is rather sensational.

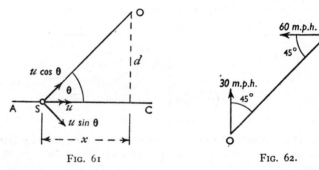

FIG. 61   FIG. 62.

EXAMPLE

A car is moving along a straight road at a uniform speed of 60 m.p.h. sounding its horn of frequency 200 vibs./sec. An observer approaches the first road along a straight side road at 30 m.p.h. Assuming that the two roads are at right angles determine the frequency of the note heard by the observer when the line joining the two cars is at 45° to the two roads. (Velocity of sound = 1100 ft./sec.)

First consider the source. Because the component of its velocity towards O is 60 cos 45 m.p.h. (see Fig. 62).

200 waves occupy $(1100 - 88 \cos 45)$ ft. $= 1100 - \dfrac{88}{\sqrt{2}}$ ft.

In 1 sec. the observer moves a distance $\dfrac{30}{60} \times 88 \cos 45$ ft. or 44 ft. towards S,

∴ in 1 sec. O receives the waves in $1100 + \dfrac{44 \text{ ft.}}{\sqrt{2}}$ But each

wave occupies $\qquad \dfrac{1100 - \dfrac{88}{\sqrt{2}}}{200} \text{ ft.,}$

∴ number of waves received per sec. $= \dfrac{1100 + \dfrac{44}{\sqrt{2}}}{\dfrac{1100 - \dfrac{88}{\sqrt{2}}}{200}}$

∴ observed frequency $= \dfrac{1131}{1100 - 44\sqrt{2}} \cdot 200 \text{ vibs./sec.}$

$$
\begin{bmatrix}
\log 1131 & 3\cdot0535 \\
\log \; 200 & 2\cdot3010 \\
& \overline{5\cdot3545} \\
\log 1038 & 3\cdot0161 \\
& \overline{2\cdot3384}
\end{bmatrix}
$$

$\eqsim \dfrac{1131}{1038} \cdot 200$

$\eqsim 218 \text{ vibs./sec.}$

66. The Doppler effect is applicable to all wave motions, but the velocity of light is so much greater than that of terrestrial sources that the change in frequency (and therefore wavelength) using these sources is not apparent to the casual observer.

Doppler originally suggested that stars going away from an observer should appear red (frequency decreased, wavelength increased) whilst those coming towards him should appear blue. Fizeau pointed out that since stars emit practically all wavelengths from infra-red to ultra-violet the effect of the velocity would be a general shift of the spectrum and the effect would not be so obvious as that expected by Doppler. He showed, however, that if a particular line belonging to an element (e.g. sodium) were considered, then this line would show a displacement from its normal position in the spectrum, which would be shown by a change in wavelength, dependent on the velocity of the star.

If the eastern and western edges of the sun's disc are viewed, in one case the edge is moving towards the earth and in the other it is moving from the earth. Thus by examining these two edges of the sun's disc with a spectrometer, the wavelength of the lines of specific elements will be altered according to which edge is viewed, and by finding this shift the velocity of rotation of the sun can be found.

For a moving source $\delta n = \dfrac{2uc}{c^2 - u^2} \cdot n$ where u is the velocity of the source, n the frequency of the spectral line and c the velocity of light.

But since $c \gg u$ $\qquad\qquad \delta n \eqsim \dfrac{2un}{c}.$

For a long time it was a subject of controversy as to whether Saturn's rings were solid or composed of small particles. If solid then the velocity of the outer edge would be greater than that of the inner. If, on the other hand, the rings consisted of tiny particles, then the particles nearer to Saturn must have a greater velocity than those farther away to balance the greater gravitational attraction.

$$\left[m\frac{v^2}{R} = G\frac{m \cdot M}{R^2} \quad \therefore \; v^2 = \frac{GM}{R} \right.$$

where G = constant of gravitation ; M = mass of Saturn ; R = radius of the orbit of a particular particle, and v its velocity,

$$\left. \therefore \; v \text{ increases as } R \text{ decreases.} \right]$$

Measurements of the change in frequency and therefore wavelength show that the inner edge produces the greater effect and it is considered therefore, that the rings are composed of swarms of individual particles.

A point worth noting is that the effect of the movement of a source of light is measured, as a change of wavelength, with the aid of the eye, whereas the effect of the movement of a sound source is measured as a change in frequency by means of the ear. A simple " aide-memoire " is that when the distance between observer and source is decreasing the frequency is increased and vice versa.

QUESTIONS

1. A smoked plate falls vertically under gravity. A trace is formed by the transverse vibrations of a tuning fork, and the lengths of two consecutive groups of 10 vibrations are 5·143 cm. and 6·640 cm. respectively. What is the frequency of the fork ?
   (g is 981 cm./sec./sec.)

2. In th falling plate experiment the consecutive lengths occupied by 25 complete waves were 9·85 and 14·1 cm. The experiment was repeated using a different tuning fork and in this case the lengths occupied by 25 complete waves were 9·0 and 12·0 cm. Calculate the frequency of each fork and derive any formula you employ.
   (g is 981 cm./sec./sec.)

3. The disc of a siren is rotating at 1500 r.p.m. and the note emitted is observed to give 60 beats with a tuning fork. When the speed of rotation of the siren is reduced to 1495 r.p.m. the number of beats per min. is reduced to 40. If there are 20 holes round the disc of the siren what is the frequency of the fork ?

4. A stroboscopic disc is revolving at 40 rev./sec. The disc contains 20 dots, and is viewed through the holes in two small pieces of aluminium, carried by the prongs of a tuning fork, and arranged so that the dots are visible when the prongs are in the undisturbed position. If the dots on the disc appear to move backwards at the rate of one every 3 sec. what is the frequency of the fork ?

5. A source of sound is emitting a note of frequency 512 vib./sec. Find the pitch of the note heard by an observer (a) when the source

is approaching him at 40 m.p.h., (b) when the observer and source are moving towards each other, each moving at 60 m.p.h.

(Velocity of sound is 1100 ft./sec.)

6. Two trains, each moving at 40 m.p.h., are approaching each other. To an observer on one train the pitch of the note from the other appears to be that of A (426·7 vibs./sec.). If the velocity of sound in air is 1100 ft./sec. find the actual pitch of the whistle.

7. A train, travelling at 60 m.p.h., blows its whistle, the frequency of which is 384 vib./sec. What will be the pitch of the note heard by an observer in another train travelling towards the first at 50 m.p.h.? Assume the velocity of sound to be 1100 ft./sec.

8. Explain Doppler's principle and give examples of its application to (a) light, (b) sound.

A whistle is attached to a flexible tube connected to an air pump and is whirled round, in a horizontal circle of 1 m. radius, at a uniform speed of 10 rev./sec. To the operator rotating the whistle, the centre of the circle being directly above his head, the note emitted is steady and of frequency 512 vib./sec. An observer some distance away hears a fluctuating note. Explain this and calculate the maximum and minimum frequencies of the note heard by a distant observer.

(Velocity of sound under the given conditions is 300 m./sec.)

9. Derive expressions showing how the apparent frequency of the note heard by an observer is affected by (a) motion of the source, (b) motion of the observer, in each instance the motion being along the line of propagation of the sound.

A motor car is fitted with twin horns differing in frequency by 256 vib./sec. Calculate the difference in frequencies of the notes by an observer when the car, sounding the horns, is approaching him at 40 m.p.h. Take the velocity of sound in air as 1120 ft./sec.

(N.U.J.M.B).

10. Explain why the motion of a sound affects its pitch as heard by a stationary observer. How can the phenomenon be demonstrated in the classroom?

What is the velocity of the source along the line joining the source to the observer if, as a result of the motion, the frequency of the note heard is (a) increased in the ratio 16 : 15, (b) decreased in the ratio 15 : 16? Assume the velocity of sound to be 1120 ft./sec. and give the result in ft./sec. Derive any formula employed.

(N.U.J.M.B.)

11. An engine travels at 45 m.p.h. towards an observer and emits a whistle of frequency 1000 vib./sec. Assuming that the velocity of sound is 1120 ft./sec. determine the frequency of the note heard by the observer. Explain the method of calculation. (N.U.J.M.B. part.)

12. A source of sound of frequency 512 vib./sec. is moving towards a wall at 300 cm./sec. Under certain conditions beats may be heard between the direct and reflected sounds. Find the number of beats heard per sec. if the observer (a) carries the source of sound, (b) is stationary between source and wall, (c) is stationary at a point remote from source and wall. Assume the velocity of sound to be 330 m./sec.

13. A car is fitted with a horn of frequency 1000 vib./sec. When passing a stationary observer the latter observes a fall in pitch of 100 vib./sec. If the velocity of sound is 1100 ft./sec. what is the speed of the car ?

14. As two trains are approaching each other, one travelling at 50 m.p.h. and the other at 30 m.p.h., the whistle of the former, of frequency 500 vib./sec., is sounded. What is the frequency of the note heard by an observer on the other train ? What would be the frequency if the speeds of the trains were interchanged ?
(Velocity of sound in air is 1120 ft./sec.)

15. The light from the star Sirius contains the blue-green hydrogen line F, whose wavelength is found to be 4862·12 A.U. When the line is produced in the laboratory its wavelength is found to be 4861·37 A.U. What deductions can you make from these figures ?
(Velocity of light $= 3 \times 10^{10}$ cm./sec.)

16. Explain Doppler's principle.

A spectrum line of wavelength 4×10^{-5} cm., in the spectrum of the light from a star, is found to be displaced from its normal place towards the red end of the spectrum by an amount equivalent to 10^{-8} cm. What velocity of the star in the line of sight would account for this ?

17. A racing car travels at 100 m.p.h. on a straight track in front of an observer. If the velocity of sound is 1100 ft./sec. find the direction from which the observer hears the sound when the car is nearest to him.

18. A vibrating tuning fork is moving steadily with a velocity of 150 cm./sec. normally towards a wall from which the sound waves are reflected. If the frequency of the fork is 512 sec.$^{-1}$, what will be the frequency of the beats heard by a stationary observer who has just been passed by the fork ? (Velocity of sound $= 330$ m./sec.)
(C.S.)

19. A train is moving with uniform velocity v on a straight track between two bridges A and B over the track, the motion being towards A. An observer on the train hears the echo of the train's whistle reflected from each of the bridges. If the velocity of sound is V find the ratio of the wavelengths of the waves reflected from A and B and the ratio of the frequencies of the echoes heard by the observer.
(C.S.)

20. Show how the apparent frequency of the note heard by an observer varies with the motion of the source, deducing expressions connecting the observed frequency with the emitted frequency for a source moving directly towards and away from an observer.

A " flying-bomb " motor makes 50 explosions per sec. and the machine travels at 400 m.p.h. Find the extreme frequencies heard by a stationary observer as the weapon passes overhead.
(Velocity of sound in air $= 1100$ ft./sec.) (O. & C.)

21. An observer on a railway station platform observed that as the train passed through the station at 60 m.p.h. the frequency of the whistle appeared to drop by 400 vib./sec. Find the frequency of the whistle. (Velocity of sound $= 1100$ ft./sec.) (C.S. part.)

CHAPTER VI

THE VIBRATION OF STRINGS, RODS AND SOLID BODIES

67. The vibrating string plucked, struck or bowed forms the basis of probably the most important class of musical instruments. The musical use of stretched strings was familiar in Old Testament times and it seems probable that these instruments were developed from the hunting bow. In sound, as in most branches of science, little advance was made in the years between the time of Pythagoras (572-497 B.C.) and Galileo (1564-1642). Pythagoras showed that the relationship between a note and its octave is always obtained when the two segments of a stretched string are divided by a movable bridge so that the lengths of the segments are in the ratio 2 : 1. Many years later Galileo discovered the quantitative relation between the frequency of vibration and the length, diameter, density and tension of the string. Independent of this Mersenne (1588-1648) carried out experiments and published his results in 1636. They may be stated as follows :

1. For a given string under a given tension the frequency varies inversely as the length $\left(n \propto \dfrac{1}{l} \right)$.

2. For a string of given length and material the frequency varies as the square root of the applied tension $(n \propto \sqrt{T})$.

3. For strings of the same length and under the same tension the frequency varies inversely as the square root of the mass per unit length of the string $\left(n \propto \dfrac{1}{\sqrt{m}} \right)$.

Consequently $n \propto \dfrac{1}{l} \sqrt{\dfrac{T}{m}}$.

At this point it is worth noting the properties of the theoretical string. Ideally it has length only, is infinitely thin and can be bent laterally in transverse vibrations without bringing into play any viscous forces in the material. Natural wires and threads fail to comply strictly with this last requirement in that they possess stiffness. This resistance to bending is the cause of vibration in a rod or bar since it provides the restoring force when the bar or rod is displaced. In a string the tension between particles replaces this resistance to bending and in the absence of this applied tension a string cannot be made to vibrate transversely.

68. Velocity of Transverse Waves along a Stretched String

The following is another method of obtaining the equation obtained in para. 16. Assuming that a wave of any given type can be propagated along the string without change of shape and with velocity v then this wave can be brought to rest in space by moving the string in the opposite direction with velocity v. Consider an element δs of the wave subtending an angle $\delta\theta$ at its centre of curvature (radius R). The resultant of the two equal tensions T acting tangentially at its ends is $2T \cdot \sin \frac{1}{2}\delta\theta \simeq T\delta\theta = T \cdot \dfrac{\delta s}{R}$. This force gives the element

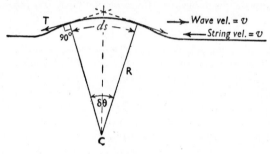

FIG. 63.

its necessary centripetal acceleration towards the centre and is therefore $m\delta s \cdot \dfrac{v^2}{R}$ where m is the mass of unit length of the string,

$$\therefore m \cdot \delta s \, \frac{v^2}{R} = T \frac{\delta s}{R}$$

or

$$v = \sqrt{\frac{T}{m}}$$

which is independent of the amplitude of the wave. Combining this with $v = n\lambda$, the equation relating frequency, wavelength, tension and mass per unit length of the string becomes $n = \dfrac{1}{\lambda}\sqrt{\dfrac{T}{m}}$.

69. Modes of Vibration of a String

Consider a string AB fixed at A and B and suppose a wave is travelling towards A. The wave is reflected at A, goes to B, is reflected at B and so on until the wave dies away. Thus the resultant motion of the string is determined by the superposition of the direct (or incident) wave and the reflected wave. In other words, standing waves are set up in the string. The simplest mode of vibration is when A and B are nodes and there is one antinode between them, i.e. AB is one half wavelength. Owing to standing waves and the persistence of vision the vibrating string forms one loop. If $AB = L$,

then since $\qquad n = \dfrac{1}{\lambda}\sqrt{\dfrac{T}{m}}, \qquad n \propto \dfrac{1}{2L}.$

If the same string under the same tension is made to vibrate and

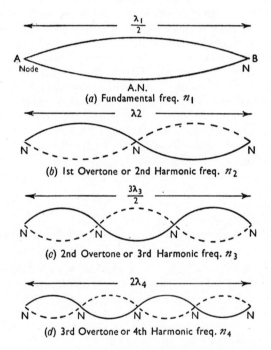

(a) Fundamental freq. n_1

(b) 1st Overtone or 2nd Harmonic freq. n_2

(c) 2nd Overtone or 3rd Harmonic freq. n_3

(d) 3rd Overtone or 4th Harmonic freq. n_4

FIG. 64. Modes of vibration of a string.

then its centre point x is damped by means of a feather, the length

AB is divided into equal loops so that $AB = L = \lambda$, $\quad \therefore\ n_2 \propto \dfrac{1}{L}.$

Repeating the experiment and damping the string at $\frac{1}{3}$, $\frac{1}{4}$, etc., of the length of the string from A, then the string vibrates in 3, 4, etc. loops

and $\qquad n_3 \propto \dfrac{3}{2L}, \ n_4 \propto \dfrac{2}{L},$ etc.

Thus the relationship between n_1, n_2, etc., is

$$n_1 : n_2 : n_3 : n_4 = 1 : 2 : 3 : 4 \text{ or Doh, doh, soh, doh}^1.$$

If s is the number of loops and L is the length of the string, then the general equation for the various partials is $n_s = \dfrac{s}{2L}\sqrt{\dfrac{T}{m}}$ where s is 1, 2, 3, etc., and represents a harmonic series of tones, and there are $(s - 1)$ points which are at rest between the fixed ends of the string. Midway between these points which are at rest are antinodes and here the amplitude of vibration is a maximum. In 1676 Noble and Piggott devised an elegant method of demonstrating the loops in vibrating strings. Small paper riders are placed on the wire, which is made to vibrate by drawing a bow across it. The mode of vibration is determined by touching the wire, at an appropriate point, by a feather at the same time that it is bowed. Only at the nodes are the riders undisturbed. In the loops they are obviously moving and most of them are flung from the string, especially at the antinodes. A similar method

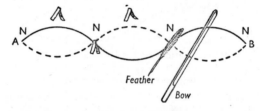

FIG. 65. Demonstration of position of nodes and antinodes in a vibrating string.

is sometimes used, especially by people who have difficulty in distinguishing beats, to indicate when a wire is tuned to the frequency of a vibrating tuning fork whose stem is placed on the sounding box on which the wire is mounted.

70. The Sonometer or Monochord

This instrument, which is normally used to study the laws of vibrating strings and for the comparison of frequencies, was invented by Pythagoras. In its simplest form it consists of a hollow wooden box (sounding box) on which is a wire fastened to a peg A and passing over a pulley P. A weight W provides the necessary tension in the string and presses the wire against two bridges, B_1 and B_2. Another adjustable bridge B is used so as to allow the operator to alter the length of wire which is vibrating. A scale is fixed between B_1 and B_2. The wire itself gives out little sound as can be proved by hanging it vertically under the same tension and plucking it (under these conditions the vibrations persist for a long time). The vibrations of the wire are communicated to the sounding box which sets into vibration a considerable quantity of air which in turn produces the sensation of a loud note in the ears of the observer. Another type of sonometer is fitted with a spring balance to indicate the tension instead of the hanging weight. The post to which the wire is fixed can be rotated, so increasing or decreasing the tension (cf. piano and violin strings). Although this is a more convenient method of adjusting the tension the accuracy is not so high as that obtained with the other type of instrument owing to the difficulty of accurate estimation of the spring balance readings.

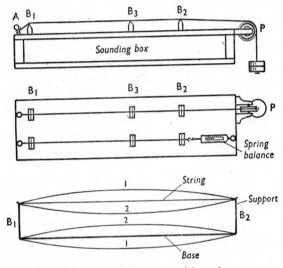

FIG. 66. The Sonometer and its action.

On the monochord usually provided in the laboratory a second string is placed alongside the first and used to provide a standard frequency.

The diagram (Fig. 66) shows how the string communicates its vibrations to the sounding board. As the string goes from rest to position 1 it bends inwards the supports at B_1 and B_2. This also takes place when the string is in position 2, and so the supports vibrate at twice the frequency of the string but the sounding board vibrates at the same frequency as the string and its corresponding positions 1 and 2 are indicated. It is worthy of note that if the baseboard and supports of the wire did not yield then no appreciable sound would be heard since the wire itself radiates very little. Yielding of the base board and supports introduces errors into the readings and so in practice these are made as rigid as experimental conditions will permit.

EXPERIMENTS USING THE SONOMETER

71. To prove Mersenne's Laws of Vibrating Strings

(a) To prove $n \propto \dfrac{1}{L}$ or nL = a constant. n and L vary, T and m constant

For this experiment several tuning forks of known frequency are required. Using the fork of lowest pitch the sonometer wire is loaded so that practically the whole length of wire must vibrate to produce a note in unison with the fork. The wire is adjusted so that its note produces beats with that of the fork and then very carefully adjusted so that the beats become slow and finally disappear. For the students who have difficulty in determining when two notes are in unison, a useful aid consists of a wooded disc about 4 in. in diameter attached at right angles to the axis of a short wooden rod. The free end of the rod is pressed on to the sonometer board and the ear placed in contact

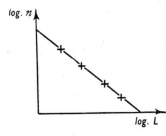

FIG. 67. Graph of $\log n = -\log L + K$.

with the disc. The vibrating tuning fork is placed with its stem on the sounding board. Both sets of vibrations are then passed along the wooden rod to the ear. The experiment is repeated several times, observations being made of the length of wire which vibrates in unison with a fork of known frequency. Since theory shows that nL is constant, the verification of the law is best shown graphically. Without a doubt the most useful graph in Physics is the straight line and so the variables should be chosen with that end in view. In this case if $\log n$ is plotted against $\log L$ and the graph is a straight line of slope $-$ 1 then the law has been verified since if nL is constant, $\log n = -\log L + K$ where K is a constant.

(b) To show $n \propto \sqrt{T}$ (n and T vary, L and m remain constant).

There are several methods of proving this law but the simplest is to use several tuning forks of known frequency. In this experiment the bridges, and therefore the length of vibrating wire, are fixed and the note of the wire is adjusted to that of the fork by varying the tension in the wire. As theory predicts a straight line relationship between n and $T^{\frac{1}{2}}$, the law is verified if the experimental work produces such a graph. An alternative method of graphing the results is to plot $\log n$ against $\log T$ when the graph should be a straight line of slope 0·5.

This law can also be proved without using a fork of known frequency, one wire on the sonometer under constant tension being used as a frequency standard. Suppose T_1 is applied to the second wire whose tension is adjusted so that a length L_1 vibrates in unison with the standard wire. Now increase T_1 to a value T_2 and increase the vibrating length of the wire until it is again in unison with the standard frequency. What is required is the frequency n_2 with which the wire would vibrate under a tension T_2 if its length had remained L_1. If the law nL is constant is assumed, then this frequency can be calculated and the frequency is given by $n_2 = \dfrac{L_2 N}{L_1}$ where N is the frequency of the standard wire and is constant. Similarly, the frequencies

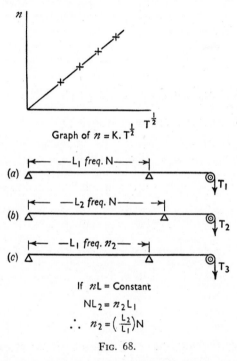

Graph of $n = K \cdot T^{\frac{1}{2}}$

If $nL =$ Constant

$$NL_2 = n_2 L_1$$

$$\therefore \quad n_2 = \left(\frac{L_2}{L_1}\right) N$$

Fig. 68.

of the second wire under different loads but with constant length vibrating can be calculated and if the graph of $\log n$ against $\log T$ is a straight line of slope 0·5, the second law is verified. As N and L_1 are constant for a particular experiment, then n is proportional to L_2, and hence another method of graphing the results is to plot $\log L_2$ against $\log T$.

(c) To prove $n \propto m^{-\frac{1}{2}}$.

Assuming again the law nL is constant, then the above law is verified if it is proved that $L \propto m^{-\frac{1}{2}}$ or $Lm^{\frac{1}{2}}$ is constant. Thus the experiment now becomes that of finding the lengths of wires of different materials which vibrate in unison with a tuning fork or the note of the standard wire under constant tension. Graphs may be plotted of L against $m^{-\frac{1}{2}}$, which should be a straight line passing through the origin, or $\log L$ against $\log m$ which should give a straight line of slope $- 0\cdot5$ for verification of the law since $\log L + \frac{1}{2} \log m = k$. The latter graph is the one recommended to the student.

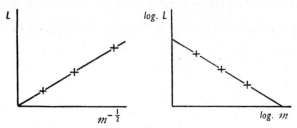

FIG. 69.   Alternative methods of showing variation of L and m.

72. To find the Density of a Heavy Mass

The weight is hung on the end of the sonometer wire and the length of the vibrating portion is adjusted until it is in unison with a tuning fork, or a frequency provided by the standard wire, first with the weight in air and secondly with the weight immersed in water. Then

$$n = \frac{1}{2L_1} \sqrt{\frac{Mg}{m}} = \frac{1}{2L_2} \sqrt{\frac{M'g}{m}}$$

where Mg and $M'g$ is the weight of the body in air and in water, L_1 and L_2 are the respective lengths of the sonometer wire which when plucked at its centre gives a note of the same frequency as the standard, and m is the mass per unit length of the wire.

Hence
$$\frac{M}{M'} = \frac{L_1{}^2}{L_2{}^2}.$$

But by Archimedes' principle the upthrust $= M - M'$ gm.

$$\therefore \text{ Volume of the body} = (M - M') \times 1 \text{ cc.}$$

$$\therefore \text{ Density} = \frac{\text{mass}}{\text{volume}} = \frac{M}{(M-M') \cdot 1} = \frac{L_1{}^2}{L_1{}^2 - L_2{}^2} \text{ gm./cc.}$$

It must be noted, however, that this does not provide a good method of finding the density of a body.

73. To find the Frequency of an Alternating Current

A small current from the A.C. source is sent along the sonometer wire (as shown in the diagram) the centre portion of which lies between the opposite poles of two magnets placed fairly close together (or between the poles of a horseshoe magnet). The tension in the wire is adjusted until resonance occurs when the natural period of the wire is the same as that of the A.C. When this occurs the wire vibrates and shows an obvious loop. The frequency can then be calculated from $n = \dfrac{1}{2L}\sqrt{\dfrac{T}{m}}.$ Since it is more convenient in this experiment to alter the tension rather than the length of wire vibrating, the sonometer fitted with a spring balance and rotating peg for altering the tension is most suitable.

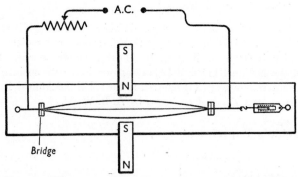

FIG. 70.   Measurement of A.C. frequency using a Sonometer.

74. Comparison of the Frequency of two Sounds

The sonometer wire is kept under constant tension and by means of the sliding bridge the length of the wire is adjusted until, when plucked at its centre, it gives out a note of the same frequency of one of the sounds. One of the previously explained methods of tuning is used to get unison and the experiment is repeated with the second sound, using the same wire under the same tension. Then since T and m are constant

$$\frac{n_1}{n_2} = \frac{L_2}{L_1}.$$

If one of the sounds is of known frequency, such as a tuning fork, then the frequency of the other sound can be determined.

75. Absolute Measurement of Frequency

When the length L of the sonometer wire vibrates with the same frequency as an unknown sound, then, if the tension and the mass per unit length of the wire are known, the frequency is given by

$n = \dfrac{1}{2L}\sqrt{\dfrac{T}{m}}$ for the fundamental mode of vibration of the wire. Since this measurement of frequency does not involve the use of any standard frequency, this is known as an absolute method of finding the frequency of a note. The method is not very suitable for accurate work for the following reasons :—

1. It is difficult to measure accurately the tension, which is liable to vary on opposite sides of a bridge.
2. The effective length of the string is uncertain. The theory assumes an ideal string having no stiffness, which is not realised in practice.
3. Yielding of the bridges affects the frequency.

To measure frequencies to 1 part in 1000, a sonometer is required which has very rigid bridges (and therefore does not radiate sound) and which is set into vibration by electromagnetic means. D. W. Dye at the National Physical Laboratory devised such an instrument and the interested student is referred to the " N.P.L. Annual Report," p. 83, 1924, or a *Textbook on Sound* by A. B. Wood.

76. Melde's Experiment

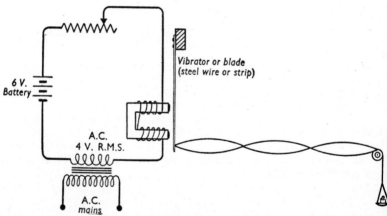

Fig. 71. Melde's experiment using an electrical vibrator instead of a maintained tuning fork. With the 6 V. polarising battery the frequency of vibration of the blade is the same as that of the mains. Without its use the frequency is double that of the mains.

A very elegant method of demonstrating the laws of vibrating strings is due to Melde. An electrically maintained fork or a vibrator running on 50 cycle A.C. provides a suitable means of exciting a string. One end of a string 2 or 3 m. in length is attached to one prong of the fork, the other end being attached to a scale pan after passing over a single fixed pulley. The pan is loaded and the fork set into vibration with its prongs moving along the direction of the string. The length of string between fork and pulley (or the load in the scale pan) is adjusted until the string shows one loop. When the load is reduced to one quarter of its original value, two loops are formed, when it is one-ninth three loops are formed and so on.

Let L be the length of the string between fork and pulley and let s be the number of loops in the vibrating string. Then since

$$v = n\lambda \text{ and } v = \sqrt{\frac{T}{m}}, \quad n = \frac{1}{\lambda}\sqrt{\frac{T}{m}} = \frac{s}{2L}\sqrt{\frac{T}{m}}, \text{ since } \lambda = \frac{2L}{s}.$$

If n, L, m are kept constant, then

$$s\sqrt{T} = \text{a constant or } s^2 T = k.$$

No. of loops s	1	2	3	4	5
Tension T .	T	$\dfrac{T}{4}$	$\dfrac{T}{9}$	$\dfrac{T}{16}$	$\dfrac{T}{25}$
$s^2 . T$ . .	T	T	T	T	T

Thus to obtain 1, 2, 3 or 4 loops, the initial value of added weights, together with scale pan and string hanging over the pulley, should be the L.C.M. of 4, 9 and 16. If for any pattern the plane of vibration of the fork is now turned through 90°, so that the fork is vibrating at right angles to the direction of the string, everything else being kept the same, the number of loops in the string is doubled, i.e. the string is now vibrating with twice its original frequency. This is explained as follows. When the fork is vibrating along the direction of the string and is in position A, i.e. its maximum displacement to the right, then the sag in the string is also a maximum. As the fork moves towards A' the string begins to move upwards so that when the prong of the fork is at A', the maximum displacement to the left, the string is taut. As the prong moves to A'' the string continues to move upwards under its

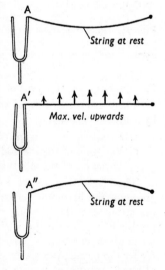

FIG. 72.   Fork vibrating along the direction of the string.

8

inertia, so that when the prong is at its maximum displacement to the right, the string bows upwards. Thus for one complete oscillation of the fork the string makes half an oscillation.

When the plane of vibration of the fork is rotated through 90° the end of the string follows the motion of the prong and this is communicated to the rest of the string. As the diagrams show, the vibration of string and fork synchronise and therefore their frequencies of vibration are the same.

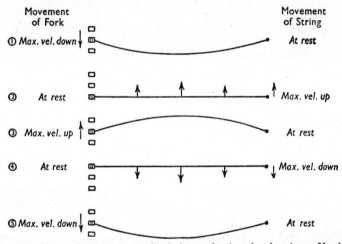

Fig. 73. Fork vibrating perpendicularly to the length of string. Vertical section showing five positions of the fork. The three rectangles represent the extreme and mean positions of one prong during its vibrations. The stem and blades of the fork are horizontal.

77. Quality of the Notes from Stretched Strings

There are three ways of varying the quality of the note given out by a stretched string.

1. Variation of the point of " attack ".
2. Variation of the method of " attack " (plucking, bowing, etc.).
3. Variation of the vibrating system to which the string is coupled.

The ideal string, i.e. perfectly flexible and between rigid supports, gives out the harmonic series of partials. In practice the stiffness of the string and the yielding of the supports results in the series of partials being sharper (i.e. slightly higher frequency) than the harmonic series given out by the ideal string. The shorter the string and the higher the partial, the greater is this departure.[1] By varying the point of attack, groups of partials can be cut out, thus altering the quality of the note, since this point cannot be a node.

[1] Shankland and Coltman, *Journ. Acous. Soc. Amer.*, **10**, p. 161, 1939.

The most usual ways of setting a string into transverse vibration, are :

(*a*) Plucking as in the harp, mandoline, etc.
(*b*) Striking as in the pianoforte.
(*c*) Bowing as in the violin, etc.

For a plucked string the harmonics depend upon the instrument used for plucking as well as the point of attack.   For the harp the strings are displaced by the fingers which, being broad and soft, do not set up sharp angles in the displaced string.   This tends to cut out the higher partials, giving the notes a sweet and mellow quality.   When a plectrum is used as in the mandoline the string is pulled into a sharp angle and the highest partials are strong and give the note a metallic or hard quality.

Strings, hammers and sounding board affect the quality of the note given out by a piano.   In this instrument the point at which the hammer strikes the string was determined by ear long before any theoretical treatment was possible.   The dissonant partials are the 7th, 9th, 11th—and the point of striking, about $\frac{1}{8}$ the length of the string from its end, is such that it practically cuts out these overtones. The sounding board, depending on its size and nature, also modifies the quality of the note as well as radiating the sound and is forced into vibration by the string.   According to Dr. Alex Wood [1] the piano has one striking defect—it is not possible to sustain the quality of a note. Like all percussion instruments its quality or tone reaches a maximum just after the moment of impact and then begins to die away.

The violin can sustain its quality or tone by the action of bowing, the bowing pressure having very little effect upon the quality of the note.   The point of attack has a great effect upon the quality, the nearer the bridge the string is bowed the more brilliant the quality. The usual limits are from $\frac{1}{7}$ to $\frac{1}{15}$ of the length of the vibrating string from the bridge.   One of the most remarkable features of this instrument is the difference in quality between the same note played on two different strings or different notes played on the same string.

F. A. Saunders made an exhaustive study of the violin with a view to finding a reason for the excellence of tone attributed to Stradivarius and other Italian violins of that period.   Among the tests made were (*a*) frequency response curves, (*b*) range of loudness consistent with good tone, (*c*) least force between bow and string to make the instrument speak, (*d*) damping (log dec) of the freely vibrating strings at various frequencies.

The results of this work indicated that there is no reason why the best modern violins should not be as good as a Stradivarius.   As Saunders points out, the old violins have been considerably modified,

[1] Alex Wood, *Physics of Music*, p. 95.

e.g. stronger bridges were needed when standard pitch was raised, and so the violins are not quite the same as when they were made. It was shown that good varnish has no appreciable effect upon tone, and there is no basis for the magical effects attributed to Cremona varnishes. The effect on tone of the ageing of the wood is uncertain, and so nothing can be said of how this may have changed the tone of the old instruments. Although some experts could recognise the tone of a Stradivarius when a test was carried out, the numbers were not sufficiently great to enable Saunders to conclude that this was due solely to the difference in tone, and when a stringed orchestra entirely composed of Stradivarius instruments played in a concert in New York in December 1937, many listeners could hear nothing unusual in their combined tone. It seems, therefore, that a good violin is a good violin whether it was made in the age of the Cremona makers or in the present time.

THE VIBRATION OF RODS AND SOLID BODIES

78. Longitudinal Vibration of Rods

When a rod is set into longitudinal vibration, cross-sections vibrate to and fro, about their position of rest, in the direction of the axis which remains undisplaced. When a rod is stretched in the direction of its length the increase in length is accomapnied by a contraction in cross-section. If the length of the rod is large compared with the cross-section, then the transverse vibration brought into play is negligible.

It can be shown that for rods of finite length the direct and reflected waves interfere to form standing waves which exhibit nodes and loops as in the case of vibrating strings, and the velocity of propagation is given by $v = \sqrt{\dfrac{E}{\rho}}$ where E is Young's modulus and ρ the density of the material.

Case 1. For a rod clamped at both ends the frequency of the partials is a complete harmonic series since in each case the ends are nodes (see Fig. 74 (1)). As explained in a previous chapter, the longitudinal vibration of a particular point is indicated by the ordinate of the graph.

Case 2. When the rod is clamped at its middle point this must be a node and the free ends antinodes. Applying these limiting conditions gives the result that the even harmonics are absent. The frequencies of the possible modes of vibration are therefore n, $3n$, $5n$, etc.

Case 3. Similarly for a rod clamped at one end and one end free, the even harmonics are absent, since this may be considered as half the preceding example.

Case 2 has a definite advantage in the method of supporting the rod, since the two equal portions react equally and in opposite directions at the mid-point, and so it is comparatively easy to ensure that the centre is a point of zero displacement. The usual laboratory method of exciting a rod is by stroking with a resined cloth. Other methods are striking with a hammer (for short stiff bars), electromagnetic, electrostatic and magnetostrictive. When a piston is fitted to the end of the rod, the vibrations can be transmitted to a gas, as in the case of Kundt's dust tube.

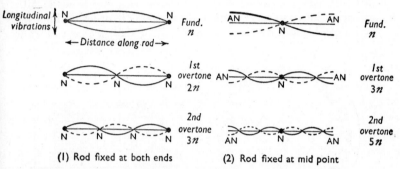

(1) Rod fixed at both ends   (2) Rod fixed at mid point

Fig. 74.   Displacement/distance diagrams for longitudinal vibrations.

79. Transverse Vibration of Rods

In dealing with the vibration of strings it has been assumed that they are perfectly flexible and are restored to their zero position, after being displaced, by the tension in them. There is no tension along a rod and the restitution is brought about by the rigidity of the material of the rod. The diagrams show the transverse vibrations of a rod executing its first three modes of vibration. A full treatment of the subject [1] shows that the overtones are not harmonics as in the case of strings or longitudinally vibrating rods, that the velocity of transverse vibrations is dependent on the frequency which is in

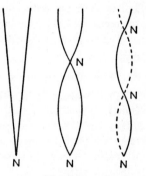

75. Transverse vibrations of rods.

turn dependent upon $\sqrt{\dfrac{E}{\rho}}$ as is the velocity of longitudinal vibrations in the bar.

[1] A. B. Wood, *Sound*, p. 111 ; E. G. Richardson, *Sound*, p. 110.

80. Resonant Frequency Indicator

A frequency meter or indicator is an instrument for indicating the frequency of an alternating current. A central laminated iron core C has a high resistance winding w round it, and carries a laminated top T. Arranged in a circle round the coil and close to the top is a series of steel reeds r, r, r, with bent-over flat tops, the lower ends of which are securely fixed into a brass base. Each reed is tuned to a different frequency of vibration and they are arranged in order of gradual increasing frequency. When an alternating current traverses the coil, that particular reed whose frequency corresponds to that of the A.C. will be set into resonant vibration, the tip of the resonant reed moving over a considerable distance. The tips of the reeds are painted white

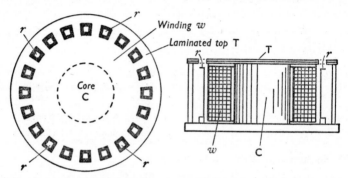

FIG. 76. Principle of resonance frequency indicator.

and so show up well against the dark interior of the instrument. As the reeds are lightly damped the selectivity curve is sharp and usually only about three reeds show any indication of vibration for a particular alternating current.

81. The Tuning Fork

This instrument is of the greatest value in sound because of its constancy as a standard of pitch. It is little affected by external conditions and if kept free from corrosion and not too badly treated it will retain its pitch for many years. Its development was due to König whose forks were remarkably pure in tone and covered a very wide range of frequencies. Some had a frequency as high as 90,000 cycles/sec.[1] In spite of many modern methods of producing sounds of known frequency, the tuning fork still maintains its place as a standard of pitch.

Chladni considered the tuning fork as a bar, with both ends free to vibrate, bent into the form of a " U ". Rayleigh,[2] on the other

---

[1] D. C. Miller, *The Science of Musical Sounds.*   [2] Rayleigh, *Sound,* 1, p. 58.

hand, considered it as two bars fixed in the same clamp. It is well worth considering how these two ideas, which at first sight appear to be contradictory, are really in close agreement.

The effect of bending a bar is to cause the two nodes $N_1 . N_2$ of the fundamental vibration to come closer together. This increases the length of the prongs and so increases the time of vibration while reducing the amplitude of vibration at the central antinode. When an additional piece of metal in the form of a stem is fitted at the central antinode, the movement becomes even less. What is equally important is that the movement of the stem must be up and down or at right angles to the direction of motion of the tips of the prongs. It is this up and down motion of the stem that sets into vibration a sounding board or resonance box, which in turn causes a considerable quantity of air to be set into vibration and so makes the fork audible at a considerable distance. These vibrations persist for a considerable time since the rate of transference of energy from the fork to the box is fairly slow. If, on the other

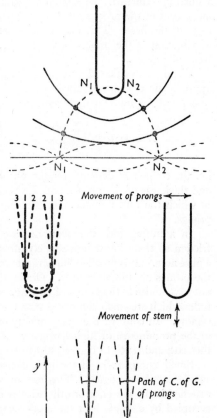

FIG. 77.   Principle of the tuning fork.

hand, *one* prong of the fork is touched by the hand, *both* prongs stop vibrating since the rate of withdrawal of energy is great.

Now, consider the tuning fork as made of two bars fixed on the same clamp such as a fairly massive piece of metal. Since the movements of the centres of gravity of the prongs are equal and opposite along the " x " axis there will be no movement of the centre of gravity of the whole instrument in this direction. The path traced out by the centre of gravity of each prong during its vibrations is the arc of a circle. The displacements along the x axis balance, those along the y axis do not; hence the centre of gravity of the block must perform a small movement in the direction of the y axis. Thus the to and fro movement of the prongs has been turned into an up and down movement of the base. This movement must depend upon the amplitude of vibration of the prongs as well as the relative mass and stiffness of base and prongs.

Wood [1] states that the frequency of a fork of this construction will approximate to that of a single clamped free rectangular bar of thickness t and the fundamental frequency will be

$$N = (1 \cdot 1937)^2 \frac{\pi}{8} \cdot \frac{t}{\sqrt{12} \cdot l^2} \sqrt{\frac{E}{\rho}} \quad \text{or} \quad N \propto \frac{t}{l^2} \sqrt{\frac{E}{\rho}},$$

i.e. the frequency depends on the physical dimensions of the length and thickness of the prongs and the velocity of sound in the material of which the fork is made. It does not depend on the width of the prongs.

In a tuning fork the overtones are damped rapidly by internal friction so that almost immediately after striking the fork is emitting a pure note. It is possible, however, to introduce harmonics by bowing the prongs at suitable points. Obviously the harmonics present will not have nodes at the points of bowing. These harmonics have amplitudes which are small compared with the fundamental and are damped rapidly. In contrast the sharp quality of the note of the violin is due to the prominence of high harmonics of which Helmholtz considered the sixth and tenth to be the most important.

Small tuning forks of the type devised by König are still used as standards of frequency. The test of whether forks are accurately matched is the presence or otherwise of beats. The longer the period occupied by a single beat the more accurately matched are the forks. In the manufacture of forks the one being made is adjusted until it gives beats when sounding with a standard fork and is then carefully adjusted until the beats disappear or one beat occupies a very long period. Under certain circumstances a beat which occupies as long as 30 sec. can be recognised.

Little of the energy of a tuning fork is radiated as sound. E. A. Harrington [2] has found experimentally, using an electrically maintained fork, that only 3·5 per cent. of the energy of the fork was radiated as sound, the remaining 96·5 per cent. being used to overcome internal friction and in vibrating the support of the fork.

[1] A. B. Wood, *A Textbook of Sound*, p. 119.
[2] E. A. Harrington, *Journ. Opt. Soc. Amer.*, **17**, p. 234, Sept. 1928.

82. Electrically Maintained Tuning Forks

An external supply of energy is provided so as to maintain the vibrations of the fork which is started by hand. This energy is in the form of electromagnetic impulses (due to the attraction of the electromagnet M, situated between the prongs) on the prongs at suitable intervals of time. The action is similar in some respects to the escapement of a watch, and is very similar to the action of the make and break of an electric bell or the vibrator of an induction coil but is not quite so simple as it may seem.

Wood [1] has shown that without inductance in the circuit the fork is not self maintaining, since, when the inductance is zero, energy is

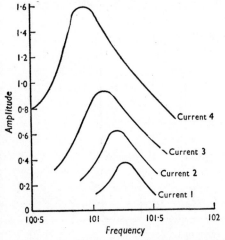

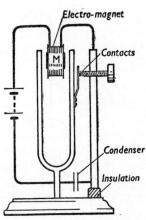

FIG. 78. Resonance curves of electro-magnetically maintained fork (Hartmann Kempf), using interrupted current. Increase of current lowers the frequency and moves the resonance maximum to the left.

FIG. 79. Electro-magnetically maintained fork.

not communicated to the fork to compensate for frictional damping, and the oscillations will die away. Unfortunately the presence of an inductance means a large back E.M.F. at break (cf. induction coil) and a consequent arcing at the contacts. This necessitates the use of resistance in the circuit, often in the electromagnet itself, and a suitable condenser across the contacts. The frequency of a fork of this type is altered to a certain extent by the electrical constants of the circuit and the amplitude of the vibrations of the prongs. For very accurate work the amplitude is adjusted to prescribed limits. In spite of these precautions this method of controlling forks is not efficient for frequencies in excess of 100 vib./sec.

[1] A. B. Wood, *A Textbook of Sound*, p. 122.

83. Valve Maintained Tuning Fork

W. H. Eccles [1] designed a method of maintaining the vibrations of a fork at frequencies up to about 2000 vib./sec. It also has the added merit that the prongs are not loaded. This method has been used at the Post Office wireless station at Rugby, the fork having a frequency of 1800 per sec. and the ninth harmonic being selected to check the frequency of oscillatory electrical circuits. The principle is that voltage oscillations applied to the grid circuit of a triode valve set up alternating current in the anode or plate circuit which maintains the vibrations of the fork. The two coils N and S are wound in opposite directions and the two condensers C_1 and C_2 are used to tune approximately the grid and anode circuits. Consider prong 1 vibrating.

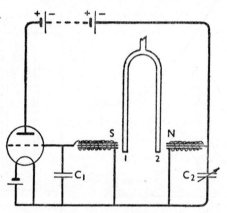

FIG. 80.   Valve maintained fork.

The movement of this induces an alternating voltage in coil S which applies this alternating voltage between grid and cathode of the valve. This causes an alternating current to flow in the anode circuit, which causes the coil N to attract prong 2 at suitable intervals. If one prong is maintained in vibration then the other prong will continue to vibrate also. It should be noted that the harmonic mentioned above is obtained by passing the current of tuning fork frequency through another valve, the output of which sets into resonant vibration a circuit tuned to a harmonic of this frequency and does not come from the fork itself.

This method of controlling a fork has the additional advantage that the sound is free from contact spring rattle. Dye [2] has developed the valve maintained fork as a precision time standard. He used a fork made of Elinvar (ELasticity INVARiable), one of the nickel steels due

[1] W. H. Eccles, *Proc. Phys. Soc.*, 1919, **31**, p. 269.
[2] D. W. Dye, *Proc. Phys. Soc.*, Aug. 1926, **38**, pp. 399-458.

to Guillaume, which has a small temperature coefficient of elasticity. In a constant temperature enclosure such a valve maintained fork is capable of remaining constant to one part in a million.

* 84. Factors Governing the Frequency of Oscillation of a Fork

These can be ascertained by the method of dimensions.   The time of oscillation will depend upon (1) linear dimensions, (2) density of the material, (3) Young's modulus of elasticity for the material.

Assume $\qquad N = k \cdot l^a \cdot \rho^b \cdot E^c.$

Now $\qquad [N] = T^{-1}\,;\ [\rho] = M \cdot L^{-3}\,;\ [E] = M \cdot L^{-1}T^{-2},$

∴ Dimensionally $T^{-1} = L^a M^b \cdot L^{-3b} \cdot M^c L^{-c} T^{-2c}.$

Equating corresponding indices

$$[T] - 1 = -2c,$$
$$[L]\ a - 3b - c = 0,$$
$$[M]\ b + c = 0,$$

$$\therefore\quad c = \tfrac{1}{2}\,;\ b = -\tfrac{1}{2}\,;\ a = -1.$$

Hence $\qquad N = k \cdot l^{-1} \cdot \rho^{-\frac{1}{2}} E^{\frac{1}{2}}$ . . . . (1)

or $\qquad N \propto \dfrac{1}{l}\sqrt{\dfrac{E}{\rho}}$ . . . . . (2)

As quoted previously Wood gives $N \propto \dfrac{t}{l^2}\sqrt{\dfrac{E}{\rho}}$ where t is the thickness of the fork. This difference is not apparent from the method of dimensional analysis since the dimensions of $\dfrac{t}{l^2}$ is L^{-1}.

From equation (1)

$$\log N = \log K - \log l - \tfrac{1}{2}\log \rho + \tfrac{1}{2}\log E.$$

Taking differentials

$$\frac{\delta N}{N} = -\frac{\delta l}{l} - \tfrac{1}{2}\frac{\delta \rho}{\rho} + \tfrac{1}{2}\frac{\delta E}{E}.$$

If changes in the various quantities involved are due to an increase in temperature $\delta\theta$,

$$\frac{\delta l}{l} = \alpha \cdot \delta\theta, \text{ and } \frac{\delta \rho}{\rho} = -3\alpha \cdot \delta\theta$$

where α is the coefficient of linear expansion of the material.   Assuming that elasticity obeys a linear relationship such as $E_\theta = E_0(1 - \beta \cdot \theta)$,

then $\qquad \dfrac{\delta E}{E} = -\beta \cdot \delta\theta,$

$$\therefore \frac{\delta N}{N} = -\alpha\, \delta\theta + \frac{3\alpha}{2}\, \delta\theta - \frac{\beta}{2}\delta\theta,$$

$$\frac{\delta N}{N} = -\left(\frac{\beta - \alpha}{2}\right)\delta\theta,$$

i.e. frequency decreases with rise in temperature.

In Tables of Physical Constants, Kaye and Laby give, for steel,

$$\alpha \fallingdotseq 11 \times 10^{-6} \text{ per deg. C,}$$
$$\beta \fallingdotseq 2\cdot 4 \times 10^{-4} \text{ per deg. C,}$$

$$\therefore \frac{\delta N}{N} \fallingdotseq - 1\cdot 15 \times 10^{-4} \, \delta\theta.$$

Putting $\qquad \dfrac{\beta - \alpha}{2} = k \quad$ Then $\quad \dfrac{\delta N}{N} = - k\delta\theta.$

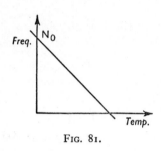

FIG. 81.

Thus the equation relating frequency with temperature is of the form

$$N_\theta = N_0(1 - k \cdot \theta),$$

and so the graph of frequency against temperature should be a straight line [Fig. 81].

Thus a rise in temperature of 1° C. lessens the frequency by about 1 part in 10,000. In a modern fork, made of "Elinvar", the effect is about one-tenth of that of an ordinary steel fork.

85. Experimental Methods of Checking Variation of Frequency with Temperature

Several of the methods which are useful for comparing the frequency of two tuning forks cannot be used in this case since the forks have to be kept in constant temperature enclosures, which obviously restricts experimental work. Since the variation of frequency with temperature will be small, then in order to obtain any degree of accuracy the forks must be made to continue vibrating for some considerable time, i.e. they must be electrically or valve maintained.

The measurement of frequency using the phonic wheel is probably the most accurate method, since the fork can be used to control the speed of the wheel and its revolutions counted over a very long period. An accuracy of 1 in 10,000 is quite easily obtainable using this method. In many cases the accuracy will be limited by the accuracy of the time-piece available.

Before considering details of this method it is worth while considering the order of magnitude of the results to be expected.

From the previous work $\dfrac{\delta N}{N} = - 1\cdot 15 \times 10^{-4}$ per deg. C. rise in temperature. Consider a fork of frequency 512 vib./sec. where N is the frequency. Then

$$\frac{\delta N}{N} = - 1\cdot 15 \times 10^{-4} \, \delta\theta.$$

Let $\delta N = - 1$ vibration, i.e. 1 beat/sec., then

$$\delta\theta = \frac{10^4}{512 \times 1\cdot 15} = \frac{10^4}{588\cdot 8} \fallingdotseq 17° \text{ C.}$$

i.e. a rise in temperature of about $17°$ C. will cause the frequency of a fork of frequency 512 vib./sec. to be reduced by 1 vib./sec.

During the experiment care must be exercised to see that the amplitude of vibration of the fork and the current supply to the electromagnet remain constant as otherwise the results may be misleading. The wheel is set rotating at the slowest rate which will just be maintained by the applied electro-magnetic impulses which are controlled by the fork. If there are n teeth on the wheel and it makes m revolutions in t sec. then $\dfrac{nm}{t}$ teeth pass each electromagnet per sec. Hence the wheel must receive $\dfrac{nm}{t}$ impulses per sec. from the fork and hence this must be the frequency of the fork. i.e. $N = \dfrac{nm}{t}$ vib./sec.

By means of a revolution counter the value of $\dfrac{m}{t}$ can be found very accurately by timing the wheel over a very large interval of time, and hence N is determined very accurately. It must be noted, however, that the value of N is the mean value during the period of timing.

During the experiment it is important that the amplitude of vibration, pressure of the contact spring, magnet current and the loading of the base be kept constant since any or all of these, as well as temperature, will affect the frequency of the fork.

86. High Frequency Vibration of Crystals

J. and P. Curie[1] found that when certain crystals were subjected to pressure they exhibited electric charges on their faces. The converse was also shown to be true—that applied voltages caused corresponding physical changes in their linear dimensions. Many crystals have this property but quartz, tourmaline and Rochelle salt are probably the best known examples. Of these, Rochelle salt gives the largest effect but is inferior mechanically to quartz and tourmaline. In the diagram representing a typical crystal the electric axes E_1E_1, E_2E_2, E_3E_3, are parallel to the bounding faces of the crystal, and plates or bars are cut so that the breadth b is parallel to the optic axis, the length l is perpendicular to an electric axis (e.g. E_2E_2) and the thickness t is parallel to this axis. When an electric field is applied in the direction of the electric axis (i.e. in the direction of the thickness) the length l and the thickness t change, one increasing and the other decreasing, the two strains being such that the volume of the crystal remains constant. If the crystal is placed under applied stresses then potential differences are set up between the faces. These are the P.D.'s used in piezo-electric pick-ups for the reproduction of sound, and the

[1] J. and P. Curie, *Comptes Rendus*, 1880, p. 204 ; *Piezo-Elect.*, *Dict. of Applied Physics*, **2**, *Electricity*, p. 598.

frequency of the potentials is well removed from the natural frequency of the crystal which would give a very undesirable effect. In pick-ups the stresses are applied either by bending or twisting the crystal as the gramophone needle moves in the grooves on the record.

Even for the largest crystals of quartz the dimensions of the slices are small and therefore the frequencies of vibration (natural) are high. For a bar these are given by $n = \dfrac{s}{2l}\sqrt{\dfrac{E}{\rho}}$ where s is 1, 2, 3, etc., and the velocity $\sqrt{\dfrac{E}{\rho}}$ depends on the particular axis chosen since for a crystal the elasticity varies with direction. For the l and t directions, as chosen in the cutting of these crystals, the difference is small and

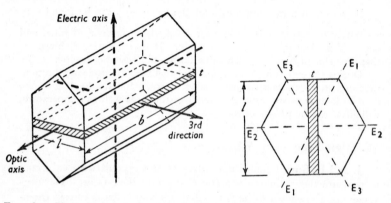

FIG. 82. Typical crystal showing direction of axis and method of cutting a slab.

for quartz the velocity of propagation is about $5 \cdot 5 \times 10^5$ cm./sec. Thus for a rod 5 cm. long and $0 \cdot 5$ cm. thick the frequencies will be approximate multiples of $\dfrac{1}{2 \times 5}\sqrt{\dfrac{E}{\rho}}$ and $\dfrac{1}{2 \times 0 \cdot 5}\sqrt{\dfrac{E}{\rho}}$ or $5 \cdot 5 \times 10^4$ and $5 \cdot 5 \times 10^5$ vib./sec.

A very important use of these crystals is as a reliable standard of frequency since they vary so little when kept at a constant temperature. The natural frequency can be found acoustically from a study of Chladni figures but a more usual method is to introduce them into an electric oscillatory circuit. A second circuit containing a known inductance L and a variable capacitance C is brought near. When this subsidiary circuit is tuned an alternating current galvanometer in the circuit indicates when the two circuits are in tune and then $n = \dfrac{1}{2\pi\sqrt{L \cdot C}}$.

87. Vibration of Plates, Chladni's Figures

Just as strings and rods possess nodal points when stationary waves are present, so two dimensional bodies such as plates and diaphragms give rise to nodal lines when set into vibration. Chladni began the experimental study of the vibration of plates. The vibrations are easily demonstrated but the mathematical theory is very complex. The figures are most easily obtained on a plate clamped at the centre of symmetry, sprinkled with fine dry sand and bowed at a suitable point. The bow sets up waves, by alternately sticking and slipping, which travel across the plate, are reflected, and set up stationary waves with the approaching train. Brass plates are commonly used, but if a glass plate is used instead its transparency allows the fingers

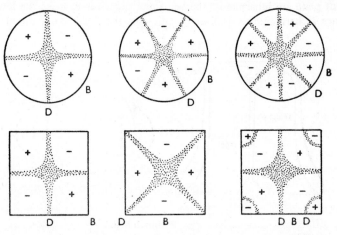

Fig. 83. Modes of vibration of circular and square plate. Lissajous showed that the sectors shown + and − are moving in opposite directions.

to be placed underneath to damp points which the arrangement of the sand above shows to be nodes, the point of bowing being an anti-node.

When the plate is bowed at B and damped at D the note emitted rises rapidly in pitch as D and B come closer together and more nodal lines appear. Rayleigh[1] states, " If all the dimensions of a plate, including thickness, be altered in the same proportion, the period is proportional to the linear dimensions, as in every case of a solid body vibrating by virtue of its own elasticity. The period varies inversely as the square root of Young's modulus, if Poisson's ratio be constant, and directly as the square root of the mass per unit volume of the substance." The patterns formed using a thin disc are of practical importance, since a thin metal plate is used in a telephone earpiece,

[1] Rayleigh, *Sound*, 1.

the other figures possess academic interest only. Chladni gives illustrations of 52 figures with a square plate, 43 circular, 30 hexagonal, 52 rectangular, 26 elliptical, 15 semicircular, 25 triangular, and even this formidable list does not exhaust the possibilities.

Savart found that fine powder, such as lycopodium, behaved differently from sand, collecting at the antinodes instead of the nodes. Faraday [1] stated that this was due to the influence of currents in the surrounding vibrating air. In a vacuum all powders move to the nodes.

88. The Bell

The bell may be considered as the development of a hollow rod or as a bent plate of non-uniform thickness. Although the tones of a bent plate are inharmonic, the bell founder strives to make the lower tones as harmonic as possible by adjusting the thickness of the metal

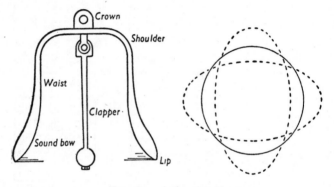

FIG. 84. A church bell.

at various sections. Most of his success is the result of practice and little is due to theory. Centuries of experience have gone into devising the best shape of bell, which is usually cast in an alloy consisting of about 13 parts copper to 4 parts of tin. The thickening at the sound bow eliminates some of the higher partials and removes the otherwise pronounced tinkling sound.

In church bells the simplest mode of vibration has two nodal meridians at right angles to each other. Round the sound bow there are 4 nodes and 4 antinodes which are equally distributed in a symmetrical bell. This is also true of any parallel section above the sound bow. The point of striking determines the position of the antinodes and therefore the nodes. If the bell is not symmetrical the point of impact of the clapper does not determine these positions. As well as vibrating at right angles to the surface of the bell, the material vibrates to and fro round the surface. This can be illustrated by drawing a

[2] Faraday, *Phil. Trans.*, 1831, p. 299.

moist finger round the top of a wine glass, which elicits a strong note due to the longitudinal vibrations of the glass, the finger being at an antinode. Submarine bells are used in charted positions under lightships and buoys for signalling to ships fitted with hydrophones. Due to the small attenuation the sound can be heard for miles. The frequency of the bell is lowered by immersion and as the loading effect is different for different partials the general character of the bell sound is completely altered.

QUESTIONS

1. Explain the meaning of the term resonance, giving in illustration two methods of obtaining resonance between the stretched string of a sonometer and a tuning fork of fixed frequency. A sonometer wire of length 76 cm. is maintained under a tension of 4 kg. weight and an alternating current is passed through the wire. A horse shoe magnet is placed with its poles above and below the wire at its midpoint, and the resultant forces set the wire in resonant vibration. If the density of the material of the wire is 8·8 gm. per cc. and the diameter of the wire is 1 mm., what is the frequency of the alternating current ? (L.H.S.C.)

2. What data would be required to predict the frequency of the note emitted by a stretched wire (a) when it is plucked, (b) when it is stroked along its length ? A weight is hung on the wire of a vertical sonometer. When the vibrating length of the wire is adjusted to 80 cm. the note it emits when plucked is in tune with a standard fork. On adding a further weight of 100 gm. the vibrating length has to be altered by 1 cm. in order to restore the tuning. What is the initial weight on the wire ? (L.H.S.C.)

3. Two identical wires stretched on a sonometer under the same tension of 5 kg. weight emit notes in unison (frequency 300 vib./sec.) when plucked. One wire has its tension increased by 100 gm. wt. and then the wires are plucked. Explain the formation of the beats and calculate the number of beats per sec. which would be heard. (L.H.S.C.)

4. Describe a laboratory apparatus for investigating the laws of vibration of stretched strings, and give an account of its use. Explain the fact that the same string under precisely the same physical conditions may emit sounds of different quality, according to the manner in which it is brought into vibration.

Two notes on a piano are four octaves apart. If the lower note is given by a wire 135 cm. long and the higher by a wire 40 cm. long, and if the tensions are the same, calculate the relative mass of each wire per unit length. (C.W.B.)

5. State the laws of vibration of a stretched string and describe how you would verify them experimentally.

A stretched wire is touched lightly with a feather at a point one-third of its length from one end, and is bowed near that end. It is found to be in unison with a fork of 512 cycles/sec. Find the length of the wire if the mass per cm. is 0·015 gm., and the tension is applied by a load of 10 kg.   (L.Inter.)

6. What factors determine the frequency of transverse vibration of a stretched wire ? How may the relation between transverse frequency and tension be established experimentally ?

A stone hangs in air from a wire which is stretched over a sonometer. The bridges of the sonometer are 40 cm. apart when the wire is in unison with a certain fork. When the stone hangs immersed in water the length between the bridges must be altered to 32 cm. to re-establish unison with the fork. Calculate the specific gravity of the stone.   (N.U.J.M.B.)

7. It is found that when the length l and the tension T of a string are varied so as to keep the frequency of transverse vibration of the string constant Tl^p is constant, p being a numerical index. Describe how you would verify the result, and determine the value of p.

Two wires A and B, made of the same metal, of equal lengths and with diameters in the ratio 7 : 4, when set into transverse vibration give notes whose frequencies are in the ratio 4 : 5. These notes are brought into unison when the tension in B is diminished by 1·5 kg. wt. Find the tension in A and the original tension in B.

      (N.U.J.M.B.)

8. How would you find the velocity of sound along a metal rod assuming that the velocity of sound in air at 0° C. is known ?

A weight of 5 kg. suspended from the lower end of a uniform wire of length 1 m. and diameter 0·36 mm. produces an extension of 2·5 mm. Find the frequency of the note emitted when the stretched wire is stroked by a resined cloth. The density of the material of the wire is 7·8 gm./cc.   (N.U.J.M.B.)

9. How would you (a) demonstrate the presence of overtones in the sound emitted by a stretched wire when it is plucked at its centre, (b) verify the relation between the frequency of the fundamental note emitted by a stretched wire, vibrating transversely, and its tension ?

Two wires vibrate transversely in unison. The tension in one wire is increased by 1 per cent. and now, when they vibrate simultaneously, three beats are heard in 2 sec. What was the original frequency of vibration of the two wires ?   (N.U.J.M.B.)

10. Describe and explain the mode of action of an electrically driven tuning fork or vibrator. How may such a fork or vibrator be used to verify the relation between the tension and wavelength of transverse waves on a stretched string or wire ?

A fine wire 500 cm. long is fixed at both ends and is under tension, the fundamental frequency of transverse vibration being 50 cycles/sec. At what distance from its centre must a bridge be placed in order that 4 beats/sec. may be heard when both sections of the wire are made to vibrate transversely ?   (N.U.J.M.B.Schol.)

11. Write down expressions for the velocity of propagation along a stretched wire of (a) transverse waves, (b) longitudinal waves. Deduce one of the expressions.

Find the ratio of the fundamental frequencies of transverse and longitudinal vibrations for a steel wire, diameter 1 mm., mounted on a sonometer and stretched by a force of 10 kg. wt.   (Young's modulus for steel is 20 × 10^{11} dynes per sq. cm.)

Describe and explain a method of finding the velocity of longitudinal waves in a long steel rod.   (N.U.J.M.B.Schol.)

12. Describe the phenomena of (a) stationary waves, and (b) beats, and explain under what conditions each phenomenon is produced.

A uniform wire is stretched over two bridges so that each unit of its unstretched length is increased by 0·1 per cent. Compare the frequencies of the fundamental notes of the stretched wire when vibrating longitudinally and transversely.   (N.U.J.M.B.Schol.)

13. Describe the phenomenon of beats, and show that the beat frequency is the difference of the frequencies of the tones producing the beats. Describe one quantitative use of the phenomenon.

A certain fork is found to give 2 beats/sec. when sounded in conjunction with a stretched string vibrating transversely under a tension of either 10·2 or 9·9 kg. wt. Calculate the frequency of the fork.   (N.U.J.M.B.)

14. Theory shows that the fundamental frequency n of transverse vibration of a stretched string of length l, radius r, tension T and

density ρ is given by $n = \dfrac{A}{lr}\sqrt{\dfrac{T}{\rho}}$ where A is a constant. Describe

how you would use a sonometer and tuning forks of known frequency to verify this relationship.

A brass wire and a steel wire, of the same length, diameter and tension, give 5 beats/sec. when mounted on a sonometer and made to give their fundamental tones simultaneously. Calculate the frequencies of vibration of the two tones, given that the densities of brass and steel are 8·4 and 7·8 gm. per cc. respectively.   (O. & C.)

15. Distinguish between progressive and stationary waves.

Describe an experiment to illustrate the formation of stationary waves (with more than one loop) on a string or wire. If a copper wire 0·193 mm. in diameter is used, what must be the tension to form loops 30 cm. long when the frequency of vibration of the wire is 64 per sec. ?   Give the result in gm. wt. (The density of copper is 8·93 gm. per cc.)   (N.U.J.M.B.)

16. What date would be required in order to predict the frequency of the note emitted by a stretched wire (a) when it is plucked, (b) when it is stroked along its length ?

A weight is hung on the wire of a vertical sonometer. When the vibrating length of the wire is adjusted to 80 cm. the note it emits when plucked is in tune with a standard fork. On adding a further weight of 100 gm. the vibrating length has to be altered by 1 cm. in order to restore the tuning. What is the initial weight on the wire ?   (Lond.H.S.C.)

17. Prove that the velocity of transverse waves in a stretched string is (tension/mass per unit length)$^{\frac{1}{2}}$.

A wire is stretched between two fixed points so that its natural length is increased by 1 per cent. at room temperature. The coefficient of linear expansion of the wire is $2 \cdot 3 \times 10^{-3}$ per cent. per deg. C. and the temperature coefficient of its Young's Modulus is $0 \cdot 012$ per cent. per deg. C. Calculate the percentage change in the frequency of transverse vibrations when the temperature of the wire rises by $10°$ C.   (O.S.)

CHAPTER VII

FREE AND FORCED VIBRATIONS, RESONANCE

89. Free Vibrations

Any source of sound which is set into vibration, and suffers no external interference, vibrates with its own natural frequency and emits a note, the loudness of which gradually dies away but the pitch remains constant. Such a vibration is called a free vibration. Air blown gently across the mouth of a test tube or bottle, a tuning fork struck or bowed, a stretched string plucked or bowed are very obvious examples. In the case of the test tube (or a series of test tubes of different sizes called the pipes of Pan), the sound ceases as soon as the blowing stops, that from a stretched string lasts a little longer, whereas the sound from a vibrating tuning fork lasts for a considerable time. These differences are due to damping which determines how quickly the sound ceases. The tuning fork is said to be lightly damped since the vibrations die away slowly, whereas the air in the test tube is heavily damped and quickly comes to rest after the driving force is removed. When a fork is set into vibration it is supplied with a certain amount of energy which appears in the vibration of the prongs. Assuming that the prongs are perfectly elastic, and so do not use up energy themselves, then the energy of the fork is lost in two ways : (1) by moving against the resistance of the air, i.e. friction, the energy appearing as heat, (2) by giving energy to the air which is carried away as sound. An alteration in either of these two factors will alter the damping of the fork and hence the time for which the sound persists. When a tuning fork is struck and held in the hand the sound lasts for a long time since the damping is small. When the same fork is given the same amount of energy and then placed with the shaft on a table the sound heard is louder but the rate of damping is increased, since a greater area of surface is set into vibration and energy is carried away at a greater rate, and so the sound dies away more rapidly.

90. Forced Vibrations

Consider a test tube or bottle over the mouth of which is held a vibrating tuning fork. Usually the sound heard from the air in the cavity will be feeble but its frequency will be the same as that of the fork. Blowing air across the mouth of the tube will produce a note of quite different frequency (and loudness). The first vibration is known as a forced vibration since the air in the cavity is forced to vibrate at the frequency of the fork. The second and louder sound is due to the free vibration of the air in the cavity. When a periodically varying force is applied to a system which can vibrate, the amplitude of the vibrations set up will usually be small and the frequency will be the same as that of the applied force. Strictly speaking, in forced vibrations the system which is being driven must not have an appreciable effect on the system which is driving. The essential conditions for forced vibrations are therefore:

1. The driving force must be great.
2. The coupling between the systems must be tight.

In musical instruments the vibrating system imposes its vibrations on another system which as a rule radiates the sound. When a violin is played the sound comes mainly from the body of the instrument and partly from the air inside it, both being forced into vibration by the vibrating string and both emitting notes of the same frequency as the string. The mounting of the string on the body of the instrument closely couples the vibrating systems. The sounding board of a piano is controlled or driven by the string which is set into vibration when struck by the hammer, and in wind instruments such as the oboe, clarinet, bassoon, the periodic force is supplied by reeds and the air column in the instrument set into forced vibration. In instruments such as the cornet and horn the lips of the player act as reeds.

91. Resonance

When the frequency of the driving system is the same as the natural frequency of the system being driven, then resonance occurs, i.e. resonance is really a special case of forced vibrations.

Galileo (1564-1642) stated that " every pendulum has its own definite and determined period of vibration which nature has given it and cannot be induced to vibrate in any other. On the other hand, even a heavy pendulum can be set in vibration by breath if we blow on it intermittently and keep time with its swings." He goes on to describe how one man alone could ring a large bell by applying his impulses at the correct time whereas when four or six men tried to stop the bell they were lifted from the ground.

An experiment devised by the late Professor Barton illustrates forced vibrations, resonance and the dependence of the sharpness of resonance on the damping of the system. It also shows that Galileo's statement was not wholly correct. A number of simple pendulums of slightly differing lengths, having bobs consisting of paper cones, are suspended from a stretched horizontal cord. Attached to the same cord is another pendulum—the driving system—having a massive bob of lead or iron and having a length equal to that of the middle pendulum of the series. The two conditions for forced vibrations are fulfilled as follows: (1) The driving force is large—a pendulum with a massive bob. (2) The systems are closely coupled—the pendulums are as close together as possible. If this latter condition is not fulfilled the result is a complicated type of motion which is not a forced vibration. When the massive pendulum is set into vibration the impulses from it are communicated along the string and set the other pendulums into vibration and they execute vibrations of the same frequency as the driving system. In this case the pendulums are heavily damped since if they are set into free vibration they quickly come to rest and the resonance effect is not sharp, cf. curve 1, Fig. 85. The experiment is repeated with an alteration to the damping of the pendulums. Wooden rings, slipped over the paper cones, increase the masses of the bobs thus reducing the damping of the pendulums, i.e. if they are now set into free vibration they swing for a longer time. The condi- tions for forced vibration are not upset since the mass of each loaded pendulum is very small compared with that of the massive bob. The forced vibrations which are now set up differ widely throughout the series and the sharpness of resonance is much increased. Only the pendulum whose effective length is equal to that of the

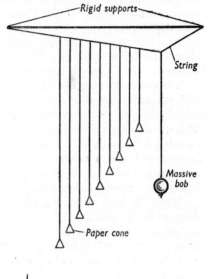

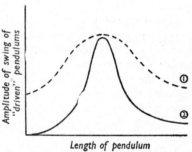

FIG. 85.   Barton's pendulums.

(1) Paper cones—heavily damped, unselective resonance.

(2) Loaded pendulums—lightly damped, selective resonance.

driver pendulum acquires a large amplitude of swing, thus showing that the resonance is selective. The time of swing of every pendulum in the series is the same as that of the driving pendulum and it is only the amplitude of vibration which varies considerably throughout the range.

Wallis [1] (1616-1703) in a paper " on the trembling of consonant strings " remarks that if one string of a lute or viol is touched by bow

[1] *Phil. Trans.*, 1677, Vol. 12, p. 380.

or hand another string on the same or on a nearby instrument will vibrate if the strings are in unison or an octave. He goes on to say, " I have heard of a thin fine Venice glass cracked with the strong and lasting sound of a trumpet or cornet near it sounding a unison or consonant note to that of the glass. And I do not judge the thing unlikely."

As a more recent example Caruso is said to have amused himself after dinner by singing loudly the note to which a wine glass resounded. The resonance set up was sufficiently violent to shatter the glass.

The resonance box, due to Marloye, is a rectangular wooden box, with one end open, constructed so that the natural frequency of the contained air is the same as that of the fork fixed to the box (see Fig. 86). This will give out a note of increased loudness no matter what vibrating fork is placed upon it due to forced vibrations. In this case the instrument is not a resonance box. When the force (tuning fork) and system (resonance box) are in unison resonance occurs, i.e. the box is only a resonance box for a fork of one definite frequency.

When the loud pedal of a piano is depressed, thereby taking the dampers off the strings, and a note is loudly sung and then suddenly cut off, some of the strings can be heard vibrating. The frequencies of these strings are that of the sung note and its overtones.

Other simple examples of the way in which resonance is used or avoided are the tuning of a wireless set, the breaking of step of a column of soldiers marching over a suspension bridge and the crossing of a stream by means of short, quick steps on a single, flexible plank. The frequency of a tuned circuit in a wireless set is usually controlled by a variable condenser and the action of tuning in the set consists of altering the value of the capacitance in the circuit until the natural frequency of the circuit agrees with that of the selected incoming signals when resonance occurs. Soldiers on the march are ordered to break step when crossing a bridge for fear lest the frequency of their step agrees with the fundamental frequency of the bridge or one of its overtones, in which case the bridge could be set into violent oscillation (cf. a pendulum). For the same reason short quick steps are used when crossing a single, flexible plank, otherwise the plank begins to oscillate, the oscillations soon becoming sufficiently violent to throw off the operator.

92. The Sharpness of Resonance

This is of considerable importance in sound and radio and expresses the fall in amplitude with change of frequency on each side of the frequency producing maximum response. When the damping is great this fall in amplitude is slow and when the damping is small this fall in amplitude is rapid.

The following experiments prove this apparently paradoxical statement.

1. When a series of vibrating tuning forks are successively held over the end of a test tube the response is greatest to the fork whose pitch is the same as that of the air in the tube. But the air in the tube does not respond only to this frequency but also to forks which may be a semi-tone or even a tone above or below the correct pitch, although the sound is feebler. The important fact remains that the air in the cavity responds to a band of frequencies.

2. Now place two tuning forks of the same frequency and mounted on resonance boxes with the open ends facing each other. Strike *A* and after a few seconds stop *A* vibrating by touching it with the finger. *B* can be heard sounding (in resonance) although it was not struck. Remove the finger from *A* and place it on *B*. *A* is once more vibrating.

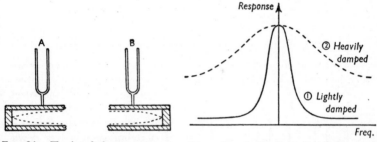

FIG. 86. Tuning forks on resonance boxes to demonstrate the sharpness of resonance.

FIG. 87. Indicating the sharpness or otherwise of resonance in good coils (1) and poor coils (2) in a radio set.

Thus *A* and *B* are interchanging energy as long as they have the same frequency. Now load *A* with a small piece of wax which may be insufficient to set up discernible beats and repeat the experiment. When *A* is stopped from vibrating *B* does not emit sound, i.e. there is no transference of energy from *A* to *B*. Thus in a lightly damped system the amplitude of forced vibrations is very small when the difference of frequency is small. In the case of the air cavity the resonance is said to be general whereas in the second (lightly damped case) the resonance is said to be highly selective. Thus in a heavily damped system the selectivity is small whilst in a lightly damped system the selectivity is high. Those interested in wireless will see an analogy here. In a cheap wireless set the tuning condenser can be turned through a considerable angle without altering appreciably the reception of a station. A good set is selective (a slight rotation of the dial tunes out the station), responding only to the frequency to which it is tuned and giving practically no response to unwanted frequencies. This is due to the damping in the coils. Cheap coils have a considerable resistance and so the signals are heavily damped whereas good coils have little resistance, hence little damping and are therefore highly selective.

VIBRATIONS OF COLUMNS OF GAS

93. Columns of gas, enclosed in tubes of uniform cross-section, may be caused to vibrate longitudinally in a manner exactly analogous to the longitudinal vibration of rods. When the tube containing the

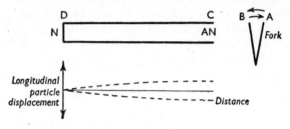

FIG. 88. Displacement diagram for air in a closed pipe.

gas is closed at one end, it is termed a closed tube, when both ends are open it is known as an open tube.

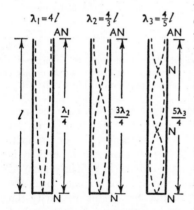

FIG. 89. First three modes of vibration of a closed tube.

$$N \cdot \lambda = v \text{ (a constant)}$$

Freq.	N	$3N$	$5N$
Overtone	—	1st	2nd
Harmonic	1st	3rd	5th

Consider one prong of a vibrating tuning fork placed at the open end of a closed tube (Fig. 88). As the fork begins to move from A to B a compression moves down the tube, is reflected as a compression from the rigid boundary D and returns to C. Here the compression overshoots the end of the tube and tends to leave a vacuum behind. This rarefaction then proceeds down the tube, and if the time taken by the compression in going from C to D and back again to C is the same as that taken for the prong of the fork to go from A to B, then the rarefaction set up by reflection of the returning compression will coincide with the rarefaction set up by the fork as it begins to move from B to A. Thus, for this to occur, the disturbance in the gas must go a distance $2 \cdot CD$ in half the period of vibration of the fork, and if this condition is realised then the compressions and rarefactions in the gas and those set up by the fork are in phase and standing waves are set up.   The gas at D cannot move and so D is a node, the gas at this point undergoing maximum variations in pressure. C is an antinode since the gas at this point can move and here the gas suffers minimum change in pressure.   The graphs

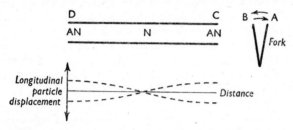

FIG. 90.   Displacement diagram for the air in an open pipe.

of particle displacement against distance along the tube, shown in the diagrams, indicate how the longitudinal displacement of a particle varies with distance along the tube.   From the boundary conditions of a node at D and an antinode at C it follows that CD is one quarter of a wavelength.   If a fork of higher frequency is used, the same boundary conditions will be applicable and will be fulfilled if a compression goes $2 . CD$ while the fork makes $\frac{3}{2}$ vibrations.   Similarly, if the wave goes $2 . CD$ while suitable forks make $\frac{5}{2}, \frac{7}{2}, \frac{9}{2}$, etc., vibrations, the essential conditions are satisfied and resonance will occur.   The frequencies of the forks must therefore be in the ratios $1 : 3 : 5$, etc., and these are the ratios of the frequencies to which a tube of fixed length will respond.   An important point to notice is that the tube will not respond to forks of an even multiple of the fundamental frequency.

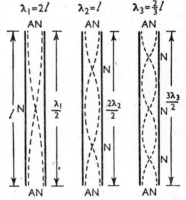

FIG. 91.   First 3 modes of vibration of an open pipe.

$N . \lambda = v$ (a constant)

Freq.	N	$2N$	$3N$
Overtone	—	1st	2nd
Harmonic	1st	2nd	3rd

Consider the same experiment carried out with an open tube (Fig. 90).   As the prong of the fork begins to move from A a compression moves down the tube.   At D this is reflected as a rarefaction and on reaching C this rarefaction is reflected as a compression.   Thus for the fork and disturbance in the gas to be in phase, and standing waves to be set up, the fork must go from A to B and back again to A

while the disturbance goes a distance $2CD$, i.e. the disturbance goes twice the length of the tube in the period of vibration of the fork. In this case the boundary conditions are that there shall be an antinode at each end of the tube. If while the disturbance goes twice the length of the tube, the tuning fork makes 2, 3, 4, etc., vibrations, i.e. more rapidly vibrating forks are used, the disturbance in the gas and the vibrations of the fork are in phase and resonance occurs. These forks must have frequencies in the ratios 1 : 2 : 3 : 4, etc.

Thus there is an obvious difference between the first three modes of vibration of an open and of a closed tube. The open tube will respond to any frequency which is a multiple of its fundamental, the closed tube will respond only to those which are an odd multiple of its fundamental. When a tube is sounded, such as in an organ pipe, harmonics are also present. The open tube, having a complete range of harmonics, will give a note of a quality different from that of a closed pipe sounding a fundamental of the same frequency since the latter lacks the even harmonics.

In considering the reflection of the wave at the open end of the tube it has been considered, so far, that this point of reflection is exactly at the end of the tube. This is not so, since some of the energy is radiated in the form of spherical waves from the end of the tube and so the air at that point is vibrating. This means that the " effective " length of the tube is greater than its physical length. The actual distance of the antinode outside the end of the tube increases with the radius of the tube. The calculation of this end correction is quite difficult and beyond the stage of this book. Values of about $0.8r$ have been obtained experimentally for pipes with large flanges, and recent experiments [1] give $0.58r$ (or approximately $0.6r$) as the correction for a flangeless pipe. Thus in the diagram for the flangeless closed pipe sounding its fundamental, $\dfrac{\lambda_1}{4} = CD + 0.58r$, and for the open pipe $\dfrac{\lambda_1}{2} = CD + (0.58r \times 2)$. As will be shown in the following section the value of this end correction can be found or eliminated in experimental work.

The actual motion of the air in a tube sounding a partial tone can be studied in a number of ways of which the following are typical examples.

1. A small coil of wire heated by an electric current is fixed to a thin rod and moved along the axis of the pipe. The rapid motion of the air at an antinode cools the wire, thus lowering its resistance which can

[1] Higgs and Tyte, *Phil. Mag.*, 1927, **4**, 1099 ; Anderson and Ostensen, *Phys. Rev.*, 1928, **31**, 267 ; Bate, *Phil. Mag.*, 1930, **9**, 23 ; 1930, **10**, 617.

be measured electrically.   At a node the air is at rest and no cooling takes place.

2. Lycopodium or any other suitable powder may be scattered in a horizontal tube (see Kundt's dust tube) to show the motion of the air.   When stationary waves are set up, the dust forms striations across the tube at the antinodes and quite large heaps at the nodes. Tobacco smoke illuminated by strong light also serves to indicate the position of nodes and antinodes.   A microscope is focused on a particular smoke particle. Under rapid vibration the particle appears as a bright line the length of which indicates the amplitude of vibration of the air at that point.

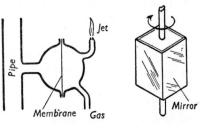

Fig. 92.   König's manometric capsule and rotating mirrors.

3. If the tube is of glass or if, in the case of an organ pipe, it has a glass front, a tray of tissue paper or oiled silk covered with dry sand, or any suitable light powder, can be lowered into the pipe.   The sand is agitated at the antinodes and undisturbed at the nodes.

4. König's manometric capsule can be fitted into the tube and the flickering of the flame studied by means of a rotating mirror.   A thin rubber membrane separates the gas supply for the jet from the air in the pipe.   The membrane responds to variations in pressure which are a maximum at the nodes and a minimum at the antinodes.   Thus at a node the jet shows maximum fluctuations as can be noted by moving the head rapidly sideways or by means of the rotating mirror mentioned above.

94. Resonance Tube Experiments

The apparatus may take the form of that shown in either Fig. 93 (a) or (b).   In Fig. 93 (a) a tube about 1 m. long and 5 cm. in diameter is connected at its lower end, by a flexible tube, to a reservoir R containing water or a light oil which has a negligible vapour pressure. The level of the water in AB is controlled by raising or lowering R and adjusting the clip C so that the water flows slowly into AB or from AB into R.   In Fig. 93 (b) the level in the resonance tube A'B' is adjusted by raising or lowering the tube in the water contained in a large vessel.

Experiment 1.   Given a tuning fork of known frequency to find the velocity of sound in air.

Adjust the level of the water in AB almost to the top of the tube and adjust the clip C so that the water slowly moves back into R. Hold the vibrating tuning fork above the tube AB while the water level is falling. When resonance occurs between the fork and air above the water in the tube, a note of considerable loudness is heard. The clip is closed when the water is at a level D when this note is of maximum loudness. A preliminary experiment may be necessary to find the approximate position of D. Note the length AD and let it be l_1 (see Fig. 93 (c)). Since the tube is closed, this length is approximately one quarter of a wavelength and as resonance will take place if the length of the air column is three-quarters of a wavelength,

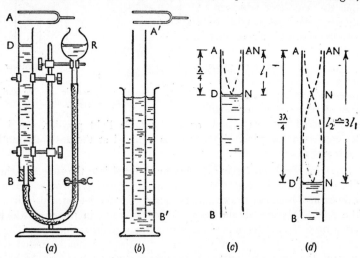

FIG. 93. (a) and (b) illustrate the forms of resonance tube apparatus. (c) and (d) show displacement diagrams for the first two modes of vibration.

the level of the water can be rapidly lowered a further distance of just less than $2l_1$ and then allowed to fall slowly until the level reaches D' when resonance again occurs. Let the distance AD' be l_2 (Fig. 93 (d)). If the end correction of the tube " e " is taken into account then the following equations are obtained.

$$\frac{\lambda}{4} = l_1 + e \qquad . \qquad . \qquad . \qquad . \quad (1)$$

$$\frac{3\lambda}{4} = l_2 + e \qquad . \qquad . \qquad . \qquad . \quad (2)$$

Hence $$\frac{\lambda}{2} = (l_2 - l_1)$$

and therefore the velocity of sound

$$v = n \cdot 2 \cdot (l_2 - l_1).$$

If the tube is sufficiently long further positions of "D" are obtainable when "AD" is approximately $\dfrac{5\lambda}{4}, \dfrac{7\lambda}{4}$, etc., and as a precaution that a position of resonance has not been missed it should be checked that the length l_1, l_2, l_3, etc., are approximately in the ratios $1:3:5$, etc.

The end correction can also be found from the equations above.

Since $$\frac{3\lambda}{4} = 3l_1 + 3e$$

and $$\frac{3\lambda}{4} = l_2 + e.$$

Then $$e = \frac{l_2 - 3l_1}{2}$$

If the velocity of sound in air is known, or found from a previous experiment, then this method may be used to find the frequency of a tuning fork.

Experiment 2. To compare the frequencies of two tuning forks. The above experiment is repeated with each fork in turn. Then if n_1 and n_2 are the two frequencies

$$\frac{\lambda_1}{2} = l_2 - l_1 \quad \text{and} \quad \frac{\lambda_2}{2} = l_2' - l_1'.$$

But $v = n_1\lambda_1 = n_2\lambda_2$ if atmospheric conditions are unchanged,

$$\therefore \frac{n_1}{n_2} = \frac{\lambda_2}{\lambda_1} = \frac{l_2' - l_1'}{l_2 - l_1}.$$

Experiment 3. Given several forks of known frequency to find the velocity of sound in air and the end correction of the tube.

In this case the length AD corresponding to the first position of resonance is measured for each fork in turn. Then

$$\frac{\lambda}{4} = l + e$$

$$\therefore \lambda = 4l + 4e. \quad \text{But } v = n\lambda.$$

Hence

$$\frac{v}{n} = 4l + 4e$$

or $$l = \frac{v}{4}\left(\frac{1}{n}\right) - e.$$

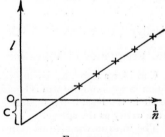

FIG. 94.

This equation is of the form $y = mx - c$ if "l" is plotted against "$\dfrac{1}{n}$" and the graph obtained should be a straight line of slope $\dfrac{v}{4}$ and

144 TEXTBOOK ON SOUND

have an intercept on the y axis of $-e$. Having obtained this graph it may be used with the same tube to find the frequency of an unknown fork.

A similar set of experiments can be carried out using open pipes which are adjustable in length, one tube sliding inside the other, the end correction being applied for each end of the tube. These may also be used to determine the harmonics present in a note by adjusting the length of the tube until it resonates at a calculable frequency. In Helmholtz's resonators the air in the cavity is almost completely enclosed and therefore there is little loss of energy into the outside air. This means that the damping is small and therefore the tuning is very sharp and for this reason is particularly suited as a detector of sound waves of a definite frequency. Helmholtz designed a series of these turnip shaped resonators in order to find the harmonics present in notes of differing quality. The exact form of the cavity is unimportant provided that its smallest dimension is con-

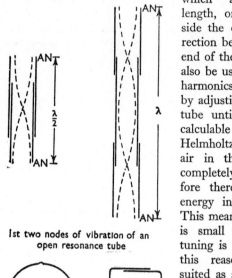

Ist two nodes of vibration of an open resonance tube

(a) Fixed   (b) Adjustable

Helmholtz resonators

Fig. 95. Open resonance tube and Helmholtz resonator.

siderably greater than that of the aperture.

*95. Frequency of Vibration of a Hollow Cavity Resonator

Consider a resonator having the dimensions shown in Fig. 96. The system in its simplest form is equivalent to a mass on the end of a spring, the air in the neck being regarded as equivalent to the mass and the air in the cavity as the spring.

The mass of the air piston in the neck is $Al\rho$ where ρ is the density of the air. If the air is made to resonate the oscillations take place adiabatically.

$$\therefore \quad pv^\gamma = \text{constant and hence } \delta p = -\gamma \cdot p \frac{\delta v}{v}$$

Consider a layer of air in the neck moved through a distance x. Then change in volume of the air $= Ax$ and the restoring force is

$$= A \cdot \delta p$$

$$= -\gamma \cdot p \cdot \frac{\delta v}{v} \cdot A$$

$$= -\gamma p \cdot \frac{A^2 x}{v}.$$

By Newton's Laws of Motion

$$M\ddot{x} = \left(-\gamma \cdot p \cdot \frac{A^2}{v}\right)x,$$

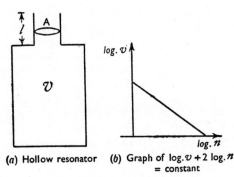

(a) Hollow resonator   (b) Graph of $\log v + 2 \log n$ = constant

FIG. 96.

i.e. the motion is Simple Harmonic and the period of oscillation T is given by

$$T = 2\pi \sqrt{\frac{M \cdot v}{\gamma p A^2}}$$

$$= 2\pi \sqrt{\frac{(l \cdot A\rho)v}{EA^2}} \text{ since } E = \gamma p$$

$$= 2\pi \sqrt{\frac{v \cdot l}{c^2 A}} \text{ since } c = \sqrt{\frac{E}{\rho}}$$

where c = velocity of sound in air, v = volume of cavity,

$$\therefore \quad n = \frac{1}{T} = \frac{c}{2\pi} \sqrt{\frac{A/l}{v}} \quad . \qquad . \qquad . \qquad . \qquad . \quad (1)$$

where $\dfrac{A}{l}$ has the dimensions of a length and is known as the conductivity of the neck.

For a particular resonator it follows from equation (1) that

$$n^2 v = \text{constant}.$$

If the volume v will resonate at a known frequency " n " (a tuning fork for example) then $\log v + 2 \log n$ = constant and the graph of $\log n$ against $\log v$ should be a straight line of gradient -2.

The adiabatic oscillation of the air in the vessel using the air in the neck as a piston is responsible for the note heard when the cork is rapidly withdrawn from a tightly stoppered bottle and the frequency of the note can be calculated from equation (1) above.

96. Aeolian Tones

The wind blowing through trees, telegraph wires, grasses, etc., produces familiar sounds which even casual observation shows vary in pitch according to the speed of the wind. When the frequency of the wind note agrees with one of the upper partials of the obstacle, resonance may occur and the sound produced may be intense. This effect is often demonstrated when quite a light breeze passes over

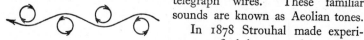

telegraph wires. These familiar sounds are known as Aeolian tones.

FIG. 97. Vortices formed at the sides of the path of an obstacle moving through a fluid.

In 1878 Strouhal made experiments to find the cause of these tones. He fixed a vertical wire at a known distance from the axis of a rotating table and measured the frequency of the tone produced. He found that this depended upon the speed of the air, the diameter of the wire, and was independent of the length and tension in the wire. Expressed in mathematical form his results

showed $n = K \cdot \dfrac{v}{d}$, where K is a constant ($\backsimeq$ 0·2), v is the speed of the air past the wire, and d is the diameter of the wire. When an obstacle, such as the fingers or a stick, is drawn rapidly through water little whirlpools, vortices, or eddies, are formed on the surface. These are found alternately on opposite sides of the track and the direction of rotation of the set on one side of the track is opposite to that on the other side of the track. If the speed of the obstacle is uniform then the eddies are evenly spaced.

In the same way the fluttering of the flag on a flagpole is due to the formation of these vortices on each side of the pole. When the frequency of eddy formation lies within the audible range of frequency then Aeolian tones are produced. The Aeolian harp consists of a number of wires of varying thicknesses mounted on a sounding board and all tuned to the same fundamental frequency which is arranged to have a large number of overtones in the range of audibility. As the wind blows over the strings one or more, according to the wind velocity and diameter of the strings, is made to resonate and gives out its particular overtones.

FIG. 98. Vortices formed by jet of air.

97. Jet and Edge Tones

Whenever a stream of gas passes a sharp edge or emerges from a jet tones are produced which are analogous to Aeolian tones.   As the air is forced through the jet in the form of a slit, eddies are formed and are found to be alternately placed on opposite sides of the jet which, after passing through the slit, has taken a sinuous form.

The tones produced when gas passes through a jet are feeble and unstable.   Their frequency is given by $n = \dfrac{KV}{d}$ where K is a constant, V the velocity of the gas at the orifice and d is the width of the jet.

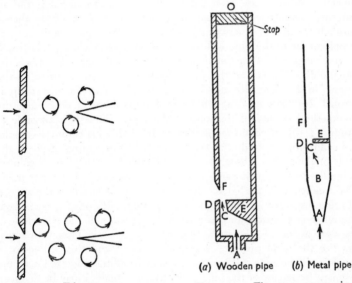

FIG. 99.   Edge tones.   FIG. 100.   Flue type organ pipes.

(a) Wooden pipe   (b) Metal pipe

If a wedge of small angle is placed in front of the jet, the edge being parallel to the slit, a stronger and more stable note is produced. Sondhaus noticed this in 1854 and since that time many scientists have worked on the problem, of whom G. B. Brown [1] carried out what was probably the most searching investigation.   He used jets from orifices of different types, impregnated the air with tobacco smoke and photographed the air stream by stroboscopic methods.   As the edge is withdrawn the speed with which the air strikes it is reduced and the pitch of the note falls, but rises an octave when the edge has moved to a critical distance from the jet.   A study of the eddy formation shows that each original eddy is now replaced by two.   Removing the edge still farther results in each original eddy being replaced by

[1] *Proc. Phys. Soc.*, 1935, **47**, 703 ; 1937, **49**, 508.

three and the pitch rises by a fifth. Thus as the wedge is moved away from the jet, the edge tones are overtones of the fundamental. After about the third jump the note ends in an irregular and confused noise.[1] If the distance of the wedge from the jet is fixed and the velocity of the jet varied a similar set of changes takes place, the frequency increasing with increase of gas velocity. In this case the frequency changes in three jumps with steady rises in frequency between them.

98. Organ Pipes

The flue pipe forms the basis of tone production in the organ and its action depends on the formation of edge tones of a suitable frequency. When made of metal the pipe is usually circular, the air entering at the tip A, passing through the foot B and from thence through the flue C, a narrow slit which gives the pipe its name. The supply of air to the pipe is adjusted by opening or closing the tip A. On the outer side of the flue is the lower lip and on the inner side is the languid E. The task of the flue is to direct a stream of air on to the upper lip F. The distance between the flue and the upper lip is termed the " cut up " and is of vital importance in determing the volume and quality of the tone of the pipe. Thus it is possible to produce : (a) an edge tone as the air from the flue impinges on the upper lip, (b) a note due to the vibration of the column of air in the body of the pipe. These two form a coupled system, the air column being the predominant partner by virtue of its relatively greater mass. The frequency of the edge tone depends on the speed of the air, i.e blowing pressure and the height of the cut up. If one of these is fixed the other is adjusted until the natural frequency of the edge tone is the same as that of the natural frequency of the air column. In actual practice the wind pressure is usually adjusted and this is known as " voicing " the pipe. That the adjustment of the edge tones to the resonant frequency of the pipe is the true explanation may be deduced from the fact that as the wind pressure is increased the pitch tends to rise but the air responds little until the edge tone frequency approaches the first overtone of the pipe when the frequency jumps and with an open pipe gives the octave. With a stopped pipe the jump is not the same since this pipe lacks the even harmonics. Some of the factors which determine the quality of the note are : [2]

1. Scale of the pipe, i.e. ratio of the diameter to the length.
2. Height of the mouth.
3. Shape of the upper lip—thick, thin, convex, concave.
4. Shape and position of the languid.
5. Nicking of the lower lip.
6. Material of the tube.

[1] Alex Wood, *Physics of Music*, p. 116.
[2] Bonavia Hunt, *Church Organ*, 1920, p. 68.

As mentioned previously, an open pipe may sound overtones which form a complete harmonic series since the top as well as the mouth is open to the air, whereas a pipe with the upper end closed may only sound the odd harmonics and therefore its tone is not so rich as that from an open pipe.   In two pipes of equal length the fundamental of

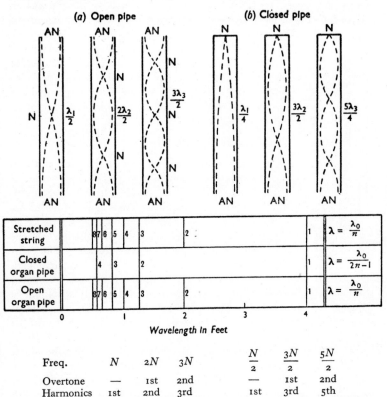

Stretched string			8	7	6	5	4	3		2					1		$\lambda = \dfrac{\lambda_0}{n}$
Closed organ pipe						4		3		2					1		$\lambda = \dfrac{\lambda_0}{2n-1}$
Open organ pipe			8	7	6	5	4	3		2					1		$\lambda = \dfrac{\lambda_0}{n}$

0	1	2	3	4

Wavelength In Feet

Freq.	N	$2N$	$3N$	$\dfrac{N}{2}$	$\dfrac{3N}{2}$	$\dfrac{5N}{2}$
Overtone	—	1st	2nd	—	1st	2nd
Harmonics	1st	2nd	3rd	1st	3rd	5th

Fig. 101 (a) and (b).   Comparison between first three modes of vibration of open and closed pipes of the same length. (c). Sound spectrum. The fundamental and overtones may be said to constitute a spectrum. The fundamental has been given (in air) of 4′ and n is an integer.

the stopped pipe is an octave below that of the open pipe and therefore if an open pipe is stopped its frequency drops an octave.

99. Reed Pipes

Beside the so-called flue pipes there are reed pipes in an organ in which the vibration of a reed is the source of sound.   The air from the bellows causes the reed R to vibrate and the reed is so strong that it vibrates at its own natural frequency, the pitch being adjusted by the metal slide S. The conical shape of the top is to encourage certain overtones and so alter the quality of the note. The pitch is determined by the reed and not the air column although in many cases the pipe is so designed that the natural frequency of the contained air is the same as that of the reed. The reed itself acts as a closed end since the reed opens and air enters when the pressure is a maximum, whereas air enters the end of an open pipe when the pressure is a minimum, and

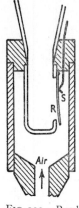

so an open reed pipe, i.e. the upper end is open, behaves like a flue pipe with the upper end closed. Although the reed pipe may be considered as a coupled system similar to the flue pipe, the edge tone being replaced by the reed, the problem is complicated and a detailed study of the subject is left to a more advanced textbook.

100. Kundt's Dust Tube

In 1866 Kundt devised one of the earliest small-scale methods of demonstrating stationary waves in gases contained in tubes. Results from this apparatus in its original and modified forms have provided information on the velocity of sound in gases under all conditions as well as valuable information on the

FIG. 102. Reed pipe.

molecular grouping of their constituents. The principle of the method is that a note of fairly high frequency, and therefore short wavelength, is sent along a column of gas enclosed by rigid boundaries and the length of this column is adjusted until standing waves are set up, i.e. the length must be a whole number of half wavelengths since each end must be a node.

In its usual form the apparatus consists of a glass tube about 150 cm long, 5 cm. in diameter and one end fitted with an adjustable piston B. Projecting into the other end of the tube is a rod of metal, glass, wood or any suitable solid which terminates in a piston A. Unlike piston B, this one clears the tube. The rod is clamped at a suitable point, usually the middle, and is set into longitudinal vibration by stroking with a damp or resined cloth. For the rod $V_R = n\lambda_R$ and

$V_R = \sqrt{\dfrac{E}{\rho}}$ and if it is clamped at its mid point $AC = \dfrac{\lambda_R}{2}$. The

bottom of the glass tube is uniformly covered throughout its length with a thin layer of lycopodium powder, cork dust or fine sand. While the rod AC is being stroked, the piston B is adjusted until stationary waves are formed. When this takes place the powder is set into violent motion at the antinodes and is moved away to form undisturbed heaps at the nodes. When the rod stops vibrating the standing waves quickly cease and the powder covers the bottom of the tubes in a regular pattern having small heaps at the nodes and thin striations across the tube at the antinodes. It is important to note that, for the rod, A is an antinode but is just outside a node for the column of gas. Careful observation of the powder when the tube is correctly

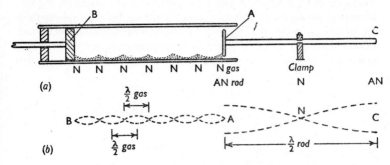

(a)

(b)

FIG. 103.   (a) Kundt's dust tube.   (b) Longitudinal displacement graphs represensenting motion of particle in both gas and rod.

adjusted shows that in the violent disturbance at the antinodes there are thin antinodal discs of powder stretching across the tube which disappear when the rod ceases to vibrate. These are so sharp and distinct that, if the vibrations can be maintained for a sufficient length of time, the measurement of the distance between the discs gives a

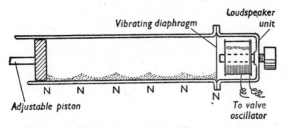

FIG. 104.   Oscillator maintained form of dust tube.

much more accurate value of half a wavelength in the gas than is obtained by measuring the distance between nodal heaps. In the experiment, of course, the distance is measured between as many antinodal discs or nodal heaps as is possible. A very convenient way of maintaining the vibrations is to use a loudspeaker or telephone earpiece driven by a valve oscillator as the source of sound. While this method is very useful for comparing the velocity of sound in gases it cannot be used for experiments to find or compare the velocity of sound in solids in the form of rods.

101. Experiments with the Dust Tube

1. To compare the velocity of longitudinal vibrations in two rods.

Using rod 1, clamped at its mid-point, with the dust tube apparatus adjust the movable piston until resonance occurs. Measure the nodal (or antinodal) separation over as large a distance as possible and so obtain an average value of half a wavelength of the sound in the gas. Measure also L_1 the length of the rod which is half a wavelength of the vibrations in the rod. Repeat the experiment with the second rod. Let the suffixes 1 and 2 represent the measurements applicable to rods 1 and 2 respectively and let $v_{1 . R}$ be the velocity of sound in the first

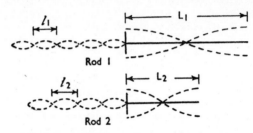

Fig. 105.   Displacement/distance diagram for the two experiments.

rod, $v_{2 . R}$ the velocity of sound in the second rod and v_g the velocity of sound in the gas in the tube. Then

$$v_R = n\lambda_R \text{ and } v_g = n\lambda_g.$$

Since " n " is the same for rod and gas

$$v_{1 . R} = v_g \cdot \frac{\lambda_{1 . R}}{\lambda_g} = v_g \cdot \frac{L_1}{l_1} \quad . \quad . \quad . \quad (1)$$

From the second experiment assuming that the velocity of sound in gas is unchanged

$$v_{2 . R} = v_g \frac{\lambda_{2 . R}}{\lambda_g} = v_g \cdot \frac{L_2}{l_2} \quad . \quad . \quad . \quad (2)$$

Hence
$$\frac{v_{1 . R}}{v_{2 . R}} = \frac{L_1}{l_1} \cdot \frac{L_2}{l_2}.$$

If the velocity of sound in air under the existing conditions is known, then the actual velocity of sound in each rod can be found from equations (1) and (2).

2. To find the velocity of torsional oscillations in a rod.

By using the cloth used for stroking the rod in experiment 1 so as to tend to twist the rod, a note of a different frequency from that produced by longitudinal vibrations can be obtained. This is due to torsional oscillations in the rod and by repeating experiment 1 the velocity of these waves can be found. This velocity is given by

$$v = \sqrt{\frac{\mu}{\rho}}$$ where μ is the coefficient of rigidity. Thus

$$\frac{\text{longitudinal velocity}}{\text{torsional velocity}} = \sqrt{\frac{E}{\mu}} = \sqrt{2(\sigma + 1)}$$

where σ is Poisson's ratio. Since σ can never exceed 0·5 the ratio of these velocities in any material can never exceed 1·73. This method provides a simple way of finding Poisson's ratio for a material in the form of a rod.

3. To compare the velocity of sound in air with that in carbon dioxide.

The basic principle of the method is to perform the experiment with the tube first filled with air and then with CO_2. In the previous

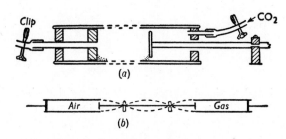

(a)

(b)

FIG. 106. (a) Showing the method of filling Kundt's tube with carbon dioxide. (b) Double tube method for comparison of velocities of sound in air and other gases.

experiments the adjustable piston may loosely fit the tube. In this experiment it is made a tight fit and is used to ensure that the tube is completely filled with CO_2. After adjusting the piston for resonance with air inside the tube, CO_2 is fed into the tube and the air withdrawn through the adjustable piston, and the experiment is repeated. Care must also be taken to see that the two temperatures are the same, otherwise a correction must be applied.

For air $v_a = n\lambda_a = n . 2 . l_a$ where l_a is the average nodal separation for air. For CO_2 $v_c = n\lambda_c = n . 2 . l_c$, n being the same since the

same rod is used in both experiments, $\therefore \dfrac{v_a}{v_c} = \dfrac{l_a}{l_c}$.

For the comparison of the velocities of sound in air and gases the double tube arrangement is useful. The rod is clamped at quarter of its length from each end (therefore its whole length is λ_R but this does not enter into the calculation for the comparison of velocities).

4. To determine Young's modulus and the modulus of rigidity.

For longitudinal vibrations $v_L = \sqrt{\dfrac{E}{\rho}}$ where E is Young's modulus of elasticity. For torsional vibrations $v_T = \sqrt{\dfrac{\mu}{\rho}}$ where μ is the modulus of rigidity.

Assuming the value of the velocity of sound in air to be given by

$$v_a = 33060 \left(1 + \frac{t}{273}\right)^{\frac{1}{2}} \text{ cm./sec.}$$ experiment 1 is performed stroking the rod to give longitudinal or torsional vibrations as required and the average nodal separations l_1 and l_2 found for the gas. If the rod is clamped at its mid-point then its length L is half a wavelength for both

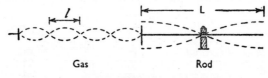

Gas   Rod

FIG. 107.

longitudinal and torsional vibrations. It follows that since the frequency of the oscillation in the rod and gas is the same

$$v_L = v_g \cdot \frac{L_1}{l_1} = \sqrt{\frac{E}{\rho}} \quad . \quad . \quad . \quad . \quad (1)$$

$$v_T = v_g \cdot \frac{L_1}{l_2} = \sqrt{\frac{\mu}{\rho}} \quad . \quad . \quad . \quad . \quad (2)$$

Thus if the value of ρ, the density of the material, is found either by experiment or reference to a table of physical constants, the value of the two moduli can be determined.

5. To find the ratio of the principal specific heats of a gas.

The tube is filled with the gas and the rod to be used to produce the sound of suitable frequency is clamped at its mid-point. The nodal separation in the gas is found and the wavelength of the sound in the rod is found from measurements of the length of the rod (see Fig. 107).

For the gas $\qquad v_g = \sqrt{\dfrac{\gamma p}{\rho_g}} = n\lambda_g = n \cdot 2l$. $\quad$. $\quad$. $\quad$ (1)

For the rod $\qquad v_R = \sqrt{\dfrac{E}{\rho_R}} = n\lambda_R = n \cdot 2L$. $\quad$. $\quad$. $\quad$ (2)

where n is the frequency of the sound in both rod and gas, γ the ratio of the principal specific heats of the gas, p is the pressure of the gas in absolute units, ρ_g, ρ_R are the densities of gas and rod, l is the nodal separation in the gas and L that for the rod.

From the equations above $\sqrt{\dfrac{\gamma p}{\rho_g} \cdot \dfrac{\rho_R}{E}} = \dfrac{l}{L}$,

Hence
$$\gamma = \frac{l^2}{L^2} \cdot \frac{E}{p} \cdot \frac{\rho_g}{\rho_R}.$$

If the value of E cannot be assumed a separate experiment must be performed to find its value.

102. Behn and Geiger's Modification of the Dust Tube

In order to keep a gas chemically pure and free from contamination by air and also to find the velocity of sound in gases of which there is a limited quantity available, Behn and Geiger had the ingenious idea

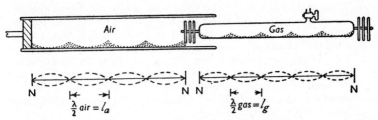

FIG. 108.   Behn and Geiger's apparatus.

of enclosing the gas in the rod used for stroking (see Fig. 108).   This rod is hollow and contains dust as well as gas, the gas being introduced at the mid-point of the rod which is also clamped.   The air column in its usual container is adjustable in length.   The gas column inside the rod is of invariable length and may not resonate to the note produced by stroking.   As the resonant frequency of the gas in the rod cannot be adjusted, the frequency of vibration of the rod is altered until they are the same.   This is done by attaching metal washers to extension pieces carried by the ends of the rod, thus altering the effective length of the rod and hence its frequency of vibration.   When the gas inside the rod resonates and arranges the dust in the usual pattern, the piston adjusting the length of the air column is manipulated until this column also resonates.   The average nodal separation in the two gases is noted then

$$v_a = n\lambda_a = n \cdot 2 \cdot l_a. \qquad v_g = n\lambda_g = n \cdot 2\lambda_g,$$

$$\therefore \frac{v_a}{v_g} = \frac{\lambda_a}{\lambda_g} = \frac{l_a}{l_g}.$$

103. Velocity of Sound in Gas at Different Temperatures

Kundt's tube provides a method of measuring the velocity of sound at different temperatures by using the tube in a thermostatically controlled enclosure. At very low temperatures, however, it is not convenient to surround a long tube with liquid air. Hunstedt and Webber carried out experiments at very low temperatures, using a Galton whistle as the source of sound (instead of the usual rod) and a short length of tube placed vertically in a Dewar flask. The whistle gave notes of high frequency, and therefore short wavelength, and a microphone placed at the lower end of the glass tube was used to indicate resonance. The tube was of a fixed length and the frequency of the note adjusted for resonance. A separate experiment, using Kundt's tube, was then carried out to find the frequency of the note used in the experiment.

WORKED EXAMPLES

1. Using a Kundt's dust tube filled with air it was found that the distance between six consecutive nodes was 48·6 cm. and that the length of the brass rod, clamped at its mid-point, was 100 cm. Find the velocity of sound in air and the ratio of the specific heats of air. It may be assumed that Young's modulus for brass is 10^{12} dynes/sq. cm., density of brass 8·5 gm./cc., pressure of the air 76·8 cm. of mercury, density of air under the experimental conditions 1·293 gm./litre, density of mercury 13·6 gm./cc., acceleration under gravity 981 cm./sec./sec.

For the rod $\quad v_R = \sqrt{\dfrac{E}{\rho_R}} = n\lambda_R = n \cdot 2L,$

$$\therefore \quad n = \frac{1}{2L}\sqrt{\frac{E}{\rho_R}} \quad \bullet \quad \bullet \quad \bullet \quad \bullet \quad (1)$$

For the air $\quad\quad v_a = n\lambda_a = n \cdot 2l,$

$$\therefore \quad v_a = \frac{l}{L}\sqrt{\frac{E}{\rho_R}} \quad \text{where } l \text{ and } L \text{ are the node separations}$$

$$= \frac{9\cdot72}{100}\sqrt{\frac{10^{12}}{8\cdot5}}$$

$$= \frac{9\cdot72 \times 10^4}{(8\cdot5)^{\frac{1}{2}}}$$

$$\begin{bmatrix} \log(10^4 \times 9\cdot72) = 4\cdot9877 \\ \tfrac{1}{2}\log 8\cdot5 \quad\quad = 0\cdot4647 \\ \hline \quad\quad\quad\quad\quad\quad 4\cdot5230 \end{bmatrix}$$

Velocity of sound in air

$$= 3\cdot33(4) \times 10^4 \text{ cm./sec.}$$

Using Laplace's correction of Newton's formula for the velocity of sound in air

$$v_a = \sqrt{\frac{\gamma p}{\rho_a}}$$

$$\therefore \gamma = \frac{v^2 \cdot \rho}{p}$$

$$= \frac{(3 \cdot 334 \times 10^4)^2 \times 1 \cdot 293 \times 10^{-3}}{76 \cdot 8 \times 13 \cdot 6 \times 981}$$

$\log \gamma = 0 \cdot 1470$

$\therefore$ Ratio of specific heats $= 1 \cdot 40(3)$

$$\begin{aligned}
\log 76 \cdot 8 &= 1 \cdot 8854 \\
\log 13 \cdot 6 &= 1 \cdot 1335 \\
\log 981 &= 2 \cdot 9917 \\
\hline
& 6 \cdot 0106 \\[4pt]
\log (33340)^2 &= 9 \cdot 0460 \\
\log 1 \cdot 293 \times 10^{-3} &= \overline{3 \cdot 1116} \\
\hline
& 6 \cdot 1576 \\
& 6 \cdot 0106 \\
\hline
& 0 \cdot 1470
\end{aligned}$$

2. In an experiment using a resonance tube positions of resonance were found when the water level was 17·42 in. and 29·42 in. from the

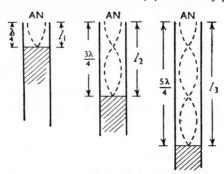

Fig. 109.

top of the tube.   What observations can be made concerning these results ?   Velocity of sound in air $= 1100$ ft./sec.

For the resonant columns the length l_1, l_2, l_3 should be approximately in the ratio $1 : 3 : 5$ (see Fig. 109).   But

$$\frac{17 \cdot 42}{29 \cdot 42} \frown \frac{18}{30} = \frac{3}{5}$$

$\therefore$ 1st resonance position has been omitted.

$\therefore$ Equations are

$$\frac{3\lambda}{4} = l_2 + c = 17 \cdot 42 + c, \qquad \bullet \qquad \bullet \qquad \bullet \quad (1)$$

$$\frac{5\lambda}{4} = l_3 + c = 29 \cdot 42 + c, \qquad \bullet \qquad \bullet \qquad \bullet \quad (2)$$

$$\therefore \frac{\lambda}{2} = 12 \text{ in.} \quad \therefore \lambda = 2 \text{ ft.}$$

But since $n = \frac{v}{\lambda}$ and $v = 1100$ ft./sec.   frequency of note used

$= 550$ vib./sec.

Eliminating λ from equations (1) and (2) gives

$$c = \frac{3l_2 - 5l_1}{2} = \frac{88 \cdot 26 - 87 \cdot 10}{2} \text{ in.}$$

$$\therefore c = 0 \cdot 58 \text{ in.}$$

Assuming that the tube was of circular section and flangeless the internal radius of the tube was 1 in.

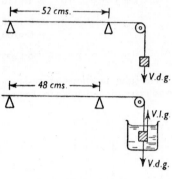

FIG. 110.

3. An unknown weight is hung from one end of a sonometer wire sounding its fundamental and the distance between the bridges is 52 cm. The suspended weight is now completely immersed in water and the distance between the bridges is reduced to 48 cm. in order that the vibrating wire shall give out the same note as before. Find the density of the unknown weight.

Let V and d be the volume and density of the unknown weight. Then for the first case

$$n = \frac{1}{2l_1} \sqrt{\frac{V \cdot d \cdot g}{m}}. \quad \text{See Fig. 110.}$$

When immersed in water the upthrust brought into play is $V \cdot d_w \cdot g$ dynes,

$$\therefore n = \frac{1}{2l_2} \sqrt{\frac{V \cdot d \cdot g - V \cdot g}{m}}.$$

Hence

$$\frac{1}{4l_1^2} \frac{V \cdot d \cdot g}{m} = \frac{1}{4l_2^2} \frac{V \cdot g \cdot (d - 1)}{m},$$

$$\therefore \frac{d}{l_1^2} = \frac{d - 1}{l_2^2},$$

$$d = \frac{l_1^2}{l_1^2 - l_2^2}.$$

$$= \frac{52 \times 52}{100 \times 4}$$

$$= 6 \cdot 76 \text{ gm./cc.}$$

4. The fundamental frequency of a stretched wire vibrating transversely between two bridges 52 cm. apart is in unison with that of an organ pipe when the temperature of the air is 12° C. When the temperature changes, the length of the wire is reduced to 50 cm. in order to maintain unison. If the tension in the wire is unaltered, what is the approximate temperature of the air? (Neglect any expansion of the pipe.)

For the string $n = \dfrac{1}{2l}\sqrt{\dfrac{T}{m}}$ and since T and m are unchanged,

$$nl = \text{a constant} \qquad . \qquad . \qquad . \qquad . \qquad . \qquad (1)$$

For the pipe $n = \dfrac{1}{\lambda}\sqrt{\dfrac{\gamma p}{\rho}} = \dfrac{1}{\lambda}\sqrt{\gamma RT}$, and under the given conditions λ is constant,

$$\therefore \; \frac{n}{\sqrt{T}} = \text{a constant} \qquad . \qquad . \qquad . \qquad . \qquad (2)$$

Hence from (1) and (2) since the notes are in unison

$$l\sqrt{T} = \text{a constant,}$$
$$\therefore \; l_1\sqrt{T_1} = l_2\sqrt{T_2},$$
$$\therefore \; T_2 = \frac{l_1^2}{l_2^2} \cdot T_1$$

$$= \frac{52^2}{50^2} \cdot 285 \qquad \begin{aligned} \log 285 &= 2\cdot4548 \\ 2\log 26 &= 2\cdot8300 \end{aligned}$$

$$= \frac{26^2}{25^2} \cdot 285 \qquad \begin{aligned} & \overline{5\cdot2848} \\ \log 625 &= 2\cdot7959 \end{aligned}$$

$$= 308\cdot(2)^\circ \text{ A}, \qquad \overline{2\cdot4889}$$

$\therefore$ Approximate temperature of air $= 35^\circ$ C.

QUESTIONS

1. Describe the natural modes of vibration of the air in an organ pipe closed at one end, and explain what is meant by the term " end-correction ".   A cylindrical pipe of length 28 cm. closed at one end is found to be at resonance when a tuning fork of frequency 864 vib./sec. is sounded near the open end.   Determine the mode of vibration of the air in the pipe, and deduce the value of the end correction. (Take the velocity of sound in air as 340 m./sec.)   (L.H.S.C.)

2. Explain the phenomenon of resonance, and illustrate your answer by reference to the resonance tube experiment.   In such an experiment with a resonance tube the first two successive positions of resonance occurred when the length of their columns were 15·4 and 48·6 cm. respectively.   If the velocity of sound in the air the time of the experiment was 34,000 cm./sec., calculate the frequency of the source employed and the value of the end correction for the resonance tube.   If the air column is further increased in length what will be the length when the next resonance occurs ?   (C.W.B.)

3. Explain with diagrams the possible states of vibration of a column of air in (a) an open pipe, (b) a closed pipe.   An open pipe 30 cm. long and a closed pipe 23 cm. long, both of the same diameter, are each sounding its first overtone, and these are in unison.   What is the end correction of these pipes ?   (L.Inter.)

4. Describe and explain the way in which a Kundt tube may be used to determine the ratio of the specific heats of a gas.   A Kundt tube

is excited by a brass rod 150 cm. long and the distance between successive nodes in the tube is 13·6 cm. ; what is the ratio of the velocity of sound in brass to that in air ? (L.Inter.)

5. Describe the dust tube experiment. How may it be used to compare the velocities of sound in different gases ? The fundamental frequency of longitudinal vibration of a rod clamped at its centre is 1500 vib./sec. If the mass of the rod is 96·0 gm. find the increase in its total length produced by a stretching force of 10 kg. wt.
(L.Inter.)

6. What is the meaning of overtone, harmonic ? Give an example of a harmonic which is not an overtone. What is the frequency of the second overtone of the air in a pipe, 1 m. long, closed at one end when the temperature of the air is 20° C. ? Assume that the end correction is 1·25 cm. and that the velocity of sound in air at 0° C. is 33,150 cm./sec. (L.Inter.)

7. Distinguish between progressive and stationary waves. Describe an experiment, based on the production of stationary waves, which shows that sound travels more slowly in carbon dioxide than in air at the same temperature. Show how to calculate the ratio of the velocities of sound in these two gases from the experimental data.
(N.U.J.M.B.)

8. Describe the way in which the air layers in different parts of an open organ pipe are vibrating when the pipe is sounding its fundamental note. What other modes of vibration are possible for this pipe ?

An open organ pipe in which the air is at a temperature of 15° C. and a sonometer wire of frequency 512 vib./sec., when sounded together, give 5 beats/sec., the organ pipe emitting its fundamental note. If a slight reduction in the tension of the sonometer wire produces unison between the two notes, what change in the temperature of the air in the organ pipe would have produced unison with the original frequency of the sonometer wire ? (C.W.B.)

9. What is meant by the terms node, antinode, in respect of sound waves ? What are beats, and how are they produced ?

Two open organ pipes, 80 and 81 cm. long, are found to give 26 beats in 10 sec. when each is sounding its fundamental note. Find the velocity of sound in air and the frequencies of the two notes. (End corrections may be neglected.) (C.H.S.C.)

10. Explain in general how stationary undulation is produced and state the features of this kind of motion.

A resonance tube has a jagged end and it is used to find the velocity of sound in air. A tuning fork of frequency 250 causes it to resound when it is filled with water to a mark 28 cm. below a reference mark near the open jagged end. A fork of frequency 500 causes resonance when the water reaches a mark 11½ cm. below the reference mark. Both these resounding lengths are the shortest possible with these forks. Find the velocity of sound from these results and also the position of the antinode at the upper end in relation to the mark. (L.H.S.C.)

11. Explain the production of the beats heard when two notes of nearly the same pitch are sounded together, and show how the frequency of the beats is related to the frequencies of the separate notes.

The first overtone of an open pipe and the fundamental tone of a pipe closed at one end give 5 beats/sec. when sounded together. If the length of the pipe closed at one end is 25 cm., what are the possible lengths of the open pipe? (Neglect end corrections, and take the velocity of sound in air to be 340 m./sec.)   (O. & C.)

12. Distinguish between progressive and stationary wave motion. Describe and illustrate with an example how stationary wave motion is produced. Plane sound waves of frequency 100 cycles/sec. fall normally on a smooth wall. At what distances from the wall will the air particles have (a) maximum, (b) minimum amplitude of vibration? Give reasons for your answer. (The velocity of sound in air may be taken as 1100 ft./sec.)   (L.Inter.)

13. Distinguish carefully between progressive and stationary waves and explain the terms node and antinode.

How would you demonstrate the existence of nodes and antinodes in an open organ pipe sounding its first overtone?

The shortest length of a resonance tube closed at one end which resounds to a fork of frequency 256 is 32·0 cm. The corresponding length for a fork of frequency 384 is 20·8 cm. Calculate the end correction for the tube and the velocity of sound in air.   (N.U.J.M.B.)

14. Explain what is meant by resonance, illustrating your answer with one mechanical and one accoustical example.

How may the frequency of a tuning fork be found by a resonance tube method when the velocity of sound in air at 0° C. is known? Discuss briefly how the observations and the final result would be affected by a rise in the temperature.   (N.U.J.M.B.)

15. The note which is emitted when the cork is rapidly withdrawn from an empty bottle is due to the air in the neck acting as a piston to the air in the bottle itself, which contracts and expands adiabatically as a whole.

Find the note at N.T.P. emitted from a Winchester quart bottle ($2\frac{1}{2}$ litres), the length and diameter of whose neck are each 2 cm. (Density of air at N.T.P. is 1·293 gm./litre : 1 atmosphere = 10^6 dynes/cm.^{2} ; $\gamma = 1·41$.)   (O.S.)

16. The exciting note in a Kundt's dust tube, filled with air, is produced by stroking a glass rod 1 m. long, clamped at its centre. The distance between adjacent nodal heaps of powder in the tube is 13·6 cm. If the velocity of sound in air is 340 m./sec., find the velocity of longitudinal waves in the glass rod.

17. In a Kundt's dust tube experiment a metal rod 160 cm. long, and of density 8·9 gm./cc., was clamped at its centre and set into longitudinal vibration. The distance between adjacent nodal heaps of powder in the tube was 11·35 cm. Assuming that the tube contained air, of density 1·293 gm./litre, under a pressure of 76 cm. of mercury, that the value of Young's modulus for the metal is 2×10^9 gm. wt./sq. cm. and the density of mercury is 13·6 gm./cc. Calculate the ratio of the principal specific heats of air.

CHAPTER VIII

THE ACOUSTICS OF BUILDINGS

104. Introductory

The acoustic properties of a hall or room have a considerable effect on speech and music. This effect varies from room to room. These simple facts have been known for many years but the problem was not investigated scientifically until comparatively recently. Public buildings are designed nowadays so as to give optimum acoustical efficiency, and architectural acoustics involves many points concerning the reflection, interference and absorption of sound. The fundamental fact is that the room in which music is being played is really an extension of the instruments and as such modifies considerably the tones produced by the instruments. The amount and character of the changes depend upon the physical dimensions of the room as well as the materials used in its construction.

In the design of public buildings the following must be considered :

(*a*) The reverberation or prolonged reflection of the sound.
(*b*) Loudness.
(*c*) Focusing due to walls and ceilings.
(*d*) Echelon effects.
(*e*) Extraneous noises.
(*f*) Resonances within the building.

It was in its application to public speech that the late Wallace C. Sabine, Professor of Physics in the University of Harvard, tackled the problem. In this country Dr. Alex Wood of Cambridge, Dr. A. H. Davis and Dr. G. W. C. Kaye of the National Physical Laboratory have taken up his work.

Sabine laid down three important rules which must be obeyed if the acoustics of a building are to be correct :

1. The sound heard by the audience must be loud enough.
2. The quality of the sound must be unchanged.
3. The successive sounds in speech and music must not overlap.

105. Reverberation

Sabine picked out the most important factor affecting speech and music in a room, namely, the prolonged reflections from walls, floor and ceiling, or reverberation. He called the time for a sound to fall from average intensity to inaudibility the " time of reverberation ". In his early experiments he used an organ pipe of frequency 512 vib./sec.

as his source of sound and a stop watch to time the reverberation after the pipe ceased to sound.   Modern apparatus is much more complicated but the principle is still the same.

Speaking in a room is far less exhausting than speaking in the open. Reflections from walls, ceiling and floor assist the voice.   During the period of spring cleaning, when carpets and curtains are removed, the time of reverberation of voice and footsteps is much increased and small movements given an abnormally loud sound.   Soft materials which are good absorbers of sound take in rapidly the energy of a sound.   The compressions and rarefactions cause air to move in and out of the pores of the material and the friction changes the sound energy into heat.   This does not offer a method of warming a room by means of music !   As an illustration of the amount of heat which could be obtained from sound, Wood [1] states that " the sound energy generated by the shouting of a cup-tie crowd throughout a match would yield just about enough heat to warm one cup of tea ".

When the earth is covered with a layer of freshly fallen snow there is a very obvious lack of noise and everywhere seems strangely quiet. Freshly fallen snow is a good absorber of sound but is not as effective when it has become hard.   Smooth water on the other hand is a good reflector and a poor absorber of sound energy and so the laughter and chatter from people sailing on lakes and rivers can be heard over a considerable distance.   As an illustration of how the normal voice is dependent on the assistance given by reflection a person suspended in the air and speaking normally would be inaudible at a distance of 11 m.

In an ordinary room a sound undergoes two or three hundred reflections before becoming inaudible.   Energy is lost at each reflection and as a result of such a large number of reflections energy is distributed uniformly throughout the room.   Rooms which have no time of reverberation such as some studios of the B.B.C. feel " dead " and the sensation of speaking is similar to that experienced when speaking from the top of an isolated tower or building.   The time of reverberation varies with the frequency of the note.   If the time of reverberation is short for high notes and long for low notes then the music sounds mellow and even dull.   If it is short for low tones and long for high tones then the music becomes excessively brilliant and possibly thin.   For calculation purposes the value used is usually that for a sound of frequency 512 vib./sec.   Sometimes artificial reverberation is used, as in the Manchester studios of the B.B.C., to give music its necessary brilliance.   The orchestra performs in a rather small studio with a small time of reverberation and so the music would lack brilliance if it were broadcast as it came straight from the studio.   The microphones in the studio feed some of the music via

[1] Wood, Alex, *The Physics of Music*, p. 222.

amplifiers to loudspeakers in underground cellars. At the other end of these cellars microphones pick up the music which has reverberated through the cellars and pass the music back to the control room. Here it is mixed in the correct proportion with the music coming straight from the studio so as to give the effect of an orchestra playing in a large concert hall.

A long reverberation time is even more undesirable than a short one. Consider a case where the time is from 4 to 5 sec. In this time even a most deliberate speaker will have uttered ten or a dozen syllables. All these will be sounding together making the utterances hopelessly confused. Increasing the loudness of the sound only makes things worse. It was to remedy a defect of this kind in a lecture room at Harvard that Sabine began his pioneer work. In this particular room the time of reverberation was from 5·45 to 5·62 sec. He attempted to reduce this to a reasonable value, i.e. one which supported the voice and did not make speech unintelligible, by placing suitable absorbing material in the form of cushions in various parts of the room. The experiment was successful and the effect of the cushions was practically independent of their position. The graph of the reciprocal of the time of reverberation against the area of cushion was a straight line which gave the relationship

$$S \cdot T = k$$

where S is the area of cushions together with the area of walls, floor and ceiling reduced to an equivalent area of cushion, T is the time of reverberation and k is a constant.

When the organ pipe used by Sabine was rated it was found to give an intensity 10^6 times the minimum audible. This enabled him to make a standard reverberation time as that required for a sound to fall to one millionth of its initial intensity. It was essential also to have some standard of absorption in terms of which all substances can be measured. Sabine chose one square foot of open window as his standard, a simple but superb standard, since all the sound which falls upon an open window passes out and so it acts as a perfect absorber. After finding the time of reverberation with cushions in the room, the experiment was repeated with the cushions removed and the area of open window was adjusted until the time of reverberation was the same as before. This gave a means of finding what area of cushion was equivalent to 1 sq. ft. of window (the result always being a fraction). This was termed the coefficient of absorption, a.

The total absorption of cushions in a room is thus the area of cushion multiplied by the coefficient of absorption, i.e. aS, and is measured in open window units (O.W.U.'s). Similar experiments with audiences enabled him to find the absorption coefficient for people and it is interesting to note that each member of an audience is approximately equivalent to $4\frac{1}{2}$ sq. ft. of open window, women being rather better absorbers than men owing to the nature of their clothing. Sabine showed that the reverberation time of a room is related to its size by

$$T = \frac{0 \cdot 05 \; V}{A}.$$

where $T =$ time of reverberation in seconds,
    $V =$ volume of the room in cubic feet,
    $A =$ absorption in open window units, and $A = \Sigma aS$;
where S is the area of surface and " a " the corresponding coefficient of absorption.

The importance of this formula lies in the fact that it can be applied to the design as well as the correction of rooms.   For a room of known volume and time of reverberation the value of ΣaS can be found which will make T suitable for speech and music, and hence the surface of a suitable absorbing material which must be placed in the room can be calculated.   This means that from the architect's plan the time of reverberation can be calculated before the building is started.

The next step was to decide what is the optimum time of reverberation.   Together with a committee of musical experts Sabine determined the time of reverberation most suitable for speech and music.   For piano music the mean value of all observations gave $T = 1 \cdot 08$ sec. For theatres the optimum value of T increased with volume varying from $1 \cdot 1$ to $1 \cdot 5$ sec. for a small theatre to $2 \cdot 3$ sec. for one of larger volume.

The presence or otherwise of an audience will affect considerably the time of reverberation, as will the size of the audience.   In order to keep the time of reverberation practically constant, seats in theatres are backed with plush which has a coefficient of absorption approxi-

TIMES OF REVERBERATION OF B.B.C. STUDIOS

Studio	Use	T	Vol. cu. ft.
Ba　.　.　.	Vaudeville, light music	1·1	30,000
Bb　.　.　.	Dance bands, octets, etc.	0·85	10,000
Concert Hall　.	Orchestral performances	1·75	125,000
4a, 4b　.　.	News	Dead	670
6c, 7c　.　.	Speech in plays	Dead	1,500
8a　.　.　.	Debates, etc.	0·45	2,100

mately the same as that of a member of the audience.   The superseding of lime plaster by hard plaster has added considerably to the reverberation problems in modern buildings since the coefficient of absorption for lime plaster is about twice that for hard plaster and one person ≡ 4·7 sq. ft. of open window ≡ 300 sq. ft. of hard plaster. This means that a room copied exactly from one built many years ago will not have the same time of reverberation unless the materials are the same or the total absorption A is made the same by a suitable choice of materials.

It is generally agreed that the time of reverberation of a broadcasting studio should be less than that of a concert hall since two times of reverberation are involved, viz. that of the studio and that of the room in which the music is reproduced. The value accepted is about two-thirds of that required for concert-room conditions.

ABSORPTION COEFFICIENTS OF VARIOUS MATERIALS

Material	Frequency in cycles/sec.		
	250	500	1000-2000
Lime plaster	0·02-0·03	0·03-0·04	0·03
Hard plaster	0·01-0·02	0·01-0·02	0·02-0·03
Unpainted brick . . .	0·03	0·03	0·05
3 ply-wood panelling . . .	0·01-0·02	0·01-0·02	0·01-0·02
Wood block in mastic . .	0·03	0·06	0·10
Heavy curtains folded . .	—	0·50-1·0	—
Axminster carpet on felt . .	0·05	0·40	0·65
Turkey carpet on felt . .	0·30	0·50	0·65
Acoustic plaster . . .	0·15	0·25	0·30
Sprayed asbestos . . .	0·50-0·60	0·65-0·75	0·60-0·75
Audience per person . . .	4·3 (O.W.U.'s)	4·7	5·0
Chairs, bent ash . . .	0·16 ,,	0·17	0·21
Cushions—plush on hair . .	1·1 ,,	1·8	1·5

Consider the case of a hall of volume 75,000 cu. ft., seating capacity 600 and the volume per seat of the audience 120 cu. ft. The following particulars apply.

Surface	Nature	Area or number	Coefficient of absorption	Absorption O.W.U.'s
Ceiling	Plaster	6000 sq. ft.	0·02	120
Walls	3-ply panelling	5000 sq. ft.	0·02	100
Doors	Wood	180 sq. ft.	0·06	10·8
Floor	Polished board	5000 sq. ft.	0·06	300
Seats	Cushion backs	400	1·0 O.W.U. chair	400
Seats	Cane	200	0·1 O.W.U. chair	20
			Total permanent absorption	950·8 O.W.U.'s

The time of reverberation of the empty hall is therefore given by

$$T = \frac{0.05 \times 75,000}{950.8}$$

$$= 3.94 \text{ sec.}$$

With an audience of 600 since each is equivalent to 4.7 sq. ft. of open window, 600×4.7 O.W.U.'s must be added, but since the seats are covered $400 \times 1.0 + 200 \times 0.10$ O.W.U.s must be subtracted.

∴ With full audience

Absorption $= 950.8 + 400 (4.7 - 1.0) + 200 (4.7 - 0.10)$

$= 950.8 + 2400$

$= 3350.8$ O.W.U.s.

Giving $\quad T = \dfrac{0.05 \times 75000}{3350.8}$

$$= 1.12 \text{ sec.}$$

With half an audience occupying the covered seats

$$A = 950.8 + 1480 \text{ O.W.U.s}$$

giving $\qquad T = 1.54 \text{ sec.}$

The results show that even when the hall is not filled to capacity it is suitable for orchestral works. In the above examples the time of reverberation should be smaller since the effect of the musicians themselves has not been taken into account. It is left to the student to find T when an orchestra of 50 players is present.

⋆ 106. Eyring's Formula

In the theories of reverberation leading to Sabine's reverberation time equation it has been assumed that the formula is a " live " room formula, and several authorities have also shown that this equation varies also with the shape of the room.[1] In December 1929, Carl F. Eyring,[2] of the Bell Telephone Laboratories, read a paper to the Acoustical Society of America dealing with the reverberation time in " dead " rooms. The analysis was based on the assumption that sound images could be used to replace the walls of a room in calculating the rate of decay of sound energy after the sound source is cut off. By means of mathematics beyond the scope of this book he showed that the decay equation was given by

$$\rho = \rho_0 \, e^{\frac{cS \log \cdot (1 - \alpha)t}{4V}},$$

where $\quad \rho =$ energy density after a time t sec.

$\rho_0 =$ initial energy density $= \dfrac{4E}{cS\alpha}.$

[1] Schuster and Waetzmann, *Ann. de Phys.*, March 1929. Also Eyring.
[2] Eyring, *Journ. Acoust. Soc. Amer.*, 1930, **1**, 217.

E = energy units/sec. emitted by the source before cut-off,
V = volume of the room,
S = area of the room,
c = velocity of sound,
α = average absorption coefficient,

and is defined by

$$\alpha = \frac{a_1 S_1 + a_2 S_2 + \ldots}{S_1 + S_2} = \frac{\Sigma a S}{\Sigma S}.$$

According to Sabine's definition the reverberation time is the time required for the energy density to fall to 10^{-6} of its initial value and so

$$\frac{\rho_1}{\rho_2} = \frac{e^{\frac{cS \log_e (1-\alpha)t_1}{4V}}}{e^{\frac{cS \log_e (1-\alpha)t_2}{4V}}} = 10^6.$$

Putting $t_2 - t_1 = T$, the reverberation time

$$\log_e 10^6 = -\frac{cS \log_e (1 - \alpha)T}{4V},$$

$$\text{or} \quad T = \frac{4V \log_e 10^6}{-cS(1 - \alpha)},$$

so that in its general form

$$T = \frac{K \cdot V}{-S \log_e (1 - \alpha)}, \quad \text{where } K = \frac{4 \log_e 10^6}{c},$$

and in British units

$$T = \frac{4 \times 13\cdot82 \times V}{-1100S \log_e (1-\alpha)}$$

$$= \frac{0\cdot05 \cdot V}{-S \log_e (1 - \alpha)}.$$

But $\log_e (1 - \alpha) = -(\alpha + \frac{\alpha^2}{2} + \frac{\alpha^3}{3} + \ldots) \fallingdotseq -\alpha$ when α is small, which is true for live rooms, and in this case the reverberation time is given by

$$T = \frac{0\cdot05 V}{S\alpha},$$

thus showing that Sabine's formula is a special case of a more general formula.

Sabine's formula obviously had no meaning for the case of a " dead " room, when ($\alpha = 1$) where there is complete absorption. The new formula gives the correct reverberation time of $T = 0$. As a point of practical importance the new formula shows that a " dead " room may be obtained by the use of considerably less absorbing material than is indicated by Sabine's formula, which was applied to rooms having reverberation times varying from $1\cdot5$ to 4 sec. Using Sabine's formula 8400 sq. ft. of absorbing material will give a reverberation time of $0\cdot54$ sec. in a fairly " dead " room such as a sound stage. Using the more accurate formula this quantity of material gives a reverberation time of 0·34 sec. If, however, 6200 sq. ft. of material is used, giving a saving of approximately 25 per cent., the desired reverberation time of 0·54 sec. is obtained.

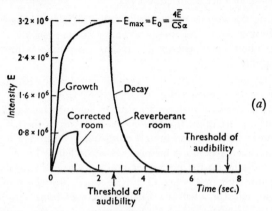

(a)

(a) Intensity/time curve for a room before and after sound absorbing material is added.

$$\text{Growth } E = E_0\left(1 - e^{-\frac{cs\alpha t}{4v}}\right) = E_0(1 - e^{-Bt})$$

$$\text{Decay } E = E_0\left(e^{-\frac{cs\alpha t}{4v}}\right) = E_0 e^{-Bt}$$

Cf. rate of change and discharge of a condenser through a resistance.

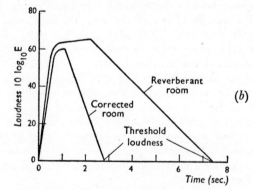

(b)

(b) Loudness curves for Fig. (a) above.

The curves show :

(1) the maximum intensity after adding absorbing material is much less than before.

(2) Loudness in a deadened room is little less than that in a reverberant room.

Fig. 111. Variation of Loudness and Intensity with time.

107. Loudness

There are two distinct ways of ensuring that the sounds which reach an audience are sufficiently loud.

1. Using the sounds which strike walls, ceiling and floor and distributing the sound energy as uniformly as possible.
2. Providing extra energy by means of public address (P.A.) equipment.

The first method is obviously very closely linked with the time of reverberation and with echoes or reflections from suitable surfaces. Reflections from plane surfaces are usually helpful whereas those from curved surfaces are often troublesome as is shown in the next section.

For music there is an optimum number of performers for a given hall, the number depending on the size of the hall. For both public speaking and singing the performer needs a sense of ease and power and there must be an absence of fatigue, often brought about by the use of undue effort in a hall that has little reverberation. High pitched notes are easily absorbed due to the increase of the coefficient of absorption with frequency, and so music can easily lose its brilliance. Simple operations, however, often effect remarkable cures as is shown by the fact that a piece of cork, normally a good absorber, becomes a good reflector when polished. In the same way the polishing of woodwork can have a considerable effect on the brilliance of music as has been demonstrated in the Leipzig Gewandhaus.

Sounding boards placed near and behind the performers so as to reflect the sound towards the audience help considerably, but to be really effective must be of considerable area, i.e. large compared with the wavelength of sound. Their nearness to the performer ensures that the reflected sound does not cause unwanted interference with the direct sound. Their presence, however, is not always desirable. Low ceilings also play a useful part in reflecting sound energy towards the audience. In order to assist the uniform distribution of this energy it is advisable to make these reflecting surfaces irregular. Useful assistance is given by pillars and boxes and even heavy relief decoration plays its part provided that the depth of the relief is of the order of one foot. Another way of using the reflection from a plane surface is to provide a clear space in front of the audience, although this is not often convenient.

When sound energy other than that produced by the performers is required, an amplifier and loudspeakers are used, often very wrongly. The loudspeakers should be above the heads of the performers so that the sounds from speakers and performers travel approximately the same distances to the members of the audience. If the speakers are placed down the hall and the direct sound is also audible then the listener hears the same sound twice. When the distance between loudspeaker and performer is 75 ft. then, under normal conditions, the time interval between the sounds will be $\frac{1}{15}$th sec. and they will be heard separately so that speech and music will become confused.

Care must be used also in the use of P.A. equipment if good reproduction is required since in most cases the amplifiers are selective, giving a greater degree of amplification to the low than the high notes.

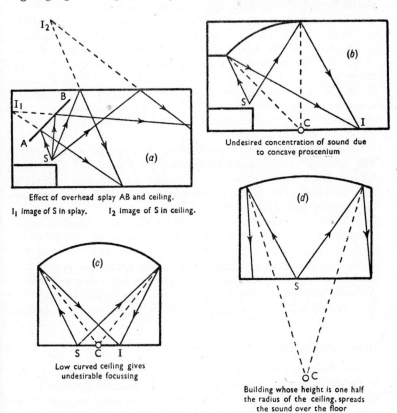

Effect of overhead splay AB and ceiling.
I_1 Image of S in splay. I_2 Image of S in ceiling.

Undesired concentration of sound due to concave proscenium

Low curved ceiling gives undesirable focussing

Building whose height is one half the radius of the ceiling, spreads the sound over the floor

FIG. 112. Effect of ceilings in the distribution of sound.

108. Focusing due to Walls and Ceilings

The reflection from the back wall of a hall is often unwanted since the sound wave reflected to the front of the audience will have travelled twice the length of the hall and so there will be a considerable time interval between direct and reflected sound. The effect is even worse if the wall is curved since the sound waves are brought to a focus giving an undesirable intensity. The fundamental principles involved are that waves reflected from a plane surface continue on their path with the same divergence, those reflected from a convex surface have increased divergence, thus helping to spread the sound energy, whilst those reflected from a concave surface have decreased divergence which may give an undesirable concentration of energy.

Careful design can often make all these surfaces useful but it must be noted that no amount of absorbing material will eliminate completely the echo from a badly placed concave surface.

Fig. 112 (b) shows the bad effect of a concave proscenium which focuses the sound over the front seats of the audience. The curved ceiling shown in Fig. 112 (c) also shows an undesirable concentration of sound. This arises when the centre of curvature of the ceiling lies on or near the floor. When the radius of curvature is made twice the height of the hall the bad focusing is eliminated and the sound is spread uniformly over the floor. The good or bad effect depends upon which side of the normal at the point of incidence the incident sound waves fall.

The Albert Hall suffers from domed ceiling and circular plan. The focusing effect is made even worse by a long path difference between direct and reflected sound. A velarium, or awning suspended from the ceiling, reduces the volume of reflected sound and so reduces the excessive time of reverberation.

The reflecting properties of an auditorium can be studied using either spark pulse or ripple tank methods. Results are obtained more easily using the latter method. Using a sectional scale model of the auditorium the effect on sound waves can be studied by placing the model in a ripple tank and using water ripples to stimulate sound waves. An important point to note is that the size of the ripples approximate fairly closely to those of sound waves on the same scale as the model.

109. Echelon Effect

An observer walking on a hard surface near a row of regularly spaced palings or towards a flight of steps may notice that each footstep is followed by an echo which has a musical ring. In both cases the note arises from the regular train of reflected sounds each consisting of a simple echo of the original sound.

If the tread of the stairs is 1 ft. (see Fig. 113 (a)), then the path difference between each consecutive echo is 2 ft. Assuming that the velocity of sound is 1100 ft./sec., the time interval between each echo is $\frac{2}{1100}$ sec., or $\frac{1}{550}$ sec. so that the observer will hear a musical echo of frequency 550 vib./sec. For the railings the path difference is $2d \cos \theta$ and therefore the frequency of the note is $\dfrac{v}{2d \cos \theta}$ vib./sec.

If this effect is undesirable it can be prevented by the irregular spacing of objects which will give rise to it, constructing the stairs so that a regular series of reflections is avoided, or the use of a stair carpet.

110. Extraneous Noises

These are nearly always air-borne and so are difficult to control or remove. For public buildings the real solution lies in the choice of a quiet site and, if possible, the quiet side of such a site. Double or even treble windows reduce extraneous noises but unfortunately this means a loss in transmitted light and also an alternative method of ventilation must be provided. Ventilating fans serve well but it is essential that the machine is free from rumble and that noise is not transmitted along the ventilation ducts even when the fan is situated some distance from the hall.

Structure borne noises also present a difficult problem. Noises made by hitting a water pipe in one class-room are often passed a

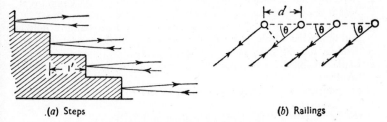

.(a) Steps   (b) Railings

FIG. 113. The echelon effect.

considerable distance round the school. Similar effects in a large hall can mar an orchestral programme. Bearing in mind the fact that the fundamental principle of the methods of reducing the transference of sound energy is that energy is lost when sound passes from one medium to another, it can be seen that the presence of discontinuities in the path of the sound will considerably reduce it in intensity. Rubber or insulating gaskets at the junctions of water pipes reduce the sound transmitted by this path to a reasonable value. Footfalls on floors and lift noises can also be very distracting. Double walls, floating floors, suspended ceilings (each providing discontinuities) are the answer to these problems, but unfortunately the methods involve considerable expense. These expensive precautions are wasted, however, unless the hall has tight fitting doors and windows.

111. Resonance within the Building

In large halls the resonant frequency of the hall itself is well below the audible range since it is proportional to $\dfrac{1}{\sqrt{\text{volume}}}$, and there is no unpleasant effect. The pulsations of the low notes of an organ in some halls and churches build up until they can be felt rather than heard. In some buildings these vibrations set up unpleasant resonances in wood panels and windows.

Although some resonances can be very unpleasant, others can be very useful. Some halls, famous for their acoustic properties, such as the old Gewandhaus, Leipzig, and the Royal Opera House, Covent Garden, have a large area of resonant material in the form of wood panelling. The Queen's Hall, now destroyed, also possessed this characteristic and the resonance of this panelling compensated for a time of reverberation which would otherwise have been considered short.

QUESTIONS

1. Explain what is meant by " time of reverberation ". Upon what does it depend and how is it adjusted to its optimum value ?
2. If you were consulted with regard to the construction of a public building what would you consider essential, in the design and furnishing, for optimum acoustical efficiency ?
3. Explain carefully with special reference to the physical principles involved :
   (a) Sounds in an empty house seem louder than when the house is furnished.
   (b) Some pulpits are equipped with sounding boards.
   (c) When walking past railings the noise of one's footsteps is often accompanied by a musical sound.
4. During bomb practice in the neighbourhood of a corrugated fence the noise of each explosion was accompanied by a shrill echo. Explain this and show by means of a rough diagram the relative positions of bomb, fence and observer.
5. An observer walking towards a flight of steps, the tread of which is 8 in., hears a musical note of frequency 825 vib./sec. What is the velocity of sound under these conditions ?
6. A hall 60 ft. long, 30 ft. wide and 20 ft. high has a hard plaster ceiling, plywood panelled walls, a wooden floor, and four wooden doors each 6 ft. × 5 ft. It is designed for an audience of 200 and an orchestra of 40. The chairs provided have cushioned backs. Find the time of reverberation (a) when the hall is empty, (b) when occupied by full audience and orchestra. It may be assumed that the coefficient of absorption for plaster and wood panelling is 0·02, for wood (doors and floor) it is 0·06, for chairs with cushioned backs it is 1·0 and that each member of audience and orchestra is equivalent to 4·7 sq. ft. of open window.

CHAPTER IX

INTENSITY OF SOUND

112. As stated in chapter 1 intensity of sound and loudness are not identical although they are related. The intensity of a sound is a definite physical quantity, determined by a rate of supply of energy, which is proportional to the square of the amplitude of vibration of the wave. Loudness, on the other hand, is a degree of sensation depending upon the intensity of sound and the sensitiveness of the ear. Near the limits of audibility a very intense sound will produce little sensation of sound, or the loudness will be considered feeble, although the rate of flow of energy in the waves is very great.

The accommodation of the ear is great and it can adapt itself to a wide range of intensities, from violent explosions to very feeble vibrations of the order 10^{-8} cm. It is quite within the capabilities of the ear to deal with sounds of amplitudes varying in the ratio $1 : 10^6$, which means intensities varying in the ratio $1 : 10^{12}$.

Weber's law states the relation between sensation and stimulus (or loudness and intensity) as follows: "The increase of stimulus necessary to produce the minimum perceptible increase in sensation is proportional to the pre-existing stimulus." In other words, if a sound wave of large intensity is producing the sensation of a loud sound in the ear then the change in the intensity of this wave in order for the ear to discern a change in loudness is proportional to the original intensity of the sound wave and therefore must be great. If all the people in a room are whispering then little extra effort is required by any one person to make his voice heard above the rest. If on the other hand they are all talking fairly loudly, a sound wave of much greater intensity is required for any one person to make his voice heard above the hubbub. The extra intensity needed to make a perceptible increase in the sound produced by one particular person on the ear of a second person, is proportional to the intensity of sound already falling on the ear of that second person.

From this law Fechner derived a very important law relating the sensation S and the intensity of stimulus I:

$$S = K \log I \text{ where } K \text{ is a constant.}$$

Hence $\qquad \dfrac{dS}{dI} = \dfrac{K}{I}$ and $\dfrac{dS}{dI}$ increases as I decreases.

Thus the relationship between sensation and stimulus is a logarithmic one and $\dfrac{dS}{dI}$ represents the sensitiveness of the ear.

Common everyday happenings such as sitting alone in an otherwise empty room shows that the sensitiveness of the ear increases as the intensity of sound decreases. Many tiny sounds normally passing unnoticed against a noisy background seem abnormally loud, i.e. the pre-existing stimulus or noise has become quite small and the increase in stimulus due to small noises, such as the creaking of doors and windows, the noise due to the shrinking of woodwork or even the movements of a mouse, is quite big enough to produce a perceptible increase in the pre-existing stimulus or the original sensation of sound.

113. From Fechner's derivation of Weber's law it can be seen that if the intensity of sound I is doubled the loudness is not doubled, but increases by equal additions since the relationship is logarithmic. When the impression of magnitude of physical quantities is proportional to the logarithms of their magnitudes then a convenient way of comparing them is on a logarithmic basis.

The common logarithm of the ratio of two powers defines a number which is expressed in " bels ". It is often more convenient to use a decibel which is one tenth of a bel. Thus the difference in level between two powers P_1 and P_2 is given by

$$S = \log \frac{P_1}{P_2} \text{ bels,}$$

or

$$N = 10 \log \frac{P_1}{P_2} \text{ decibels.}$$

Before applying this to sound, consider its application to radio where it is very widely used. The response curves of microphones, pick-ups, radio sets, etc. show decibels against frequency, since the former indicate the behaviour of the instrument with respect to a definite level.

Suppose that in a radio set the power valve is delivering 1 watt to the loudspeaker and that this is then increased to 2 watts. To say that the power has increased by 1 watt means little unless it is stated that the original power or level was 1 watt. In this case the increase in power is 100 per cent. whereas if the valve had been giving out 100 watts the increase would be only 1 per cent. The great advantage of decibels is that being logarithmic their addition is equivalent to multiplication with ordinary numbers.

Consider again the case of the speaker being driven by a valve giving out 1 watt. Then on increasing the power to 2 watts

$$N_1 = 10 \log \frac{P_1}{P_2} = 10 \log \frac{2}{1} = 3 \cdot 010 \text{ decibels (increase of 100 per cent.).}$$

Suppose that the power delivered by the valve increases by another watt, i.e. it is now giving out 3 watts, then

$$N_2 = 10 \log \frac{3}{2} = 1 \cdot 761 \text{ decibels (increase of 50 per cent.).}$$

Considering now the total increase in power with respect to the original level, i.e. 3 watts as against the original 1 watt,

$$N = N_1 + N_2 = 4 \cdot 771 \text{ decibels}$$
$$= 0 \cdot 4771 \text{ bels.}$$

From logarithmic tables anti-log $0 \cdot 4771 = 3$ which gives the number of times the new power is as great as the original power. The percentage increases on the other hand do not give a correct result if they are added since it would indicate a final level of 150 per cent. above the original level whereas it is really 200 per cent. above the original level.

Consider a pick-up which when connected directly to a radio set gives an output of $4 \cdot 761$ decibels above the standard level, i.e. its output with amplification. By means of a transformer between the pick-up and amplifier the output is now increased by $5 \cdot 239$ decibels. Then the total increase above the standard level is $4 \cdot 761 + 5 \cdot 239$, i.e. 10 decibels or 1 bel. But 10 is the number whose logarithm is 1, so that with transformer and amplifier the pick-up is giving out 10 times the output it would give without their assistance.

Unfortunately in radio no standard reference level has been uniformly adopted and it is usual therefore to state a reference level, e.g. 20 decibels (0 decibels is $0 \cdot 006$ watts). This is a measure of increase of 100 times above the reference level since 20 decibels $= 2$ bels and anti-log 2 is 100. In this case, since the reference level is stated, it is possible to calculate the absolute output since

$$\frac{P_2}{P_1} = \frac{W_2}{W_1} = \frac{W_2}{0 \cdot 006} = 10^2,$$

therefore $\qquad\qquad W_2 = 0 \cdot 6 \text{ watts.}$

Since $W = \dfrac{E^2}{R}$ the number of decibels change in level can be stated as follows :

$$\text{Decibels} = 10 \log \frac{W_2}{W_1} = 10 \log \frac{E_2{}^2 R_1}{E_1{}^2 R_2} = 20 \log \frac{E_2}{E_1} + 10 \log \frac{R_1}{R_2}.$$

If the resistance is the same, then this reduces to

$$\text{decibels} = 20 \log \frac{E_2}{E_1} \text{ since } \log \frac{R_1}{R_2} = 0.$$

12

In the case of microphones the specification usually refers to an output above or below 1 volt, i.e. the reference level is 1 volt and a negative sign indicates that for a stated frequency the output is below 1 volt.

Using decibels $= 20 \log \dfrac{E_2}{E_1}$,

-50 decibels means $\log \dfrac{E_2}{E_1} = -\dfrac{50}{20} = -2\cdot5 = \overline{3}\cdot5 = 0\cdot00316$ volts (RMS)

-60 decibels means $\log \dfrac{E_2}{E_1} = -\dfrac{60}{20} = -3\cdot0 = \overline{3}\cdot0 = 0\cdot001$ volt (RMS)

-70 decibels means $\log \dfrac{E_2}{E_1} = -\dfrac{70}{20} = -3\cdot5 = \overline{4}\cdot5 = 0\cdot000316$ volt (RMS)

In telephone practice the reference level generally used is 6 milliwatts into 500 ohms, although 6 milliwatts into 600 ohms is also used. This is done because the signals are usually developed across a definite impedance and so if the same impedance is used throughout, the gain or loss in decibels can be found from voltage measurements. The following shows examples of the relationship between decibels and power ratio.

Power ratio	1·2589	1·5849	1·9953	2·5119	3·1623	10	10^2	10^3	10^4
Decibels	1·0	2·0	3·0	4·0	5·0	10	20	30	40

Since the response of the ear varies with frequency (see Fig. 2), the reference level in sound must be fixed as a standard loudness at a definite frequency. The standard frequency is that of 1000 cycles/sec., and so using this standard frequency and a standard level of intensity, it is possible to define a standard of loudness. This unit of loudness is known as the *phon*.

It must be carefully noted that the decibel is not a unit of loudness but a unit of change of power. The phon, however, is a true unit of loudness. If the ear were equally responsive at all frequencies then the phon and decibel would be identical. The decibel bears no relation at all to the response of the ear and only at the standard frequency of 1000 cycles/sec. will the level in phons be numerically equal to the level in decibels. Having chosen the standard frequency in order to account for the characteristics of the ear, it only remains to state a reference level.

Let S' be the sensation produced with respect to a definite zero level for a definite intensity of sound I and let the intensity I_0 be that required for the zero level of the scale, i.e. the intensity just not sufficient to enable an observer to hear a sound or in other words the intensity required to make the sound reach the threshold of audibility.

Then $$S' = \log \frac{I}{I_0} \text{ bels,}$$

or as before $$N = 10 \log \frac{I}{I_0} \text{ decibels}$$

when $$I = I_0, \qquad \log \frac{I}{I_0} = 0,$$

therefore $$S' = 0.$$

When $I = 2I_0$, $\log \dfrac{I}{I_0} = \log 2 = 0.3$ bels $= 3$ decibels approximately.

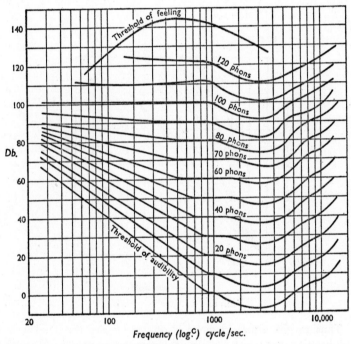

FIG. 114.

Zero reference level is taken as the average limit of audibility which has been standardised as a sound pressure (R.M.S.) of 0.0002 dynes/ sq. cm. or an energy flux of 10^{-16} watts/sq. cm.

Thus the loudness of any sound in phons is numerically equal to the sound intensity in decibels of an equally loud pure note of 1000 cycles/sec.

Using this definition it is now possible to compare the loudness of different sounds by comparing them with a pure note of 1000 cycles/sec. The note is fed from an oscillator into a single earpiece and controlled by an attenuator calibrated in decibels. The attenuator consists of a network of resistances which is designed to introduce a known loss into the circuit.

Considering Fig. 114 and taking as an example a medium radio set of loudness 70 phons it follows from the definition that for frequencies of 1000 cycles the loudness must be 70 phons. From the graphs the following relationships are obtained between phons and decibels.

Frequency		phons	Db
50 cycles/sec.		70	84
100	,,	70	80
1000	,,	70	70
3000	,,	70	67
10,000	,,	70	83

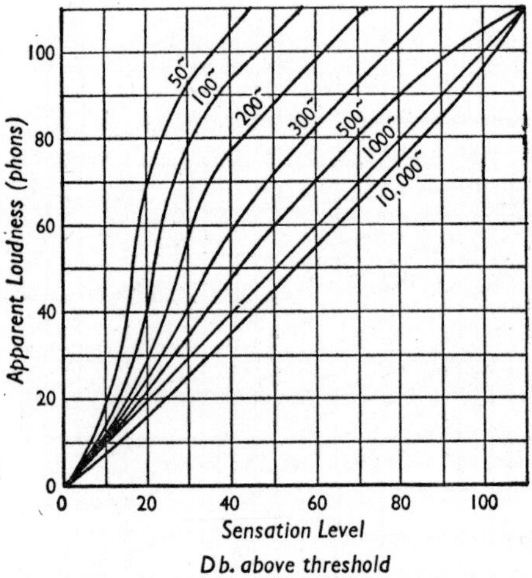

FIG. 115. (After Fletcher.)

Thus to give equal loudness at all frequencies the loudspeaker must handle power which is dependent upon the frequency. The valve must either provide extra power for the low and high frequencies or the speaker must have a response curve which shows it is more sensitive at low and high than at medium frequencies. The valve must deliver 14 decibels more acoustic power at 50 cycles than at 1000 cycles/sec. By a suitable choice of resistances and condensers in a tone control, more of the medium frequency power is by-passed to earth than the low or high frequency. This is done by making the impedance of the resistance condenser network lower to medium frequency current than it is to low or high frequency current. This, however, results in a lowering of the total output of the set.

The following table shows the relationship between well-known sounds and units of loudness.

Phons	Sound
130	Threshold of feeling or pain.
110-120	Vicinity of aeroplane engine.
105-110	,, pneumatic drill.
100-105	,, loud motor horn.
90-95	Interior of tube train, windows open.
90	,, noisy motor vehicle or loud radio.
80	,, main-line train, windows open.
70	,, quiet motor car, medium radio.
60-75	Conversation average to loud.
40-50	Suburban district (residential).
20-30	Quiet country residence.
0	Threshold of audibility.

It is interesting to use some of these values and show how fortunate it is that nature has arranged that loudness is proportional to the logarithm of the energy. Consider a number of singers each producing notes of equal intensity at 1000 cycles and a loudness level of 60 phons.

Number of singers	Loudness	Energy (watts/sq. in.)
1	60 phons	$1 \times 60 \times 10^{-16} = 6 \times 10^{-15}$
2	$60 + 10 \log 2 = 63$ phons	$2 \times 6 \times 10^{-15} = 1 \cdot 2 \times 10^{-14}$
100	$60 + 10 \log 100 = 80$,,	$10^2 \times 6 \times 10^{-15} = 6 \times 10^{-13}$
1000	$60 + 10 \log 1000 = 90$,,	$10^3 \times 6 \times 10^{-15} = 6 \times 10^{-12}$
10^6	$60 + 10 \log 10^6 = 120$,,	$10^6 \times 6 \times 10^{-15} = 6 \times 10^{-9}$
10^{12}	$10 + 10 \log 10^{12} = 180$,,	$10^{12} \times 6 \times 10^{-15} = 6 \times 10^{-3}$

Dr. Alex Wood was of the opinion that at some time in the future, the phon scale for loudness will replace the indefinite " p " and " f " markings on the music score.

Stokowski makes use of a phon meter, although the present type of direct scale reading instrument is cumbersome and expensive, and interprets his score as follows :

ppp = 20 phons f = 75 phons
pp = 40 ,, ff = 85 ,,
p = 55 ,, fff = 95 ,,
mf = 65 ,,

CHAPTER X

ANALYSIS, RECORDING AND REPRODUCTION OF SOUND

114. When two or more notes of different pitch are sounding simultaneously, the vibration of the air is the complex resultant obtained by compounding the individual vibrations. In general the ear is able to analyse this vibration and to distinguish the separate notes. Two obvious exceptions to this statement arise when the notes are very nearly of the same pitch and beats are set up, and when the intensity of one note is below a certain minimum value relative to the others.

The fundamental law in physiological acoustics was propounded by G. S. Ohm (the originator of Ohm's law in electricity) in the statement that a simple harmonic vibration is the only vibration that gives to the ear the sensation of a pure tone, and that the ear resolves any other complex vibration into its harmonic components and perceives them as a summation of pure tones. Thus the complicated movement of the ear drum under the sound waves from an orchestra is resolved into a whole series of separate tones for each of the various instruments producing the sound. Since few notes are really pure it is instructive to determine the constituent tones of a particular note thus demonstrating the harmonic series into which the note is resolved by the ear and also the mixture of the harmonics which gives the notes from each musical instrument their own peculiar quality (see plate 3).

115. Analysis by Resonators

The note given out by a jug or bottle when it is filled under the tap rises in frequency as the filling proceeds. This is because the air in the space above the liquid acts as a resonator and as the volume of air is diminished the resonant frequency rises. As has been mentioned previously, Helmholtz devised a series of resonators to determine the harmonics present in notes of the same frequency but of different quality. These resonators were designed so that their natural frequencies formed a harmonic series for the note to be analysed. By using each in turn it was possible to ascertain what harmonics were present and to make some estimate of their relative strengths.

116. Analysis by Graphical Methods

For every vibration there is an appropriate displacement curve, the ordinate representing the displacement of the medium at the point, or for the instant of time for which that ordinate is drawn. If such a graph is obtained it is possible, as will be shown later, to analyse the curve so as to obtain a series of curves representing a fundamental and a series of harmonics.

117. The Phonodeik

This instrument was designed by D. C. Miller[1] and is shown diagrammatically in Fig. 116. A horn H collects the sound waves and directs them on to a thin glass diaphragm D. One end of a thin wire is fixed to the centre of the diaphragm and after passing once round a small drum the other end is held in tension by a light spring. The spindle supporting the drum is jewel mounted and carries a small mirror M on to which light is directed from a pinhole I, the reflected beam being focused by means of the lens on to the moving film F. The sound waves falling on the diaphragm cause it to vibrate and these

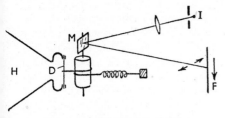

FIG. 116. Miller's Phonodeik.
H = horn ; D = diaphragm ; M = mirror ;
I = pinhole ; F = film.

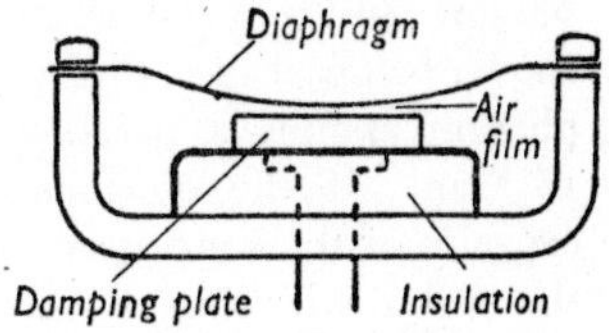

FIG. 117. Condenser microphone.

vibrations are transmitted to the drum by means of the spring loaded wire. As a result of the oscillatory motion of the drum the spot of light will move from side to side on the vertically moving film, the movements of spot and film combining to give the displacement curve. With this type of instrument a movement of the diaphragm of the order of 10^{-4} cm. will move the spot a distance of about 4 cm., the exact figure depending on the setting up of the apparatus. One of the defects of this arrangement is the distortion of the curve due to the resonant frequencies of the glass diaphragm and the air in the conical horn. Miller obtained a calibration curve for the instrument and used it to correct the displacement curve shown on the film.

Practically all the early methods of sound analysis and sound recording employed a diaphragm as a sensitive receiver. König's manometric capsules and Edison's phonograph used a diaphragm and consequently suffered from resonances in the diaphragm as well as other parts of the apparatus.

[1] D. C. Miller, *Science of Musical Sounds*, Macmillan, 1916.

118. Electrical Methods

For low frequency sounds, i.e. up to 1000 and 1500 vib./sec. the Einthoven string galvanometer (see sound ranging) or the Duddell galvanometer can be used to obtain an oscillograph, but both require an applied correction relating the natural frequency of the moving part and the impressed frequency. The Cathode Ray Oscilloscope, on the other hand, is equally sensitive to all frequencies from practically zero to the order of many megacycles, the inertia of a moving electron being negligible in comparison to that of the fine wire of a string galvanometer. The sound wave is collected in a piezo-electric receiver or a Wente condenser microphone, passed through a good distortionless amplifier, and then applied to the " Y " plates of a Cathode Ray Oscilloscope. When the time base is adjusted to the correct sweep frequency the picture appears to be stationary on the fluorescent screen and so can be photographed or studied at will.

The Wente condenser microphone is an electrostatic form of microphone in which a potential difference is applied between the diaphragm and a metal electrode embedded in the insulating material shown below it (see Fig. 117), the effect of which is to make the diaphragm assume a paraboloidal form leaving an air space of about 10^{-3} cm. If the distance between the plates is altered, then the capacity of the condenser will be altered and hence the P.D. between the plates will change. As the air gap increases and consequently the capacity diminishes, the P.D. will increase ($Q = V.C$), and so an oscillation of the diaphragm causes a ripple in the P.D. between the plates. At low frequencies the air film provides viscous damping, the air surging with the diaphragm, and at high frequencies it acts as a buffer since the motion of the diaphragm is too rapid for the air to follow. These two factors combine, however, to give uniform response over a very considerable range of frequencies, usually about 300 to 5000 vib./sec.

119. Analysis of the Graphs

The basis of this analysis is a very important theorem propounded by F. B. Fourier (1768-1830) in 1822.[1] This may be stated as follows : Any periodic vibration, however complicated, can be built up from a series of simple harmonic vibrations whose frequencies are in the ratio $1 : 2 : 3 : 4$, etc., and whose relative phases and amplitudes are suitably chosen. Thus, for example, if the displacement curve for a particular note is obtained, the harmonics required to give the resultant curve its particular shape can be found, using Fourier's theorem.

[1] *Théorie de la Chaleur (Paris, 1822).*

Consider the curves $y = A \sin \theta$, $y = \dfrac{A}{2} . \sin 2\theta$ plotted on the same graph. On adding the ordinates the resultant curve, the thick curve, is obtained. In the same way the graphs of $y = A . \sin \theta$

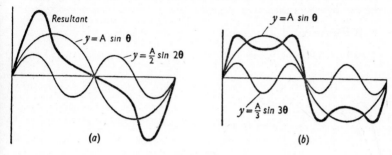

FIG. 118.

(a) Fundamental + 2nd harmonic. (b) Fundamental + 3rd harmonic.

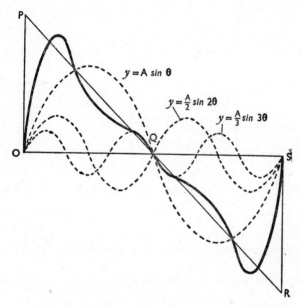

FIG. 119. Fourier components of a saw-tooth wave.

and $y = \dfrac{A}{3} . \sin 3\theta$ may be compounded to give the resultant curve.

Fig. 118 (a) is very similar to that obtained when the note from an open pipe is picked up by a microphone and after amplification applied to the " Y " plates of a C.R.O. and indicates that the second harmonic is quite strong.

From the figures above it may be noted that the presence of the second harmonic makes the two halves of the curve unsymmetrical, whereas the addition of the third harmonic to the fundamental makes the two halves of the curve symmetrical.

If the curves of $y = A \sin \theta$, $y = \dfrac{A}{2} \sin 2\theta$ and $y = \dfrac{A}{3} . \sin 3\theta$ are

plotted on the same graph and compounded, the resultant curve is as

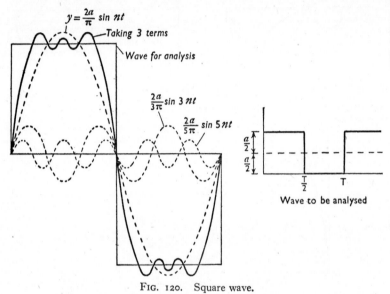

FIG. 120. Square wave.

shown in Fig. 119. If the whole series of curves $y = A . \sin \theta + \dfrac{A}{2}$, $\sin 2\theta + \dfrac{A}{3} . \sin 3\theta + \ldots$ to infinity, is plotted and compounded, the resultant graph is the curve $OPQRS$—the saw-tooth wave, which bears little resemblance to its individual components.

120. In its general form Fourier's theorem may be expressed as follows :

If $y = f(x)$ then

$$y = a_0 + a_1 \sin x + a_2 \sin 2x + a_3 \sin 3x + \ldots a_n \sin nx$$
$$+ b_1 \cos x + b_2 \cos 2x + b_3 \cos 3x + \ldots b_n \cos nx,$$

where a_1, a_2, etc., b_1, b_2, etc. are the amplitudes of the component simple harmonic vibrations. When these amplitude values are found, it may happen that all the sine or cosine terms disappear.

Thus for a square topped wave (Fig. 120), the equation becomes

$$y = f(nt) = \frac{a}{2} + \frac{2a}{\pi}\left[\sin nt + \frac{1}{3}\sin 3nt + \frac{1}{5}\sin 5nt + \ldots\right],$$

whereas for two straight lines meeting at $y = a$ at a time $t = \dfrac{T}{2}$ (see

Fig. 121), the equation becomes

$$y = f(nt) = \frac{a}{2} - \frac{4a}{\pi^2}\left[\cos nt + \frac{1}{3^2}\cos 3nt + \frac{1}{5^2}\cos 5nt + \ldots\right].$$

The calculation of the coefficients of a Fourier Series may be very laborious. Large and complicated machines have been devised to carry out the necessary integrations accurately and rapidly. These are

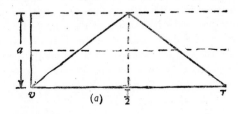

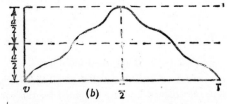

Fig. 121.   Two intersecting straight lines.

(a) Curve to be analysed.   (b) Addition of 3 terms.

used not only in sound but in astronomy, meteorology, vibration of machinery, electric, wireless and tidal waves. It is sufficient to say that the preceding simple treatment indicates how from a displacement diagram the harmonics present in a particular note can be calculated.

121. Wave Filters

The Bell Telephone Laboratories have developed a method of analysing the quality of sounds by means of filter circuits. The sound waves are picked up by a microphone and the alternating voltages produced are passed to a suitable amplifier. By means of specially designed circuits the currents corresponding to any desired sound frequency can be retained or rejected. The frequency of the alternating voltage from the microphone is the same as that of the sound waves falling on it, and thus, by cutting out or rejecting various harmonics, only the fundamental is converted back into sound by the loudspeaker.

The fundamental, or any one or group of overtones, can be eliminated by the use of filters of the correct type, and the relative strength and importance of the harmonics can be estimated from the output of the loudspeaker.

In this way it has been shown that notes of different qualities such as the piano, cello and French horn have the same almost indistinguishable fundamental, and that the higher harmonics are more important in the piano and cello than in the French horn. It has also been demonstrated that when the fundamental and some of the overtones are cut out the ear still distinguishes the pitch of the note as that of the missing fundamental. This is sometimes used to avoid the cost and bulk of the massive organ pipes required to sound very low notes. Smaller pipes sounding the appropriate overtones are provided instead, the ear supplies the impression of the missing fundamental.

In connection with their experiments the Bell Telephone Company have produced two sets of records which are identical except that in one all the frequencies below a certain limit have been filtered away.

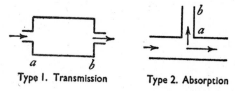

Type I. Transmission   Type 2. Absorption

Fig. 122.   Simple mechanical filters.

The two records sound very similar although all the fundamental notes are missing from one record and are supplied by the ear. The small horns of now out of date gramophones and wireless sets acted as " high pass " filters and cut out practically all the low frequencies, these had to be provided by the ear, and it has been shown that some fairly modern wireless sets pass practically no frequencies below 250 vib./sec., and yet, to the average listener, the reproduction is quite satisfactory.

Mechanical filters have also been made to give the same results as electrical filters but these are more bulky and not made so easily. A Helmholtz resonator with a small ear opening transmits a sound of one frequency only. This resonator need not be of the usual turnip shape but can be cylindrical in form, as shown in type I of Fig. 122, and transmits the resonant frequency of the column *ab*.

Type 2 is a Quincke filter and absorbs the resonant frequency of the column *ab*. Every electrical filter has its mechanical counterpart although some of these are not practicable.   G. W. Stewart[1] developed mechanical or sound filters and the interested student is referred to his papers as the work is beyond the scope of this book.

[1] *Phys. Rev.*, 1922, **20**, 528 ; 1925, **25**, 90.

RECORDING ON WAX

122. In 1859 Leon Scott made what was probably the first instrument for the recording of sound. He patented the instrument as the Phonautograph and it was later improved by König. Scott's intention was to make an instrument which would record the vibrations of the air responsible for sound so that he could calculate their frequency. A large parabolic horn, the narrow end being closed by a membrane, was used to collect the sound. One end of a lever bent at right angles rested on the membrane and the other end carried a pencil which drew a trace on a drum rotated by hand.

Edison replaced the lever with a stylus attached to the membrane which cut a furrow of varying depth in the material of the cylinder or drum, i.e. the recording was " hill and dale ". As the cylinder rotated it also moved parallel to its axis so that a wavy helical groove was cut in its surface. In his early efforts the record was cut in tin-foil and for reproduction the stylus was placed at the beginning of the groove and made to retrace its path as the cylinder was rotated. Bell varied this by recording on a wax cylinder which was cut by a sharp stylus carried by a stiff membrane. For reproduction he used a blunt stylus attached to a limp membrane.

It was not until 1878, however, that Edison produced the phonograph, the first practical talking machine, which he demonstrated to the Royal Society for Arts in May 1878. With this instrument rubber tubes were used to conduct the vibrations of the air to the two ears of each listener. A big improvement in the quality of reproduction was brought about by the introduction of lateral or " side to side " recording by Berliner in 1887. The disc on which the record was made consisted of metal with a smooth covering of wax, the movement of the stylus removing some of the wax and exposing the metal. Acid was then used to " bite " the trace into the metal. The reproducing apparatus was hand driven and the sound came out of a small horn.

Berliner improved his apparatus and in 1898 he introduced a new and improved model. This was clockwork driven and the horn ended in a flare. This instrument was immortalised by Francis Barraud in his famous and familiar picture which suggested the name " His Master's Voice " to the Gramophone Company and gave the name " Dog Model " to that type of gramophone.

For many years the quality of recording and reproduction steadily improved, mainly due to improvement in the quality of the material used rather than technical advances. A vibrating diaphragm with its unwanted resonances was used for recording and reproduction, and it was not until 1924 that a very important advance was made with the introduction of electrical recording. This used the power from thermionic valves to drive the cutting tool instead of that from the sound collected by a horn. Up to this time loud sounds had been essential for recordings but now even very feeble sounds could be recorded since the power driving the cutting tool could be varied at will.

123. The actual processes of recording and preparing copies of the original is as follows :

1. The cutting style is arranged to vibrate, under the action of the amplified current from the microphone, along a radius of the disc, thus cutting a wavy spiral in the smooth surface of the soft wax disc. If this recording is played back, it is damaged and cannot be used to make copies, and so several records are made simultaneously so that the success of the recording can be tested forthwith.

2. The surface of the disc is coated with graphite or some similar conducting material and then by means of electrolysis, using a copper voltameter, its surface is coated with a thin layer of copper. This copper master shell, which is a negative or " male " disc, is stripped from the wax.

3. The master shell is also treated so that when it is copper plated the deposition can be stripped off giving a " female " or positive disc, identical with the original wax disc except that it is made of copper.

4. If the master shell were used to make copies, it would wear rapidly and so the female or positive disc is in turn electroplated giving another negative which, after nickel plating, mounting on a heavy copper disc, and having the central hole drilled, is ready for fixing in a press. When pressed on to suitable material this negative will give a positive, i.e. one in which the wavy spiral is identical with that on the wax disc.

5. In order to make a copy, a quantity of recording material (shellac, copal resin, carbon black and slate powder) is placed on a hot press and softened to the required plasticity. The upper and lower faces of the press, which can be heated and cooled, carry the negatives for making the two sides of the record. The press is closed, pressure applied and the dies are steam heated. After a suitable interval of time water is passed through the dies and the disc is cooled, removed from the press, polished and tested.

The grooves on the disc are 0·006 in. wide at the top, the needle point is between 0·002 in. and 0·003 in. across, and the distance between the grooves is approximately 0·004 in. For the same intensity of sound at different pitches the amplitudes must be inversely proportional to the square of the frequency, i.e. the swing of the needle is doubled every time the note drops an octave. If this is carried out indefinitely, then either the groove spacing, and consequently the size of the disc, must be considerably increased or else one groove will cut into the next.

As a compromise it is arranged that for frequencies above 250 vib./sec. the needle moves with constant velocity and that below 250 vib./sec. the recording is made to follow a constant amplitude characteristic, which means that the same amplitude holds for a given acoustic power at all frequencies below 250 vib./sec. This is equivalent to a drop of 6 decibels per octave (since an octave is a frequency ratio of 2 : 1) and hence to obtain an overall level response from a record the pick-up used for reproduction, or of course the amplifier used with it, should give a

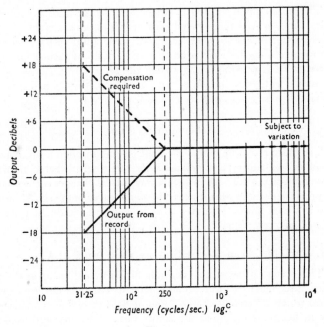

FIG. 123.

compensation to all frequencies below 250 of 6 decibels per octave (see Fig. 123).

124. Long Playing Records

The chief disadvantages of disc recordings are the short time of playing and the considerable space required for storing. In order to try and find an answer to magnetic recording on tape or wire, which combines long time of playing with ease of storing and also has the additional point in its favour that the same material can be re-used indefinitely for recording, the Columbia Recording Co. have developed a record made of high grade plastic (unfilled vinyl) which will play for up to 25 minutes.

The following data compare the two types of recordings :

	Long playing	Ordinary recording
Number of grooves per in. . .	224-260	96-100
Rotation speed . . .	$33\frac{1}{3}$ r.p.m.	78 r.p.m. (approx.)
Special stylus (tip diam.) needle .	0·001 in.	0·002-0·003 in.

The minimum recording diameter is little changed, being about $4\frac{3}{4}$ in., but a special type crystal pick-up with a head weight of 6 gm. is needed for satisfactory reproduction. The absolute level recorded is from 4 to 6 decibels down on that of an ordinary record, but good reproduction is possible up to 12,000 vib./sec. Great care, however, is essential in the production of the records and it is claimed that each individual pressing is carefully checked.

RECORDING ON FILM

The basic principle is that the light passing through a slit, valve or any other mechanism, and falling on the film to give what is known as the sound track, shall vary in such a way that its changes correspond to the pressure changes constituting the sound waves in the air. The two ways in which this is done give what is known as variable density and variable area recording.

125. Variable Area Recording as used by R.C.A.

This system of recording depends for its operation upon the amplified speech signals from a microphone actuating an electromagnetic device which effectively causes a line of light of constant intensity to vary in length according as the signals vary. The line is focused and so imparts on the moving film a trace which varies in length across the film with the varying sound impulses. A schematic arrangement is shown in Fig. 124. The exposures lamp which consumes power at the rate of about 20 watts provides a point source of light, and is run off high frequency A.C. of about 30 to 120 kc./sec. or from accumulators, since a frequency within the audio range would produce recordings of this frequency throughout the length of the film. Some of the light from this lamp is collected by a condenser lens, and passed through an aperture plate and a pair of shutter vanes. These vanes are automatically operated so as to cut off the light when no signal is being received and so reduce the recording of extraneous noise. The light from the M shaped aperture is focused on the small mirror of a galvanometer, which is so constructed that the mirror swings up and down under the action of the amplified speech currents from the microphone and hence the M shaped patch of light is also swung in the same direction. A condenser focuses the swinging light on to a narrow slit and the light which passes through the slit consists of two lines which vary in length from the mean half track AA' to a minimum BB' and a maximum CC'. An ultra-violet filter placed near to this slit allows only light towards the violet end of the spectrum to fall on

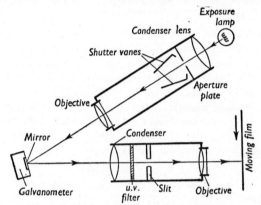

Schematic arrangement of system

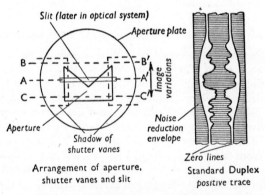

Arrangement of aperture, shutter vanes and slit

Standard Duplex positive trace

FIG. 124.   Variable area recording (R.C.A.).

the film. Experiments have shown that this light produces the least internal reflection in the film emulsion and so the outline is more sharply defined than if white light is used. The objective lens now produces a diminished image of the strip of light on the film. As the sound waves cause fluctuating movements of the galvanometer mirror the area exposed on the moving film also varies and when developed gives a negative track. The positive track is produced in the same way that a photographic print is made from a negative.

A pure tone produces a sine wave from the microphone and so the sound track recording of this will also be sinusoidal. The film is arranged to move at the standard rate of 90 ft. a minute and so for a note of 260 vib./sec. one complete oscillation will occupy rather less than $\frac{7}{100}$ of an in. on the film.

126. Variable Density Recording (as used by Western Electric Film Corporation)

The variable area method of recording separates the sound track into irregularly shaped areas and in the type of recording shown in the diagram three areas are opaque and two clear, whereas the variable density method achieves the same result by varying the instantaneous density of the sound track across its whole width.

In the Western Electric system the light intensity and the width of the film exposed is constant, the variable factor is the length of the exposed area along the film which varies the resulting density of negative and positive from instant to instant.

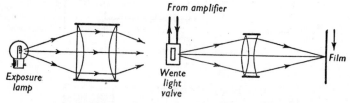

From amplifier

Exposure lamp

Wente light valve

Film

FIG. 125. Variable density recording (Western Electric).

The light from the exposure lamp is focused by means of a condenser system on to a light valve (see Fig. 125). This consists of a metallic ribbon, normally duralumin, 0·006 in. wide and 0·0005 in. thick formed into a loop and stretched in a plane at right angles to a magnetic field. The length and tension of the ribbon are adjusted so that its natural frequency of vibration (9,500 cycles) is well beyond the limit of the frequencies to be recorded. The loop or slit in the ribbon is 0·001 in. wide and about $\frac{1}{4}$ in. long and this is the part which actually lies between the pole pieces of the magnet. When a current flows round the loop the slit opens or closes depending on the direction of flow of the current (Fleming's Left Hand or the motor rule) and a half size image of the slit is formed on the moving film by the objective lens. When the slit is a maximum the image will be twice as wide as when the slit is its mean value, and as the film runs at a uniform rate it will take twice as long to pass the exposure area as during the mean position with a corresponding increase in density of the film when developed. The variation in density is also produced by the overlapping of exposed areas and so the striations across the sound track vary in length and density (see plate 4).

127. Modulated Tube Method of Variable Density Recording

In this method of recording the image of the slit is of constant area but the intensity of illumination of that image, and therefore the density of the negative, is controlled by the sound wave. The sounds to be recorded are picked up by microphones and amplified in the usual way. The output of the last stage of amplification is passed through a gas discharge lamp of special design which modifies the intensity of the light emitted. When the voltage across the tube is increased the brightness of the light is increased and vice versa. This modulated glow is projected, by a suitable optical system, through a narrow slit so as to form a thin line of light on the moving film. As the film is continuously moving, the resulting sound track is a series of striations but differs from the previous method of recording in that the rectangles of different density which overlap all have the same area.

Although many systems do not use the modulated tube method, probably because the earlier tubes were not very reliable, the principle of the method is excellent since the discharge tube is free from inertia and resonances which are unavoidable in light valves. Using this method frequencies up to 15,000 vib./sec. are readily recorded.

For a more detailed account of these and other methods of recording, such as class A and B push pull, the student is referred to more specialised works on the subject such as " Sound and the Documentary Film ", by Cameron.

128. Reproduction of Sound from Films

The photo-electric effect was discovered by Hertz in 1887 whilst investigating Hertzian waves. In 1888 the German chemist Hallwachs described fully Hertz's and other experiments and it became known subsequently as the Hallwachs' effect. Since the photo-electric cell is essential for the reproduction of sound from film some brief mention of it must be made here but the student is referred to standard textbooks on the subject of the photo-electric effect.[1]

There are three principal types of photo-electric or light sensitive cells.

1. The alkali metal cell. All writers are in agreement in calling this a photo-electric cell since there is an electron emission across a vacuum or gaseous space when light falls on a suitable cathode.

2. The selenium cell. This is typical of a group of cells which exhibit similar characteristics, viz. the cell is a semi-conductor of electricity and the resistance of the cell varies when exposed to light. Cells of this group are sometimes classified as photo-conductive or conductivity cells.

---

[1] Walker and Lance, *Photo Electric Cell Applications ;* Tolansky, *Introduction to Atomic Physics ;* Crowther, *Ions, Electrons, Ionising Radiations,* etc.

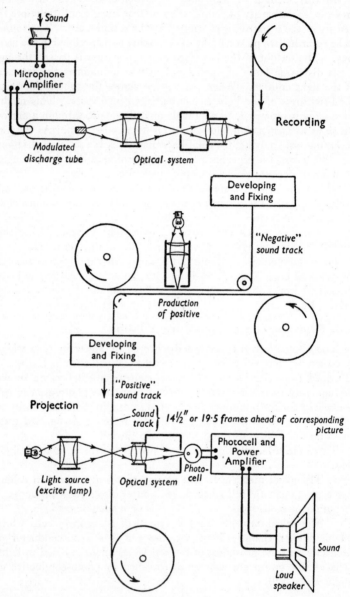

FIG. 126.   Schematic diagram of recording and projection of sound.

3. The rectifier cell.   This is known in America as the barrier layer cell and the Sperrschicht cell in Germany and in its simplest form is the same as the metal rectifier used for charging accumulators, etc.   If an alternating potential is applied across the combination of a plate of copper in close contact with a thin layer of cuprous oxide, electrons pass more readily from copper to copper oxide than in the reverse direction, which gives the familiar rectifying action.   When such a combination is exposed to light without an applied potential, then a current will flow from the copper oxide to the copper.   In this type of cell the electronic action takes place at the boundary and the mode of preparing this boundary determines whether the pair exhibit photo-sensitivity or not.

The alkali metal cell is used for sound reproduction from films and so this type only will receive further treatment.   It was found that seven elements give a considerable photo-electric emission when acted on by visible radiation.   These are Lithium, Sodium, Potassium, Rubidium, Caesium, Stron-
tium and Barium and each of
these shows a maximum re-
sponse at some point in the
visible spectrum.   X-rays or
Gamma rays on the other
hand, always produce photo-
emission from a metal.   The
earliest cells therefore had a

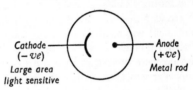

FIG. 127.   Schematic cross-section of photo-electric cell.

light sensitive cathode of one of these seven metals, but later develop-ments showed that a more satisfactory cell was produced by using a cathode coated with one of these metals on a prepared base such as oxidised copper or silver.   The cell itself is of simple structure consisting of a light-sensitive cathode of large area for collecting a considerable quantity of light and maintained at a suitable negative potential, and another metal electrode, the anode, maintained at a positive potential.   The anode may take the form of a ring of wire or gauze, grid, or a straight metal rod.   These two electrodes are enclosed in a glass envelope which may be evacuated or filled with an inert gas.   Within the limits laid down for a particular cell the current emitted is proportional to the light energy falling on the cathode.

The light from a suitable source, an exciter lamp, passing through a slit is modulated by the passage of the film between it and an optical system which focuses the light on to a photo-electric cell.   As the light varies so does the photo-emission and so an alternating current passes through the cell.   This is similar to the current given out by the microphone when the sound was recorded and so after the usual amplification the sound from the loudspeaker is similar to that which fed the recording microphone.

The moving picture passes through the gate in a series of jerks, the persistence of vision producing the sensation of a steady change, while obviously the sound track must move at a uniform speed. To do this the sound track is not registered opposite the corresponding picture but is 14·5 in. or 19·5 pictures ahead and a loop of film is formed between the picture and sound gates during projection. This means that although the motion of one is uniform and the other intermittent the average speed is the same and this loop of film compensates roughly for the time required for the sound to travel from loudspeakers behind the screen to seats in the centre of the average cinema. In all other positions the sound is slightly out of synchronisation but the amount is usually so small as to be unnoticeable.

129. Recording on Wire or Tape

In 1898 the Danish scientist Poulsen, whilst experimenting with the findings of Faraday, discovered that he could magnetise a track on a circular disc of steel and later play back the recording. This experiment was all the more remarkable in view of the fact that Poulsen had no thermionic valve amplifier. He took out patents for his idea, which were deposited with the London Patents Office. Little notice however was taken of his experiments, probably because his work was overshadowed by that of Edison and Berliner and their introduction of the phonograph and gramophone. Stille however developed Poulsen's idea and later another German named Blattner bought one of Stille's machines which he popularised as the Blattnerphone.

Improved forms of this instrument using a narrow steel tape for recording were manufactured in England by the Marconi Company and were known as Marconi-Stille recorders. Later models used a plastic instead of a steel tape with one side coated with iron oxide. Engineers in the U.S.A. favoured wire instead of tape for recording and their researches were equally successful.

The basic principles of both instruments are the same. When a wire (or a tape) is moved across the pole of a magnet, then magnetism is induced in the wire. If by some means the strength of the magnet is varied while the wire moves across the pole, then the magnetism along the length of the wire will also vary.

Suppose sound waves are collected by a microphone, turned into electric oscillations, amplified and fed to a small electromagnet, then the strength of the magnet will vary with the sounds falling on the microphone. Thus the magnetism induced in the wire moving across a pole will vary in like manner. If, after magnetising the wire, the magnet is removed, and the variably magnetised wire is passed through a coil of wire connected to an amplifier and loudspeaker then, due to the changing flux through the coil, corresponding back E.M.F.s will be set up, which when amplified will set the cone of the loudspeaker into vibration, with the consequent sensation of sound.   If the speed of movement of the wire is the same in each case, then the speaker

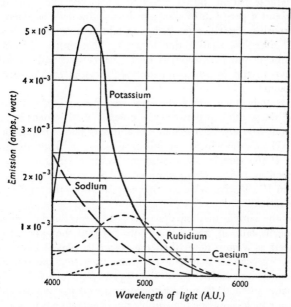

FIG. 128.   Average emissions for alkali metals (thick films).

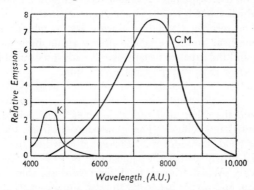

FIG. 129.   Relative emission of Caesium on Silver oxide (thin film) C.M. and potassium K (thick film) cathodes.

will give out sounds identical with those originally collected by the microphone.

In its simplest form, the apparatus consists of a steel wire 0·0004 in. in diameter which passes across a small gap in the pole pieces of a small electromagnet.   This simple mechanism is termed the sound head and the only other requirement is that the magnetism in the core of the magnet shall follow faithfully variations in the current feeding it. Soft iron is therefore useless since it retains some magnetism for a considerable period, but it was found that the alloy produced by adding about 3 per cent. of silicon to iron and known as stalloy, has a greater specific resistance (so reducing eddy currents), less hysteresis loss and gives less trouble due to ageing than iron. This material (like mumetal and permalloy) is easily magnetised and quickly loses its magnetism and so provides a suitable material for the core of the electromagnet.

The trough down which the steel wire passes is about 0·0006 in. wide and deep, the gap between the poles is about 0·0001 in. and the A.C. output from the microphone-fed amplifier passes round the winding W. Hence the wire is variably magnetised as it moves along the groove. If the wire is now moved in the same direction, and at the same speed as before, along the groove, then the back E.M.F.s developed in W will give (after suitable amplification) the same sounds as used for recording.

With the simple method described, the reproduction obtained is by no means faithful, and a pure note fed into the apparatus is not reproduced as a pure note when the record is played back. It was found by experiment that if at the same time that the sounds were being recorded an oscillation of about 30 kc./sec. was fed to the wire by the same method, then the recording was greatly improved. This oscillation which is outside the audible range and is known as a " bias " can also be used to wipe out unwanted recordings in a manner similar to that in which a watch repairer demagnetises a watch, using an A.C. magnet. The recording and reproducing heads, which may be one and the same head, must be small, otherwise an unpleasant hum is introduced, and the gaps are usually closed with some suitable material such as solder so as to stop pole-piece vibration.

Fig. 130 (*b*) shows details of the Webster head (U.S.A.) which consists of two coils wound on the same core, one for recording or play back and the other used to provide bias oscillations and also to erase unwanted recordings. The dimensions indicate the smallness required for good reproduction. The speed at which the wire moves is immaterial provided that the same value is used for recording and playing back.[1] When wire is used for recording, some mechanism such as a cam and rocker is needed to raise and lower the head as the wire comes off the drum. This is not needed when tape is used since the tape unwinds in the same way that a film comes off a spool. With tape-recording the apparatus is arranged so that the gap in the pole-pieces is at right angles to the length of the tape.

[1] For high fidelity recording the tape speed is 30 ins./sec.

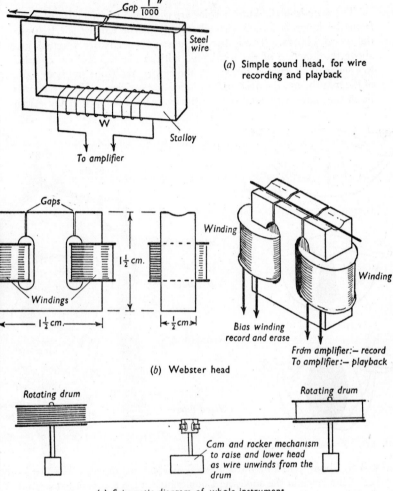

(a) Simple sound head, for wire recording and playback

(b) Webster head

(c) Schematic diagram of whole instrument

FIG. 130. Recording on wire.

Advantages of this method of recording are :

1. The recording is ready for immediate playing.
2. The same tape or wire can be used many times.
3. It is little affected by mechanical vibration and shock.
4. The reproduction is free from needle scratch.
5. Continued playing has little effect on the volume obtained from the record, e.g. after 200,000 playings the drop in volume was less than 5 phons.[1]

[1] *Electronics*, Sept. 1938.

130. The Human Voice

The sounds of the human voice are produced when a current of air from the lungs is forced through the glottis or narrow slit between the vocal chords. These two membranous reeds are situated just above the junction of the wind pipe with the larynx and are coupled to a series of air cavities formed by the larynx, the front and back parts of the mouth, and the nose and its associated cavities. The two chords lie in the same horizontal plane, run from front to back of the throat

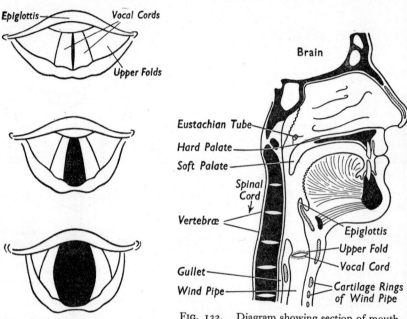

FIG. 131.   Action of vocal chords.

FIG. 132.   Diagram showing section of mouth, throat, etc., position of glottis, vocal chords, etc.

and are about $\frac{3}{4}$ in. long in men and $\frac{1}{2}$ in. long in women. The breaking of the voice in the adolescent boy is due to the comparatively rapid doubling of the length of the chords. The opening between the vocal chords or glottis is about half its maximum size during respiration and widens and narrows rythmically with each breath. In order to produce a sound the free edges of the chords are brought close together to form a parallel sided slit, the width and tension of which is controlled by muscles. The amplitude of vibration of the chords, and therefore the intensity of the sound given out, depends upon the pressure of the exhaled air current but the precise action of setting up resonant vibrations in the upper cavities is not fully understood. The average speaking voice of the male has a frequency of 145 vib./sec. and a range of about 12 tones, that of the female is about 230 vib./sec. and has approximately the same range.   The range of the singing voice varies considerably from 66 vibrations for a basso profundo to the highest soprano note of 1056 vib./sec., or four octaves above.

Helmholtz, and many other writers, regarded the chords as reeds or stretched strings, vibrating transversely with a frequency depending on the tension, thickness and length of the chord ; this vibration being passed directly to the cavities above.   This theory is supported by the fact that the vocal chords of men are one and a half times as long as those of women.   More recent writers have suggested that the function of the chords is to induce vortex formations into the air stream, but agree that the tension of the chords also plays an important part and that the action is not completely analogous with Aeolian tones.   Further support for the Helmholtz theory is provided by the fact that two thin pieces of rubber stretched across a tube can be used to imitate the vocal chords, the pitch of the note emitted depending on the tension and length of the strip and the air pressure used to set up vibrations.

When the vocal chords are set into vibration, then articulate speech is produced in the mouth and pharynx.   Whispered speech is produced without the assistance of the vocal chords and the air is breathed through the resonant cavities of the mouth and pharynx.   Speech sounds may be divided into two distinct types, vowels and consonants. When different vowel sounds are produced at the same frequency, so that the vocal chords are under the same conditions, the different sounds are produced by altering the size of the two resonant cavities in the mouth, which are created by the position of the tongue, and the shape of the lips.   (The shape of the cavity is relatively unimportant.) The cavities of mouth and pharynx act like connected resonators of differing resonant frequencies and the remaining cavities alter the quality, without affecting the enunciation, of the vowel.

This was demonstrated by Sir Richard Paget [1] who made plasticine models of the different shapes taken up by the resonant cavities and reproduced most strikingly the various vowel sounds.   Consonants such as t, p, k, s are generated by interrupting the air flow and do not come from the action of the vocal chords.   These are termed unvoiced sounds.

131. The Ear

The ear is the most marvellous instrument for the detection and analysis of sound.   For convenience of description it is usual to divide it into three parts.

1. The outer ear.   This includes the pinna or the visible external part.   In animals this is often movable and as well as enabling the

[1] *Human Speech*, Kegan Paul, 1930 ; Alex Wood, *Physics of Music*, p. 75.

animal to decide the direction from which the sound comes, also collects sound waves. In man the pinna serves no useful purpose unless the ears are very protuberant. From the pinna a passage known as the " auditory meatus " leads to the tympanum or ear drum. This drumskin closes the inner end of the passage and when sound waves vary the pressure in the meatus the drumskin vibrates with the same frequency.

2. The middle ear. The drumskin separates the outer ear from the middle ear. To this membrane is attached a chain of three little bones or ossicles. Because of their shape these are known as the hammer (malleus) anvil (incus) and stirrup (stapes). The hammer is attached to the tympanum and the stirrup is attached, at the oval window, to another membrane which separates the middle from the inner ear. Thus through the lever mechanism of these bones sound vibrations from outside are transmitted to the inner ear through the oval window. The movement of the bones is such that the movement of the oval membrane is reduced, but the force on it is increased fifty or sixty times, compared with that of the ear drum. The only outlet from the middle ear is by way of the Eustachian tube which leads to the back of the throat. This is normally closed but opens during the action of swallowing and serves a double purpose, that of drainage tube and also of pressure equaliser. If the pressure on the outer ear suddenly changes, as when a train enters a tunnel, the difference in pressure on the two sides of the drum prevents it from vibrating. The act of swallowing equalises the pressures and removes the temporary deafness. Gunners open their mouths at the instant of firing so as to prevent a large difference in pressure between the two sides of the ear drum which may burst the drum, and earache results when the valve in the Eustachian tube ceases to open and causes a considerable pressure on the ossicles which is passed to the oval window.

3. The inner ear is the true seat of the sense of hearing, and sound can still be heard without the assistance of the mechanism previously described. The vibrations must reach the oval window, either by conduction through the skull itself or by means of a conductor such as hard cotton wool leading from the outside to the oval window. The inner ear consists mainly of the semi-circular canals, which are associated with the sense of balance and play no part in hearing, and the cochlea which is the principal part of the organ of hearing. As its name implies it is shaped like a snail shell. It is filled with a liquid, has rigid bony walls, and is a spiral of two and a half turns. Stretched across the middle and coiling down its entire length is the basilar membrane to which are attached nerves connected to the brain. This membrane is about 3 cm. long, 0·16 mm. wide at one end and 0·52 mm. wide at the other and tapers in the reverse direction to the cochlea, being narrowest near the oval window and widest at the apex. It is

made up of a large number of fibres, of varying length and tension, which stretch across its width and in some respects is similar in construction to a harp.   When the stapes pushes in the oval window the vibrations are passed through the incompressible liquid and cross the membranes.   The pressure is relieved by the bulging of another membrane-covered aperture, the round window, whose movements are opposite to those of the oval window.   The vibrations of the fibres in the basilar membrane stimulate the nerves connected to the brain.

132. The Resonance Theory of Hearing

This seems to have been first suggested by Cotugno (1736-1822), Charles Bell (1774-1842), and later developed in greater detail by Helmholtz.[1] On this theory the transverse fibres of the basilar membrane act like fairly heavily damped resonators.   Only those fibres which have the same frequency as the incoming wave are set in vibration by resonance and these send a nerve current to the brain.   Any theory of hearing must explain the fact that the ear responds to pure tones over a range of ten or eleven octaves and that pitch discrimination is most acute over the middle of the range of audibility.   It must also account for the fact that beats are heard when two notes of nearly the same frequency are sounded simultaneously and that beats are not heard when the difference in frequency is too large.   There are many other points which it must explain, by no means the least of which is Ohm's law, which states that when the ear receives a note it analyses it into its harmonic constituents which are separately perceived.   One thing is hardly in doubt, although the resonance theory is by no means universally accepted, sensitiveness to pitch is distributed along the basilar membrane, sensitiveness to high notes being located where the fibres are short—near the oval window, and sensitiveness to low pitch being located where the fibres are long.

Support for this theory is provided by direct experiment and everyday observation.   Localised damage to the cochlea of a guinea pig can be produced by means of a very fine drill, and the animal is afterwards found to suffer only from deafness to notes of a particular pitch. Workmen who are subjected to loud and continuous noises also suffer from selective deafness, e.g. boilermakers' deafness, which is accounted for on the resonance theory by assuming localised damage to the basilar membrane.

The telephonic theory states that hearing does not take place by resonance at all and that the basilar membrane vibrates as a whole. On the resonance theory the sensation of pitch is produced by a particular nerve sending a current to the brain whereas the telephonic theory maintains that the sensation of pitch is determined by the brain

[1] Alex Wood, *Physics of Music*, p. 87.

because the nerve currents have the same frequency as the sound. On this theory the whole of the analysis takes place in the auditory centre of the brain and it would appear that the cochlea is unnecessarily complicated for such a purpose.

The resonance theory of hearing gives a picturesque representation of the process of hearing and seems to hold most promise, but so far no completely satisfactory theory has been propounded.

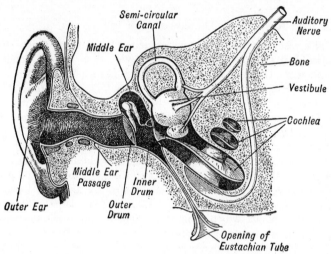

FIG. 133. Sectional diagram of the ear.

133. The Gramophone Sound-box and Pick-ups

If the apparatus used to reproduce sound from a gramophone is a mechanical type, it is known as a sound box (see Fig. 134). This type of instrument, however, is rapidly becoming out-of-date. It consists of a thin diaphragm D mounted between rubber gaskets G and connected by means of a lever S to a pivot P. As the needle performs its side to side vibrations in the record groove the movements are communicated to the diaphragm, which is made to move backwards and forwards, thus producing compressions and rarefactions in the air similar to the original sound waves. In order to damp the natural resonances of the diaphragm the lever or stylus is often fixed to it by a number of feet known as a spider.

Modern pick-ups belong to one of four types (a) moving iron, (b) moving coil, (c) electrostatic, (d) piezo-electric. These are essentially devices for converting the mechanical vibrations of the needle into corresponding oscillatory electrical voltages which after suitable amplification are reproduced by the loudspeaker as sound. In the moving iron pick-up a light soft iron armature A is pivoted at B and lies in the small gap between the poles P of a permanent magnet around the yoke of which is a winding W of fine wire which is connected to the terminals C and D. The lateral vibrations of the needle N causes A to move, thus producing corresponding variations in the magnetic flux which in turn gives rise to corresponding back E.M.F.s in the windings W which are passed to a suitable amplifier. The average pick-up has an output of about o·5 to 1·5 volts R.M.S.

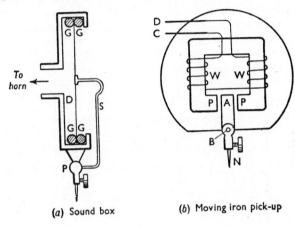

(a) Sound box   (b) Moving iron pick-up

FIG. 134.

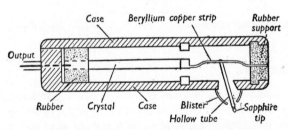

FIG. 135.   Modern lightweight crystal pick-up.

In moving coil pick-ups the needle is attached to a small coil of wire pivoted between the poles of a permanent magnet. The ends of the coil are connected to the pick-up terminals.

134. In a modern lightweight pick-up the crystal consists of two slabs of Rochelle salt. One electrode is between them and the other is in contact with the outer surfaces. The twisting action of the needle as it moves in the grooves of the record sets up a potential difference across the faces of the crystal. This potential difference is proportional to the amplitude of movement of the needle and not the velocity. A

feature of this type of pick-up is the high output and fidelity of reproduction. The output is of the order

1·0 to 0·7 volts at 1000 cycles/sec.

3·2 to 2·5 volts at 250 cycles/sec.

The waveform distortion of this type of pick-up, as shown on the
Cathode Ray Oscilloscope, is less than 2 per cent. This is less than
the value set by manufacturers for high fidelity apparatus.

The high output at low frequencies and falling off at high frequencies
is very useful since it removes the necessity for the bass compensation
which is required with moving iron and moving coil pick-ups, where
the output depends on the velocity with which the needle moves.

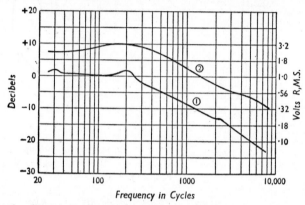

FIG. 136. Crystal characteristics : (1) High fidelity crystal pick-up ; (2)
General purpose crystal pick-up.

135. The Horn

The sound box on a gramophone acts like a transformer which
converts the swing of the needle point into changes of air pressure in
the throat of a horn. A similar action is performed by the diaphragm
driven by the coil in the moving coil loudspeaker fitted to a horn.
Only a small fraction of the energy of the diaphragm, however, actually
appears as pressure variations of the air, or sound. The sound waves
produced in the throat of the horn expand as they move along the
horn until they are large enough to transfer their energy into space
without undue disturbance of the air. The theory of the action of
the horn was only developed between 1919 and 1925 when it was
shown that its function was to increase the resistance against which the
diaphragm works, and transform waves of high particle velocity distributed over a small area (the throat) into waves of low particle velocity
and spread over a large area (the open end). The factors involved in

the design of a horn are (1) the throat area, (2) the mouth area, (3) the taper.

If the throat is too small the frictional resistance to air motion is high and also the length of the horn becomes excessive if the mouth is to be the right size. The usual area of the throat is about 1 sq. in. It can be shown that the horn cuts down all wavelengths which are greater than one quarter of the circumference of the open end and if it is assumed that the lowest frequency to be transmitted is 25 cycles/sec. the diameter of the open end must be about 13 ft. If the cut-off frequency is 70 cycles/sec. then the horn must be 4 ft. in diameter and about 15 ft. long. The earlier horns were conical in shape but it was found that the " exponential horn ", in which the area of cross-

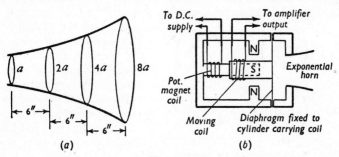

FIG. 137.

Exponential horn with rate of expansion of 6 in., i.e. area of cross section doubles itself for each increment of 6 in. measured along the axis of the horn. Moving coil drive attached to horn.

section doubles itself at constant intervals measured along the axis, is more efficient (see Fig. 137).

Theory shows that to radiate effectively a wavelength of 10 ft. the area of cross section of the horn must double itself about every 6 in., and hence the size of the mouth is determined by the lowest frequency to be handled. The highest frequency to be radiated is determined by the mass of the moving diaphragm. An effective horn must therefore be large and so that it does not take up too much room it is often folded or bent, a process which affects little the quality of the sound produced. The horn tends to concentrate the sound along its axis, a tendency which increases with frequency, and so horns for public address purposes are fitted with deflector vanes so as to spread evenly the energy for all frequencies.

136. Cone Diaphragm Loudspeakers

In moving iron and moving coil loudspeakers, the diaphragm is fairly large so that it acts directly on a considerable volume of air. A large piece of plane wood or a baffle is necessary to separate the air in

14

front of the diaphragm from that behind, since when the cone compresses the air in front it rarefies that behind, and unless precautions are taken these two neutralize instead of propagating sound waves. At low frequencies the time between compressions is greatest and so this effect is likely to be pronounced unless a large baffle is used. This effect may be demonstrated using a tuning fork and a piece of cardboard as shown in Fig. 138. When the cardboard is placed so as to stop the circulatory currents the loudness of the note is much increased.

The diaphragm of a loudspeaker is usually made of paper, linen, balsa wood, or aluminium alloy, the last named being the most efficient.[1] The driving system may be either the moving iron or moving coil type, but as the former are comparatively insensitive, give poor reproduction at low frequencies, and are practically out of date, only the latter type will be considered. The moving coil instrument is more sensitive, has a more constant impedance over the audio frequency range and in essential details resembles the moving coil microphone.

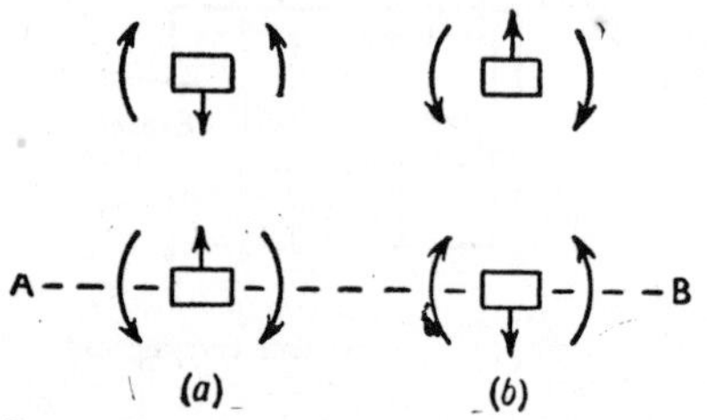

FIG. 138. Circulatory air currents round prongs of a vibrating tuning fork. Insertion of card along *AB* stops circulation and increases the loudness of the note.

The moving coil, from which the instrument gets its name, is wound on a light cylindrical tube or former of cardboard or other insulating material, and suspended so that it can travel backwards and forwards, in the direction of its axis, through a distance of about $\frac{1}{4}$ to $\frac{1}{2}$ in., but cannot move in any other direction. The coil lies in the radial field of a pot magnet, either permanent or electromagnetic in type, which is thus at right angles to the coil at any point (see Fig. 139). When a current flows round the coil it is acted on by an electro-dynamic force and moves, the direction of motion being along its axis as is shown by applying the motor or Fleming's Left Hand Rule. When alternating current flows, the coil performs an oscillatory motion and as it is firmly fixed to the diaphragm, the latter performs a similar motion and the air in contact with it is set into vibration with the same frequency, and with an amplitude depending on the amplitude of motion of the coil.

The diaphragm and coil are fixed to the framework of the loudspeaker by a ring of silk, leather, or other flexible substance (in many cases the rim of the cone itself is corrugated) and a " spider " in the centre ensures axial motion of the coil. This free suspension permits relatively large motion of the coil and cone and so gives good reproduction at low frequencies.

[1] *Admiralty Handbook of Wireless Telegraphy*, Vol. II, n. 52.

137. The Carbon Microphone

Almost simultaneously with Bell's invention of the electro-magnetic telephone, Hughes (1878) discovered the action of the microphone. He found that when a loose connection in a circuit containing a battery and a telephone was vibrated it produced a loud sound in the telephone.

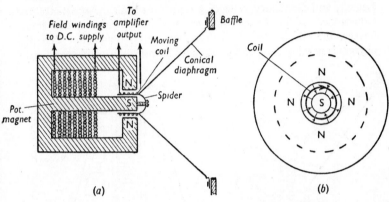

FIG. 139. Moving coil drive fitted to conical diaphragm. (a) Section of M.C. speaker ; (b) front view of coil round pot magnet with speaker, etc. removed. The coil moves in and out of the plane of the paper.

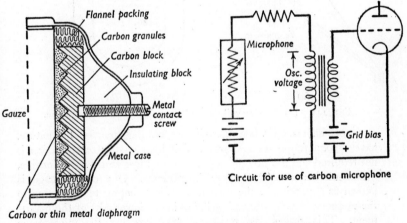

FIG. 140.   Carbon microphone and its circuit.

Instead of using a loose connection he devised a microphone consisting of a carbon rod held loosely between a pair of carbon blocks and his original instrument can still be viewed in the Science Museum, South Kensington.   The principle of the instrument is that the resistance between two carbon surfaces varies approximately in an inverse ratio to the pressure between them. When sound waves fall on the thin metal or carbon diaphragm, as shown in Fig. 140, they set it into vibration, thus varying the pressure on the carbon granules placed between it and a carbon block. This varies the resistance of the microphone and if a constant E.M.F. and a resistance or inductance are placed in series with it, the current in the circuit varies in a similar manner, and oscillatory voltages are set up across the resistance and inductance. If the inductance is replaced by the primary of a transformer, the advantage of a voltage step-up is obtained. The diaphragm is suitably damped by cotton wool washers to avoid pronounced

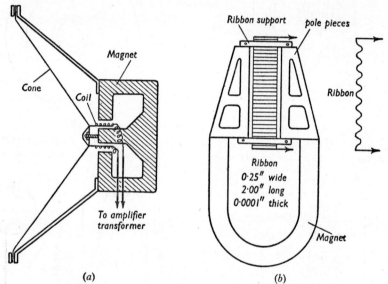

(a)   (b)

FIG. 141.   (a) Moving coil microphone ; (b) Ribbon microphone.

resonance effects. Carbon microphones are non-directional in nature, have a good frequency response and if high quality reproduction is not required and the presence of background hiss is not objectionable, make suitable general purpose instruments. One disadvantage is known as " packing ", the carbon granules clinging together due to the presence of moisture and wedging in the lower part of the instrument. This makes the resistance very low and the microphone insensitive.

138. Moving Coil Type Microphone

The moving coil microphone is very similar in appearance to a small moving coil loudspeaker. As shown in the diagram (Fig. 141), a small light coil is attached to a diaphragm, the whole being capable of movement across a strong radial magnetic field set up by a pot magnet. Sound waves falling on the diaphragm move the coil and the induced E.M.F.s set up in it are passed on to a suitable amplifier.

A further variety of moving coil instrument is seen in the more modern ribbon microphone. The light ribbon, made of aluminium or other suitable metal, is corrugated at right angles to its length and suspended between the poles of a magnet. The concertina-like structure allows the ribbon to move backwards and forwards, but not sideways in the direction of the pole pieces. As the ribbon moves at right angles to the magnetic field, under the action of sound waves, E.M.F.s are induced in it which are fed to a suitable amplifier. As would be expected from its construction, the output is considerably less than that from the more familiar moving coil instrument, but ribbon microphones have better response curves. The cut away pole pieces allow rapid circulation of the air from front to back of the instrument. When the difference in distance to the two sides of the ribbon is appreciably less than one quarter wavelength of the sound wave falling on it the resulting force exerted against the ribbon is proportional to the frequency and the pressure gradient, or particle velocity of the wave, and so this type of instrument is commonly called a velocity microphone.[1]   The cutaway pole pieces ensure a fairly uniform response to 10,000 cycles/sec. The microphone has pronounced directional properties since sound waves from the side strike the front and back of the ribbon at the same instant and so produce no resultant force. Its principal disadvantage is that it cannot be used close to a source of sound, since under these conditions it over-emphasises the low frequencies.

[1] Terman, *Radio Engineering*, p. 782.

CHAPTER XI

THE COMBINATION OF SIMPLE HARMONIC
MOTIONS

139. When a body moves in a straight line under the action of a force which is proportional to the distance of the body from a fixed point and is directed towards that point, then the body executes a Simple Harmonic Motion. Amongst familiar examples are the vertical oscillations of a mass suspended on a spring or elastic cord, a pendulum whose oscillations are small, a magnet making small oscillations in a magnetic field and the particles of gas when transmitting a pure note.

Mathematically this motion is represented by $m\dfrac{d^2x}{dt^2} = -\mu x$, but it is often useful to represent a S.H.M. as the projection, on any fixed

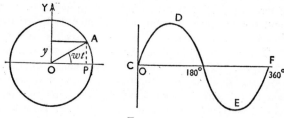

Fig. 142.

straight line, of a uniformly rotating vector. If the axis OY is chosen as the fixed line, and OA as the rotating vector, then $y = a \sin wt$ where the angle AOP is " wt ". When the appropriate ordinates for values of " wt " from 0° to 360° are plotted, the sine curve $CDEF$ is obtained and this representation of a Simple Harmonic motion is used for the combining of these motions by graphical methods. If the x axis is chosen as the fixed line, the equation, for the figure shown, becomes $x = a \cos wt$.

140. Simple Harmonic Motions in the same Straight Line

Consider a point moving under the action of two S.H.M.s of the same frequency acting in the same straight line. Then for a point A (Fig. 143), the ordinates AB and AC represent the displacements of the point due to the individual motions. Thus the resultant displacement is given by the simple addition of the ordinates at any point, so that $AD = AB + AC$. By repeating this process for various values of wt, or time (since the angular velocity is constant), the resultant displacement, shown by the thick curve, is obtained. The process is the same whether the motions are in phase or not, as is shown by the

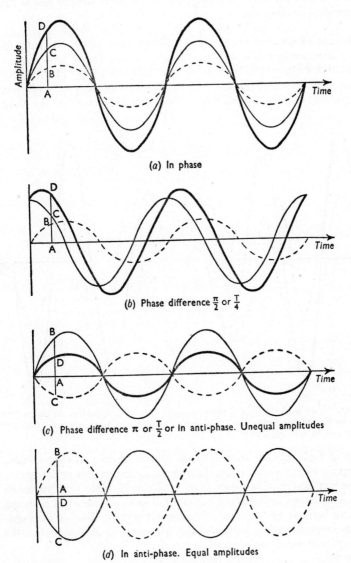

(a) In phase

(b) Phase difference $\frac{\pi}{2}$ or $\frac{T}{4}$

(c) Phase difference π or $\frac{T}{2}$ or in anti-phase. Unequal amplitudes

(d) In anti-phase. Equal amplitudes

FIG. 143.   S.H.M.s of same period.

Thin and dotted curves = Individual S.H.M.s.   Black line = Resultant curve.

curves, *b*, *c*, *d*, which also show that the resulting motion is also simple harmonic, of the same frequency, and in the same straight line as the individual components.

The same method may be used to combine Simple Harmonic Motions of differing amplitudes and frequencies which are acting in the same straight line, but on the whole these are of little interest except for the particular case of two S.H.M.s of slightly different frequency. Considering two such motions which make 4 and 5 vib./sec. respectively, then the resultant displacement (shown by the thick

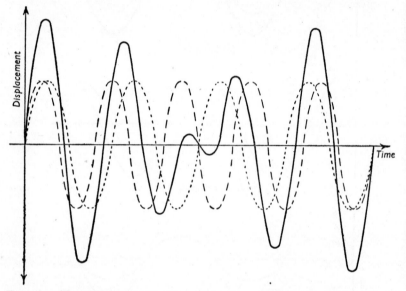

FIG. 144. Two S.H.M.s in the same straight line of frequencies in the ratio 5 : 4 (shown by dotted lines) combined to give the resultant displacement curve (thick line). The variation in amplitude of the resultant curve gives the sensation of beats.

line in Fig. 144) is obtained by the simple addition of the ordinates from the two separate motions (shown by the dotted lines in the figure). The resultant motion varies from a maximum value to a minimum once a sec. and indicates the rise and fall in amplitude when beats are set up between two sounds. The greatest contrast between the maximum and minimum values of the beat wave is obtained when the component waves are of equal amplitude.

141. Combination of Two Simple Harmonic Motions at Right Angles

The equations of two such motions having the same frequency are $x = a_1 \sin (wt + \theta_1)$ and $y = a_2 \sin (wt + \theta_2)$ where x and y are the magnitudes of the projections of the rotating vectors on a single straight line.

(a) Considering the simple case when the motions are on phase, i.e. $\theta_1 = \theta_2 = 0$. Then

$$x = a_1 \sin wt \quad \text{and} \quad y = a_2 \sin wt$$

$$\therefore \frac{x}{y} = \frac{a_1}{a_2} \quad \text{or} \quad y = \frac{a_2}{a_1} \cdot x,$$

i.e. the resultant motion is along a straight line indicated by BA in Fig. 145.

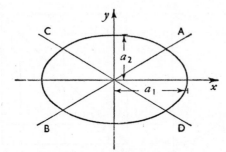

FIG. 145.   Combined simple harmonic motions.

(b) If the phase of the two motions differ by 180° then the equations are

$$x = a_1 \sin wt \quad \text{and} \quad y = a_2 \sin (wt + 180) = - a_2 \sin wt$$

$$\therefore \frac{x}{y} = - \frac{a_1}{a_2} \quad \text{or} \quad y = - \frac{a_2}{a_1} \cdot x$$

and the resultant motion is along the straight line DC.

(c) When the phases differ by 90° then

$$x = a_1 \sin wt \quad \text{and} \quad y = a_2 \sin (wt + 90) = a_2 \cos wt$$

$$\therefore \frac{x^2}{a_1^2} + \frac{y^2}{a_2^2} = \sin^2 wt + \cos^2 wt = 1,$$

i.e. the resulting motion is an ellipse and it can be shown that it is swept out in a clockwise direction.

If the equations are

$$x = a_1 \sin wt, \quad y = a_2 \sin (wt - 90) = - a_2 \cos wt$$

then the ellipse is traversed in the opposite direction. If in addition the amplitudes are equal, i.e. $a_1 = a_2$, then the equation of the figure becomes $x^2 + y^2 = a_1^2$ and the figure is a circle. For any other difference in phase the figure is an ellipse with its axes inclined to the directions of the component vibrations.

When two Simple Harmonic Motions act at right angles to each other, the resultant vibration may be simple or complicated, depending

on the frequencies, phase difference, and to a small extent on the amplitudes of the individual vibrations. The resultant curve formed by
such a combination is known as a Lissajous' Figure. Four of the
principal methods of obtaining these figures are as follows.

142. Graphical Method

This makes full use of the fact that when a point moves in a circle
with uniform speed, then the angle swept out in a given time by the
radius joining the considered point to the centre of the circle is

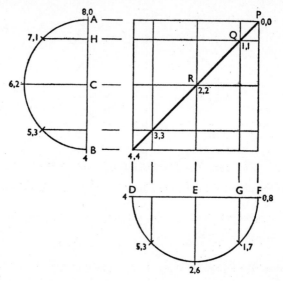

FIG. 146. S.H.M.s same amplitude, same frequency in phase.

proportional to its speed and hence to the frequency of the simple harmonic motion which its projection on to a diameter represents.

Consider two S.H.M.s of equal amplitudes, in phase and acting
at right angles. These may be represented by $x = a \cos wt$ and
$y = a \cos wt$. Construct two semicircles with diameters AB and
DF at right angles, and such that $AB = DF = 2a$ (see Fig. 146).
As the frequencies are the same, the representative radius vectors sweep
out equal angles, and in this case equal arcs, in the same time. To
indicate this fact, divide the arcs AB and DF into the same number of
equal parts. In this particular example four is a suitable number.

As the S.H.M.s are in phase it means that they both must be at
the positive extremities of their sweeps at the same time and so the
measurement of time must start from A and F. Starting from these
points number the intervals along the circumference from o to 8, the

projections of these points on to the respective diameter will then represent one complete oscillation of the S.H.M.s As the first "x" displacement is FG and that for "y" is AH the displacement of a body moving under both simple harmonic motions will be PQ. After the second interval of time the displacements will be FE and AC and so the body will be at R. Continuing thus and plotting points 3, 3. 4, 4., etc., the complete curve representing the resultant motion is obtained.

If the amplitudes of the simple harmonic motions are not equal then the diameters of the semicircles must be made proportional to

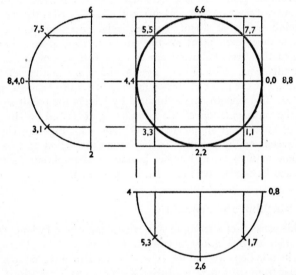

FIG. 147. S.H.M.s same amplitude, same frequency, phase difference of $\pi/2$.

the amplitudes. When the simple harmonic motions are not in phase then allowance for the phase difference must be made when fixing the starting points on the representative circles. Fig. 147 shows this for two simple harmonic motions of the same amplitude and frequency and having a phase difference of 90°.

As a rather more difficult exercise consider two simple harmonic motions acting at right angles, the ratio of whose amplitudes is 4 : 3, periodic times 3 : 4, and having a phase difference of one quarter of a period. The mathematical representation of these motions is

$$y = 3a \cos \frac{2\pi}{4} \cdot t$$

and

$$x = 4a \cos \left(\frac{2\pi}{3} t + \frac{\pi}{2} \right),$$

i.e. the one acting along the " x " axis leads that acting along the " y " axis. Construct two semi-circles with their diameters at right angles, the diameters being proportional to $4a$ and $3a$ along the x and y axis respectively (see Fig. 148). A suitable value of " a " such as 1 cm. or $\frac{1}{2}$ in. must be chosen so as to make the diagram a reasonable size. As the periods are in the ratio 3 : 4, divide the arcs into 3 or 4 equal parts, or suitable multiples of these numbers (6 and 8 are very useful for this particular figure). If the S.H.M.s were in phase then both would be at the positive extremities of their sweeps at the same time but as the x motion leads the y motion by one quarter of a period the representative point on the x motion will be one quarter of the circle in advance of the y motion. Hence at the starting time the representative points will be at B and A respectively. Starting from these two points number each point on the arc 0, 1, 2, 3, 4, etc., since they represent the distances swept out in equal intervals of time. Under the simultaneous action of both motions the representative point would start at 0.0 or the point P, thence moving to 1.1 or Q and so on to 2.2, 3.3, etc. The smooth curve obtained by joining the points so plotted gives the representation of the complete path traced out by a body moving under both simple harmonic motions. Fig. 149 shows the path traced out by a body moving under the action of two simple harmonic motions at right angles having equal amplitudes, starting in phase and having periodic times in the ratio 1 : 3.

143. Blackburn's Pendulum

This consists of a string or fine wire about 6 or 8 ft. long, attached to a rigid beam B (Fig. 150) at two points A and C. The string or wire is cut at its middle point and the ends so formed are attached to a funnel. The exit from the funnel is restricted (drawn out if it is glass), so that when it is filled with sand a fine stream falls on to a horizontal sheet of paper placed below it. As sand is continually leaving the funnel, then obviously the mass of the sand in the funnel is altering. In itself this is not very important, but what is of prime importance is that the position of the centre of gravity of what serves as a pendulum bob is continually altering, the effective length of the pendulum is continuously lengthening, and hence the time of swing is not constant. To counteract this a large mass of iron or lead is firmly fixed to the funnel so that the mass of sand is negligible compared with the mass of metal. This may be conveniently in the form of a ring which carries the funnel.

Swinging perpendicular to the plane of the paper the pendulum will have an effective length BG. A clip placed at D so as to bring the two strings together will have no effect on the time of swing perpendicular to the plane of the paper. It means, however, that the portion

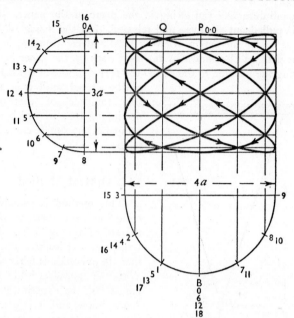

Fig. 148. Amplitudes 4 : 3, periodic times 3 : 4, x leads y by $\pi/2$.

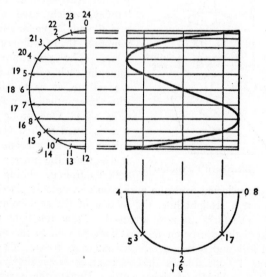

Fig. 149. S.H.M.s equal amplitude. Periods in the ratio 1 : 3 in phase.

$$x = a \cos \frac{\omega t}{1} \qquad y = a \cos \frac{\omega t}{3}.$$

of the pendulum *DG* can swing in the plane of the paper. If the funnel is pulled out slantwise and released, then the massive " bob " will move under the action of two S.H.M.s at right angles, and the resultant path will be shown by the sand track on the paper beneath. By altering the position of the clip *D* the period of one of the S.H.M.s can be altered until it is a suitable multiple of that of the pendulum *BG*, in which case a comparatively simple curve is obtained.

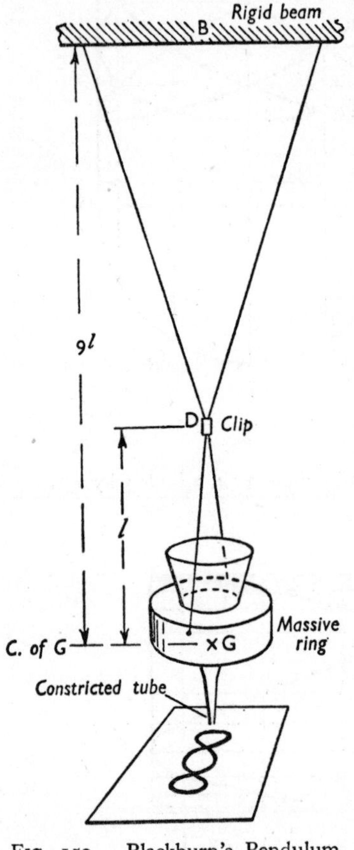

FIG. 150.　Blackburn's Pendulum.

144. Optical Method

This method is usually described as being performed with the aid of tuning forks. If the forks are electrically maintained, then the operation is fairly simple. With the non-electrically maintained fork the experiment is far from simple and it is often advantageous to substitute lengths of strip steel, such as used in the Ribbon Attwood and Fletcher's Trolley, which have a longer period and larger amplitude of vibration than ordinary tuning forks. The procedure is the same in each case. The forks are set up so as to vibrate in directions mutually at right angles (Fig. 151). One prong of each fork is fitted with a very small mirror so that a beam of light incident on the mirror will be reflected from it. Using one fork only the light reflected from the mirror on to a suitably placed screen will trace out a straight line, the motion of the spot being simple harmonic. The forks are now arranged so that the light which is reflected from the mirror on the first fork falls on to the mirror on the second fork and is thence reflected on to a screen. The motion of the spot of light follows the resultant curve obtained by compounding two S.H.M.s at right angles. Due to the persistence of vision and the speed at which the spot of light follows the resultant path the curve appears continuous to the eye.

When the phase difference between two S.H.M.s at right angles is $\frac{\pi}{2}$, the figure obtained is *closed*. If the figures due to two forks of frequency n_1 and n_2 are studied they will be found to be continuously changing, but if the two frequencies are not widely different they may be compared from a study of the Lissajous' figures. Let the time between two consecutive closed figures be t sec. Then in this time one fork has gained one vibration on the other. Hence equating the number of vibrations made in this time

$$n_1 \cdot t = n_2 \cdot t \pm 1,$$
$$n_1 = \frac{n_2 \cdot t \pm 1}{t}.$$

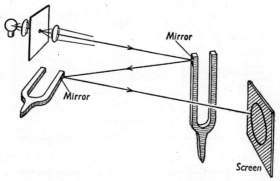

FIG. 151. Combination of S.H.M.s at right angles using two tuning forks and a beam of light.

By loading one fork with a small piece of plasticine it can be determined whether the operative sign is $+$ or $-$.

If the frequencies are exactly equal and the phase difference is $\frac{\pi}{2}$ the Lissajous' figure will remain closed and will be a circle or an ellipse depending on the amplitudes of vibration of the forks.

145. Method Using Cathode Ray Oscilloscope

This is, without a doubt, the most elegant method of demonstrating Lissajous' figures since, due to the afterglow of the fluorescent screen, the whole of the resultant curve is clearly visible and by a suitable manipulation of inductance, capacitance or resistance a very wide variety of curve is readily obtainable. The oscilloscope consists of four distinct parts, (a) an electron gun which is responsible for the production of a narrow beam of electrons, (b) an accelerating and focusing system or electron lens, (c) two pairs of parallel plates mutually at right angles through which the electron beam must pass, (d) a fluorescent screen, the afterglow of which is determined by its chemical composition and may vary according to this composition from a small fraction of a second to a considerable number of seconds.

The pairs of parallel plates are known as the X and Y plates since, if a potential is applied across them, the spot of light on the fluorescent screen is deflected along the equivalent of x and y axes. If an alternating potential is applied across either the X or Y plates, then the movement of the spot on the screen will be simple harmonic and will be shown as a straight line on the screen. Thus the application of alternating potentials to the X and Y plates simultaneously will move the electron beam under two S.H.M.s at right angles and the spot will trace out a Lissajous' figure on the fluorescent screen.

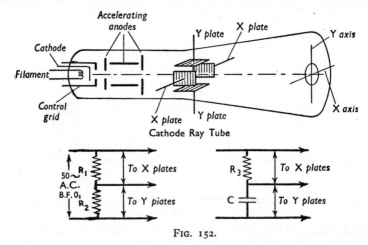

FIG. 152.

If two equal resistances R_1 and R_2 are in the same circuit and carry the same current then they have the same potential drop across them. Connecting the two resistances as shown across the X and Y plates will move the electron beam under two S.H.M.s at right angles, equal in amplitude and in phase. The resultant curve will be a straight line diagonally across the tube.

When a condenser is placed in a circuit with an alternating voltage applied to it, then the current through the condenser leads the voltage across it by a phase angle of $\frac{\pi}{2}$. If a condenser is placed in series with a resistance in an A.C. circuit then the voltage across the condenser lags behind that across the resistance by $\frac{\pi}{2}$, since both current and voltage are in phase in a resistive component. This means that a condenser and resistance in series will give two alternating voltages which are $\dfrac{\pi}{2}$ out of phase and if the amplitudes of these voltages can be made equal then the Lissajous' figure should be a circle. The reactance of a condenser, i.e. its resistance to alternating current, is given by $R = \dfrac{1}{wC} = \dfrac{1}{2\pi n C}$ where n is the frequency and C the capacity in fards. For a 2 microfarad condenser used with an alternating voltage of 50 cycles/sec. $R = \dfrac{1}{2\pi \cdot 50 \times 2 \times 10^{-6}} = \dfrac{10^6}{400\pi} \backsimeq 800$ ohms.

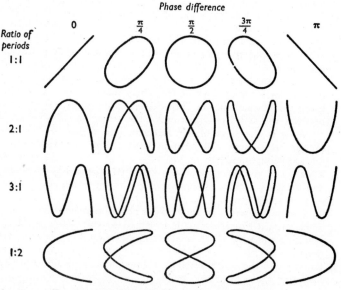

FIG. 153.   Common forms of Lissajous' Figures.

Thus the resistance R_3 (Fig. 152) should be of this order and can conveniently be a variable resistance of 1000 ohms.   In order to produce a circle on the fluorescent screen the value of R_3 will not be exactly equal to the reactance of C since the sensitivity of the X and Y plates is not quite the same.   A harmonic-free and calibrated oscillator is often used in the laboratory, rather than A.C. mains, since the latter contains harmonics, the presence of which can be demonstrated by the imperfect sine wave form when A.C. mains are applied to the Y plates and a time base to the X plates.   The relative frequency of two simple harmonic motions can be obtained by counting the number of peaks of the Lissajous' figure.   For reasons which are fairly obvious from the diagram of Fig. 153 the motions should not be in phase.   The frequency ratio is one half of the total number of peaks.

MISCELLANEOUS QUESTIONS

1. How does the velocity of sound in a medium depend upon the elasticity and density ? Illustrate your answer by reference to the case of air and a long metal rod. The velocity of sound in air being 1100 ft./sec. at 0° C., and the coefficient of expansion 1/273 per degree. Find the change in velocity per °C. rise of temperature. (L.Inter.)

2. How would you find by experiment the velocity of sound in air ? Calculate the velocity of sound in air in cm./sec. at 100° C. if the density of air at S.T.P. is 0·001293 gm./cc., the density of mercury at 0° C. 13·60 gm./cc., the specific heat of air at constant pressure 0·2417 and the specific heat at constant volume 0·1715. (L.H.S.C.)

3. Assuming that the frequency of transverse vibration of a stretched string is inversely proportional to its length, describe how you would investigate the relation between the frequency and the tension. How would you plot your observations and what result would you expect ?

   A stretched string and an air column closed at one end both resound to a tuning fork of frequency 256 vib./sec., the vibration being the fundamental in both cases. State briefly the differences between the states of vibration of the string and the air column.

   What is the next higher frequency to which (a) the string, (b) the air column will resound without their dimensions or the tension being altered ? (L.H.S.C.)

4. How would you compare (a) the velocities of sound in wood and air and (b) the velocities of transverse and of longitudinal disturbances in a stretched wire ?

   A stretched wire 1 m. long gives a note of frequency 2000 vib./sec. when stroked lengthwise with a resined leather. How is the string vibrating and what is the speed of propagation along it of the vibrations ? (L.H.S.C.)

5. Explain why the note emitted by a closed organ pipe differs in quality from that of a note emitted by (a) an open pipe, (b) a violin.

   The fundamental note emitted by a stretched wire vibrating transversely between two bridges 50 cm. apart is in unison with that of an organ pipe when the temperature is 12° C. Find approximately the change in length between the bridges necessary to restore unison when the temperature of the air in the pipe rises to 20° C., the tension in the wire remaining unaltered. (N.U.J.M.B.)

6. Describe in detail how to determine the frequency of a tuning fork by the falling plate method.

   Describe how the frequency of an alternating current, such as that from A.C. mains, may be determined with a sonometer. (N.U.J.M.B.)

7. Describe the nature of the disturbance set up in air by a vibrating tuning fork and show how the disturbance can be represented by a sine curve. Indicate on the curve the points of (a) maximum particle velocity, (b) maximum pressure.

   What characteristics of the vibration determine the pitch, intensity and quality respectively of the note? (N.U.J.M.B.)

8. Discuss the terms intensity and loudness as applied to sound.

A concert hall has a domed ceiling which is a portion of a sphere whose centre of curvature is at floor level. Assuming that source of sound to be at this level explain why, from the acoustical standpoint, the design is not good and would be much improved by doubling the radius of curvature of the dome without altering its maximum height above the floor.

Explain why the accoustical properties of a concert hall may vary with the size of the audience. (N.U.J.M.B.)

9. Write a short essay on methods of recording and reproducing sound. (N.U.J.M.B.)

10. What is meant by reverberation and reverberation time ?

What factors determine the reverberation time of a concert hall and why does the magnitude of this time affect the suitability of the hall for speech and music ? Indicate briefly other aspects of the hall which affect its acoustical quality. (N.U.J.M.B.S.)

11. Describe in detail the stroboscopic method of determining the frequency of vibration of a tuning fork. Outline two other methods which are available for measuring the frequency and discuss the respective merits of all the methods you have described.

An outer ring of twelve dots and an inner ring of eight dots, all uniformly spaced, are painted on a disc which can be rotated about its axis and which is viewed by means of a tuning fork of frequency 100 vib./sec., the disc being seen once in each vibration of the fork. Calculate the minimum rate at which the disc must be rotated so that the outer ring shall appear at rest with the normal spacing between the dots.

The disc is then speeded up until both rings appear to be at rest. Determine the rate of revolution when this first occurs and account for any peculiarity in the appearance of the outer ring.

Mention some other application of the stroboscope principle. (N.U.J.M.B.S.)

12. Describe the formation and properties of stationary wave motion. Describe how a resonance tube and sources of sound of known frequencies may be used to determine the velocity of sound in air. Show how the velocity at $0°$ C. may be calculated from the value at room temperature. (N.U.J.M.B.)

13. Show that the total energy of a particle performing simple harmonic motion is independent of time and that it is proportional to the square of the amplitude and to the square of the frequency of the motion.

The tension in the wire of a sonometer is equal to the weight of 100 gm. If the wire is 100 cm. long, and vibrates in its fundamental mode with a maximum amplitude of $0·1$ mm. calculate the energy of the vibration. (The frequency n of vibration of the wire is related to the tension T, the mass per unit length m, and the length l by the formula

$$n = \frac{1}{2l}\sqrt{\frac{T}{m}}.$$ (C.S.)

14. Describe experiments to illustrate the production of Lissajous' figures and construct the figures resulting from two S.H.M.s whose amplitudes and frequencies are in the ratio 1 : 3 and 1 : 2 respectively, and which start initially $\pi/2$ out of phase.

15. Calculate the density of the material of a sonometer wire 1 m. long and 0·70 mm. in diameter if, when stretched with a load of 20 kg., the first overtone it gives when vibrating transversely has a frequency of 250 sec.$^{-1}$. (Assume g to be 1000 cm. sec.$^{-2}$.)

16. How does the velocity of sound in a gas depend on temperature and pressure ?

    The observer in an aeroplane flying horizontally at 240 m.p.h. releases a bomb and hears the sound of the explosion 20 sec. afterwards. Find the height of the aircraft, neglecting air resistance. (Velocity of sound in air = 1100 ft./sec.)   (O.S.)

17. Explain how sound waves are propagated in solids, liquids, and gases. Describe briefly three methods of measuring the velocity of sound, one for each type of medium.   (N.U.J.M.B.)

18. Describe, briefly, a method of measuring the velocity of sound in air.

    An army sound ranging apparatus is capable of measuring the direction of arrival of sound waves from an aircraft. An aircraft flying on a straight course at a speed of 200 m.p.h. passes 10 miles from the apparatus. Draw a graph showing how its measured direction varies with time during the flight. (Velocity of sound = 750 m.p.h.)

19. Derive an expression for the velocity of plane sound waves through a gas. Discuss the effect of (a) pressure, (b) temperature, on the velocity. Neglecting end corrections, calculate the change in frequency of a 10 ft. open-end organ pipe when the air temperature changes from 5° C. to 25° C.   (O.)

20. What do you understand by the Doppler effect ? A whistle of 1000 cycles/sec. pitch is attached to one end of a light tube 2 ft. long so that it can be sounded while the tube is rotating freely in a vertical plane about a horizontal axis through the other end. If the velocity of the whistle when the tube is horizontal is 16 ft./sec., find the upper and lower limits of the pitch of the sound heard by an observer on the ground viewing the motion end-on. (Velocity of sound = 1100 ft./sec.)   (O.S.)

21. A loudspeaker is using a power of 50 mW. The volume control is then turned so that the power used becomes as follows : (a) 500 mW., (b) 1000 mW., (c) 200 mW. Express these changes in decibel form and, from their addition, show that the final output is four times its initial value.

APPENDIX

★ Analytical Treatment of Simple Harmonic Motion and Forced Vibrations

Harmonic Motion

The equation of motion of a particle moving in a straight line so that its acceleration is always directed towards a fixed point in the line and is proportional to the distance from that point is

$$\ddot{x} = - w^2 x.$$

Multiplying both sides by $2\dot{x}$, then

$$2\dot{x}\ddot{x} = - 2w^2 x\dot{x}.$$

On integration this gives

$$(\dot{x})^2 = - w^2 x^2 + \text{a constant of integration}$$
$$= w^2(a^2 - x^2) \text{ say.}$$

Hence
$$\frac{dx}{dt} = \pm w \sqrt{a^2 - x^2}.$$

Taking the upper sign this gives

$$wdt = \frac{dx}{\sqrt{a^2 - x^2}}.$$

and so
$$wt = \sin^{-1} \frac{x}{a} + \alpha.$$

where α is a constant of integration.

Hence
$$x = a \sin (wt + \epsilon)$$

or
$$x = A \sin wt + B \cos wt \qquad . \qquad . \qquad . \qquad . \qquad \textbf{(1)}$$

If the lower sign had been taken the form of solution would have been the same, an inverse cosine replacing the inverse sine.

Forced Oscillations

The equation $\ddot{x} = - w^2 x + f \cos pt$ represents a S.H.M. disturbed by a periodic force proportional to $\cos pt$.

The general solution of $\ddot{x} + w^2 x = f \cos pt$ is obtained by adding a particular integral to the solution of $\ddot{x} + w^2 x = 0$.

To find the particular integral substitute $x = C \cos pt$ in the equation.

Then
$$- Cp^2 \cos pt = - w^2 C \cos pt + f \cos pt,$$

and so
$$x = C \cos pt$$

is a solution if
$$Cp^2 = w^2 C - f,$$

or
$$C = \frac{f}{w^2 - p^2},$$

$$\therefore x = \frac{f}{w^2 - p^2} \cos pt$$

is the required particular integral and the general solution is

$$x = A \sin wt + B \cos wt + \frac{f}{w^2 - p^2} \cos pt \qquad . \qquad . \quad (2)$$

and represents an oscillation made up of " free " and " forced " oscillations, the frequency of the latter, $\frac{2\pi}{p}$, being the same as that of the disturbing force.

Consider two cases :

(1) $p^2 \fallingdotseq w^2$. Then the amplitude of the forced oscillations $\frac{f}{w^2 - p^2}$ is large.

(2) $p^2 = w^2$. The solution in the case is not of the form $x = C \cos pt$. Substituting $x = Ct \sin pt$ in the equation gives the solution $x = \frac{f}{2p} . t . \sin pt$ as can be checked by differentiation, i.e. the oscillation increases continuously with time.

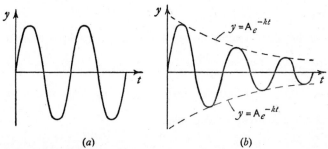

Fig. 154. (a) Undamped oscillation. (b) Damped oscillation (see equation 4).

Damped Oscillations

In all practical cases, the motion of the body is resisted by various frictional effects, usually due to air. Assuming the resistance to vary as the velocity the equation of motion may be written

$$\ddot{x} = - w^2 x - 2k\dot{x},$$

or $$\ddot{x} + 2k\dot{x} + w^2 x = 0.$$

Trying $x = e^{mt}$ as a solution of the equation, then
$$m^2 e^{mt} + 2km e^{mt} + w^2 e^{mt} = 0,$$
and the solution is valid if
$$m^2 + 2km + w^2 = 0.$$

If m_1 and m_2 are the roots of the equation, the solution is
$$x = C_1 e^{m_1 t} + C_2 e^{m_2 t}, \qquad . \qquad . \qquad . \qquad . \quad (3)$$
where m_1 and m_2 are

$$= \frac{- 2k \pm \sqrt{4k^2 - 4w^2}}{2} = - k \pm \sqrt{k^2 - w^2}.$$

There are three forms of solution of equation (3) according as m_1, m_2 are real and different, equal or complex.

(1) Real roots $k > w$ or $k^2 - w^2 = q^2$ say.

Then
$$x = C_1 e^{(-k+q)t} + C_2 e^{(-k-q)t}$$
$$= e^{-kt}(C_1 e^{qt} + C_2 e^{-qt}),$$

and the motion is aperiodic or dead beat. This is reproduced in practice by using a moving coil galvanometer with a low resistance across its terminals or a pendulum moving in a viscous medium.

(2) $w^2 = k^2$. The solution is $x = e^{-kt}(C_1 + C_2 t)$ which can be verified by differentiation. This is also a non-oscillatory motion and the case is known as that of critical damping since there is just no oscillation.

(3) $k < w$ or $k^2 - w^2 = -q^2$.

Then
$$x = e^{-kt}(C_1 e^{iqt} + C_2 e^{-iqt}),$$
or
$$= e^{-kt}[C_1 (\cos qt + i \sin qt) + C_2 (\cos qt - i \sin qt)],$$
since $\cos \theta + i \sin \theta = e^{i\theta}$.

$$\therefore \quad x = e^{-kt}[(C_1 + C_2) \cos qt + i(C_1 - C_2) \sin qt]$$
$$= e^{-kt}[C \cos qt + C' \sin qt],$$
$$x = C'' e^{-kt} \cos (qt + \epsilon). \qquad . \qquad . \qquad . \qquad . \qquad . \qquad (4)$$

which represents a simple harmonic motion with an amplitude decreasing exponentially with time. There are damped oscillations and e^{-kt} is the damping coefficient. The frequency is now $\dfrac{q}{2\pi}$ where $q^2 = w^2 - k^2$ but the change in frequency is extremely small if the damping is sufficiently small.

Example. Suppose $\dfrac{q}{2\pi} = 500$ cycles/sec. and the amplitude falls away to $\dfrac{1}{e}$ of its original value in 1 sec. Then

$$\frac{1}{e}C'' = C'' e^{-k \cdot 1} \quad \text{and} \quad \text{so } k = 1.$$

Also
$$q^2 = 10^6 \times \pi^2 \fallingdotseq 10^7 \quad \text{and} \quad w^2 = q^2 + k^2 \fallingdotseq 10^7 + 1.$$

Thus $\delta(q^2) = 1$, $\therefore 2q \cdot \delta q \fallingdotseq 1$ and so $\dfrac{\delta q}{q} \fallingdotseq \dfrac{1}{2q^2} \fallingdotseq \dfrac{1}{2 \times 10^7}$,

i.e. w exceeds q by 1 part in 2×10^7 and so the effect of this damping on the frequency is negligible.

Damped Forced Oscillations

Considering the two preceding sections then
$$\ddot{x} + 2k\dot{x} + w^2 x = f \cos pt$$

is the equation of motion of a damped forced oscillation. The complete solution is obtained by adding a particular integral to the solution of
$$\ddot{x} + 2k\dot{x} + w^2 x = 0.$$

To find this particular integral, substitute as a trial solution

$$x = A \cos pt + B \sin pt.$$

This satisfies the equation if

$$- Ap^2 \cos pt - Bp^2 \sin pt + 2k(- Ap \sin pt + Bp \cos pt) + Aw^2 \cos pt + Bw^2 \sin pt = f \cos pt.$$

A and B must be chosen so that the equation is true for all values of t. Equating to zero the coefficients of $\sin pt$ and $\cos pt$, then

$$- 2kpA - Bp^2 + w^2B = 0,$$

or

$$- 2kpA + (w^2 - p^2)B = 0, \qquad \bullet \quad \bullet \quad \bullet \quad (5)$$

and

$$- Ap^2 + 2kpB + Aw^2 = f,$$

$$\therefore \ (w^2 - p^2)A + 2kpB = f \qquad \bullet \quad \bullet \quad \bullet \quad (6)$$

From equation (5)

$$A = \frac{w^2 - p^2}{2kp} . B \quad \text{or} \quad B = \frac{2kp}{w^2 - p^2} . A,$$

and substituting these in turn in equation (6) gives

$$\frac{(w^2 - p^2)^2}{2kp}B + 2kpB = f \quad \text{and} \quad (w^2 - p^2)A + \frac{4k^2p^2A}{(w^2 - p^2)} = f,$$

whence

$$\frac{A}{w^2 - p^2} = \frac{B}{2kp} = \frac{f}{(w^2 - p^2)^2 + 4k^2p^2}.$$

Therefore the required integral is

$$x = \frac{f[(w^2 - p^2) \cos pt + 2kp \sin pt]}{(w^2 - p^2)^2 + 4k^2p^2}$$

$$= \frac{f . \cos (pt + \phi)}{[(w^2 - p^2)^2 + 4k^2p^2]^{\frac{1}{2}}},$$

where

$$\tan \phi = \frac{- 2kp}{w^2 - p^2}.$$

Thus using the results from the previous section the complete solution is

$$x = C'' e^{-kt} \cos (qt + \epsilon) + \frac{f . \cos (pt + \phi)}{[(w^2 - p^2)^2 + 4k^2p^2]^{\frac{1}{2}}}$$

$$= C'' e^{-kt} \cos (qt + \epsilon) + D \cos (pt + \phi) . \qquad \bullet \quad \bullet \quad (7)$$

where $q^2 = w^2 - k^2$ and the amplitude of the forced vibration

$$D = \frac{f}{[(w^2 - p^2)^2 + 4k^2p^2]^{\frac{1}{2}}}.$$

The two terms of equation (7) represent the free and forced vibrations respectively. Owing to damping the free oscillations die away exponentially and the forced vibrations alone persist.

Resonance

Consider the system some time after the free oscillations have died away. Then the amplitude D of the forced oscillation is

$$D = \frac{f}{[(w^2 - p^2)^2 + 4k^2p^2]^{\frac{1}{2}}}, \qquad \bullet \quad \bullet \quad \bullet \quad (8)$$

and D is greatest when the denominator is least, i.e. when

$$\frac{d}{dp}[(w^2 - p^2)^2 + 4k^2p^2] = 0,$$

or $$- 4p(w^2 - p^2) + 8k^2p = 0,$$
$$p^2 = w^2 - 2k^2.$$

Thus the amplitude of oscillation is a maximum when the forcing frequency is $\dfrac{(w^2 - 2k^2)^{\frac{1}{2}}}{2\pi}$, which is slightly less than either the natural frequency $\dfrac{(w^2 - k^2)^{\frac{1}{2}}}{2\pi}$, or the value in the absence of damping $\dfrac{w}{2\pi}$.

Substitute this value of the frequency for maximum amplitude in equation (8). Then

$$D_{\text{max.}} = \frac{f}{2k(w^2 - k^2)^{\frac{1}{2}}} \backsimeq \frac{f}{2kw} \quad \text{if} \quad w \gg k,$$

or $$D_{\text{max.}} = \frac{f}{2k(k^2 + p^2)^{\frac{1}{2}}} \quad \text{since} \quad w^2 - k^2 = p^2 + k^2.$$

It follows that the lower the value of the damping constant k the greater the maximum amplitude. For small values of damping, $w^2 \gg 2k^2$ the amplitude is greatest when the forced frequency is the same as that of the free vibration in the absence of damping, $\dfrac{w}{2\pi}$, a condition which is known as amplitude resonance.

Considering the velocity of the particle at any instant, this is given by $\dot{x} = - Dp \sin (pt + \phi)$ and in the mean position the velocity is a maximum and equal in magnitude to Dp. This value is known as the velocity amplitude.

From equation (8)

$$Dp = \frac{pf}{[(w^2 - p^2)^2 + 4k^2p^2]^{\frac{1}{2}}}$$

$$= \frac{f}{\left[\left(\dfrac{w^2 - p^2}{p}\right)^2 + 4k^2\right]^{\frac{1}{2}}},$$

which is a maximum when the denominator is least, i.e. when $w^2 = p^2$, and hence

$$(Dp)_{\text{max.}} = \frac{f}{2k},$$

i.e. the velocity amplitude has a maximum value when the forcing frequency is the same as the natural frequency in the absence of damping. In order to distinguish it from a free or forced oscillation this is sometimes termed a maintained oscillation, and it is the normal condition of resonance.

ANSWERS

CHAPTER III (p. 59)

1. 331 m./sec.
2. 346 m./sec.
3. 264 m.
   330 m./sec.
4. 1680 ft.
   9⅛ ft./sec.
5. 1490 m./sec.
6. 0·33, 0·40, 0·53 sec.
7. 53° 8'.
9. 1261 m./sec.
10. 1·425 × 10⁶ dynes/sq. cm.
11. 341·1 m./sec.
12. 388·6 m./sec.
13. 4554 ft.
14. 900 m.
    24° from second position.
15. 6900 ft.
16. 0·169 cals.
17. 1·39.
18. 344 m./sec.

CHAPTER V (p. 100)

1. 256 vib./sec.
2. 380, 452 vib./sec.
3. 499 vib./sec.
4. 400⅛ vib./sec.
5. 541, 601 vib./sec.
6. 383·(5) vib./sec.
7. 445·(2) vib./sec.
8. 648, 423 vib./sec.
9. 270 vib./sec.
10. Approaching : 70 ft./sec.
    Receding : 74·7 ft./sec.
11. 1063 vib./sec.
12. 9·4, 0, 9·2.
13. 54·8 ft./sec.
14. 556·(2), 554·(6) vib./sec.
15. Receding : 46·29 km./sec.
16. Receding : 75 km./sec.
17. 83° 3' with the track.
18. 4·67 per sec.
19. $\dfrac{\lambda_A}{\lambda_B} = \dfrac{V-v}{V+v}, \dfrac{n_A}{n_B} = \left(\dfrac{V+v}{V-v}\right)^2$.
20. 107·2, 32·6.
21. 2484 vib./sec.

CHAPTER VI (p. 129)

1. 49·6 cps.
2. 3976 gm. wt.
3. 3 beats/sec.
4. 22·5 : 1.
5. 74·9 cm.
6. 2·78.
7. $A = 8\frac{1}{8}$ kg. wt., $B = 4\frac{1}{8}$ kg. wt.
8. 2490 cps. if wt. an antinode,
   1243 vib./sec. if wt. a node.
9. 300 cps.
10. 5 cm.
11. 1 : 40 (trans : long).
12. $10\sqrt{10}$: 1 (long : trans).
13. 268 cps.
14. 132·5, 137·5 cps.
15. 39·3 gm. wt.
16. 4 kg. wt.
17. 1·2 per cent.

CHAPTER VII (page 159)

1. 1st overtone, $c = 1·51$ cm.
2. 512, $c = 1·2$ cm, 81·8 cm.
3. 1 cm.
4. 11·0 : 1.
5. 0·011 cm.
6. 424 vib./sec.
8. 5·7° C.
9. 33,700 cm./sec.
   208, 210·6 vib./sec.
10. 330 m./sec., 5 cm. above mark.
11. 98·5 cm., 101·5 cm.
12. 5½, 11, 16½, etc. ft. from wall.
13. 1·6 cm., 344 m./sec.
15. 131·7 vib./sec.
16. 2·5 × 10⁵ cm./sec.
17. 1·41.

CHAPTER VIII (page 174)

5. 1100 ft./sec.
6. 3·91, 1·33 sec.

234

MISCELLANEOUS EXAMPLES
(p. 226)

1. 2 ft./sec.
2. 38,830 cm./sec.
3. (a) 512 string damped in middle.
   768 string plucked in middle.
   (b) 768 cps.
4. 4×10^5 cm./sec.
5. 7 mm. decrease.

11. $8\frac{1}{3}$ rps., $12\frac{1}{2}$ rps.   Half spacing.
13. 0·242 ergs.
15. 8·3 gm./cc.
16. 4200 ft.
19. 2 vib./sec.
20. 1018 and 990 vib./sec., or 1010 and 983 vib./sec.
21. $+$ 10 db. $+$ 3 db. $-$ 7 db.
    6 db. $\stackrel{\frown}{=}$ 4 : 1

INDEX